Electronics and Radio—An Introduction

BOOKS BY M. Nelkon

Published by Heinemann Educational Books
ADVANCED LEVEL PHYSICS (SI) (WITH P. PARKER)
ADVANCED LEVEL PRACTICAL PHYSICS (SI) (WITH J. OGBORN)
SCHOLARSHIP PHYSICS (SI)
PRINCIPLES OF ATOMIC PHYSICS AND ELECTRONICS (SI)
OPTICS, SOUND AND WAVES (SI)
MECHANICS AND PROPERTIES OF MATTER (SI)
GRADED EXERCISES AND WORKED EXAMPLES IN PHYSICS (SI)
NEW TEST PAPERS IN PHYSICS (SI)
INTRODUCTION TO MATHEMATICS OF PHYSICS (WITH J. H. AVERY)
ELEMENTARY PHYSICS, BOOKS I AND II (WITH A. F. ABBOTT)
REVISION BOOK ON ORDINARY LEVEL PHYSICS (SI)
REVISION NOTES IN PHYSICS: BOOK I MECHANICS, ELECTRICITY,
            ATOMIC PHYSICS (SI)
  BOOK II OPTICS, WAVES, SOUND, HEAT, PROPERTIES OF
    MATTER (SI)
SOLUTIONS TO ORDINARY LEVEL PHYSICS QUESTIONS (SI)
SOLUTIONS TO ADVANCED LEVEL PHYSICS QUESTIONS (SI)

Published by Arnold
ELECTRICITY (ADVANCED LEVEL, SI)

Published by Blackie
HEAT (ADVANCED LEVEL, SI)

Published by Chatto & Windus
PRINCIPLES OF PHYSICS (ORDINARY LEVEL, SI)
EXERCISES IN ORDINARY LEVEL PHYSICS (SI)
C.S.E. PHYSICS (SI)
REVISION BOOK IN C.S.E. PHYSICS (SI)
SI UNITS: AN INTRODUCTION FOR ADVANCED LEVEL

ELECTRONICS AND RADIO—
An Introduction

THIRD EDITION

M. Nelkon
M.Sc., F.Inst.P.
formerly Head of the Science Department, William Ellis School, London

and

H. I. Humphreys
C.Eng., M.I.E.R.E.
Lecturer, Electronic and Radio Engineering Department,
Riversdale Technical College, Liverpool

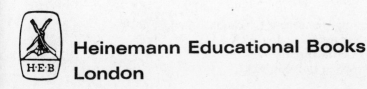

Heinemann Educational Books
London

Heinemann Educational Books Ltd

LONDON EDINBURGH MELBOURNE TORONTO
AUCKLAND JOHANNESBURG SINGAPORE
HONG KONG IBADAN NAIROBI LUSAKA
KUALA LUMPUR NEW DELHI

ISBN 0 435 68335 7
© M. Nelkon and H. I. Humphreys 1969, 1971, 1975
First published 1969
Second edition 1971
Third edition 1975

Published by Heinemann Educational Books Ltd
48 Charles Street, London W1X 8AH
Printed in Great Britain by
Fletcher & Son Ltd, Norwich

Preface to First Edition

This book covers the basic principles of electronics and radio. It is intended for students at technical colleges taking basic radio courses, such as those of the City and Guilds, or for students who may require a background knowledge in training courses such as those on radio servicing. Although no specific syllabus is covered, some of the topics discussed in using transistors will be found useful in a number of other courses. In particular, with the growing importance of Applied Physics in schools, it is hoped that the book will make a useful contribution to the development of electronics and radio.

The book begins with an introduction to the essential electrical theory. D.C. circuits, power, electrostatics, capacitors and electromagnetic principles have been discussed, with special reference to radio applications. SI units have been used throughout. Experience with a wide variety of students have shown that a.c. circuits can be well explained by vector methods for basic theory, and phasor diagrams have therefore been used extensively.

In the electronics and radio sections, prominence has been given to semiconductors, junction diodes, transistors and their associated circuits. Topics covered include rectification, a.f. amplifiers, power amplifiers, r.f. amplifiers, oscillators, modulation and detection. Although the radio valve has been superseded in most cases, we are of the opinion that, educationally, many principles can be introduced through the valve. The consideration of junction diode and transistor circuits has been preceded therefore by valve circuits. The treatment in the text is concise and further details of circuitry must be obtained from more advanced books. Summaries have been provided at the end of chapters and, as a help to the student, questions in the exercises have been graded. Details of practical work necessary in a basic course are beyond the scope of this book. These and further reading may be obtained from references listed at the end.

The authors are very much indebted to the late J. V. Talbot, C.Eng., M.I.E.R.E., Northern Polytechnic, London, for reading the MS and for his valuable advice on numerous points. They also acknowledge the generous assistance with technical detail supplied by Dubilier Condenser Company, Goodmans Loudspeakers Limited, Standard Telephones and Cables Limited, Chloride Electrical, Mullard Educational Limited, and the kind permission to reprint questions set in past Radio and Telecommunications examinations of the City and Guilds of London Institute.

Preface to Third Edition

In view of their importance in computers, this edition includes an introduction to the use of the transistor in logical gates and pulse circuits, and to Boolean algebra. We are particularly indebted to K. E. J. Bowden, B.Sc., A.Inst.P., M.I.E.E., senior lecturer in telecommunications, Northern Polytechnic, London, for his valuable advice in this section. An account of the field effect transistor, and the action of the differential amplifier, have also been added in an Appendix.

Contents

Electronics and Radio—An Introduction

1: Introduction—Carriers of Electricity

The Electron

Matter is made up of millions of tiny particles called *molecules*. Molecules themselves consist of one or more *atoms*. For many years it was thought that an atom of hydrogen, the lightest element, was the smallest particle in existence, but about the end of the last century Sir J. J. Thomson showed that there was a particle much lighter than the hydrogen atom. It was subsequently called an *electron*. As we shall see, it plays a vital part in conduction of electric current. The mass of the electron is about 1/1840th of the mass of a hydrogen atom and is thus extremely light.

Experiment shows there are two kinds of electricity (p. 45). We could call them A and B, or X and Y, to preserve their difference of identity, but experiments also show that the two kinds of electricity behave in an opposite way. They are consequently known as *positive* and *negative* electricity (p. 45). Experiment shows that the electron carries a minute but definite amount of negative electricity. Quantity of electricity is measured in *coulombs* (p. 6). The electron carries an amount equal numerically to about $1 \cdot 6 \times 10^{-19}$ coulomb, which is given the symbol e. Thus

$$electron\ charge = -1 \cdot 6 \times 10^{-19} \text{ coulomb } (-e)$$

Atomic Structure

A normal atom cannot possess any surplus of either negative or positive electricity. Otherwise we should be able to detect this in our everyday handling of the element made up of these atoms.

The structure of the hydrogen atom, the lightest and simplest atom, is represented diagrammatically in Fig. 1.1. The central core or *nucleus* of the atom is a particle called a *proton*. A single electron revolves in a circle round the nucleus. Since the electron has a negative charge $-e$, the proton has an equal positive charge $+e$.

The relative sizes concerned in the 'structure' of the atom may perhaps be gauged by the analogy that if the atom could be magnified to the size of St. Paul's Cathedral, the proton and electron would each be about the size of a pin's head! The electron is extremely light, however. Thus practically the whole of the *mass* of the atom is concentrated in its nucleus.

Accepting this picture of the hydrogen atom, three facts should be noted:

1. The electron in the orbit is the particle inside the atom which is free to move, i.e. the electron is mobile, but is bound to the nucleus by the attraction between opposite charges (p. 45).

2. The electron is so light that the whole of the mass of the atom can be considered to reside in the nucleus.

3. The positive and negative quantities of electricity in the whole of the atom are numerically equal.

As we proceed from hydrogen to the heavier atoms the electrical structure becomes more and more complex. Electrons then revolve

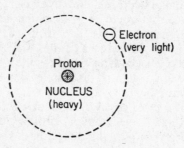

FIG. 1.1. Hydrogen atom

in more than one orbit round the nucleus, just as the planets revolve round the sun. Copper has 29 of these mobile electrons. Also the nucleus becomes more complex and contains numerous protons and particles called *neutrons*, about as heavy as protons but carrying no charge. It is not within the scope of this book to consider atomic structure in detail (and research is going on at the present day). But facts (1), (2) and (3), previously stated for the hydrogen atom, are still true. Thus in every atom the electrons are the mobile particles; the nucleus contains comparatively massive protons and neutrons at the centre of the atom; and the total amount of negative electricity on the electrons is equal to the amount of positive electricity on the nucleus.

Ions

The electrical structure of matter plays an important part when atoms combine and form a compound. When solid sodium chloride (common salt) is formed, for example, a sodium atom gives up one of its outer electrons to a chlorine atom. The sodium atom is then left with a positive charge numerically equal to that on an electron, while the chlorine atom has gained a negative charge. The 'solid state' is due to the strong force of attraction between the opposite charges on the remaining sodium and chlorine atoms. This binds the atoms together.

Atoms which have gained or lost one or more electrons are called *ions.* In a sodium chloride molecule, for example, sodium is a positive (+) ion; the chloride is a negative (−) ion, Fig. 1.2 (i). The transferred electron is so light that the masses of the two ions are practically the same as the atoms from which they were formed.

When water is added to solid sodium chloride, the force of attraction between the ions is reduced to about one-eightieth of its previous value (see p. 46). The ions then become relatively free from each other's influence. They wander about independently in the sodium chloride

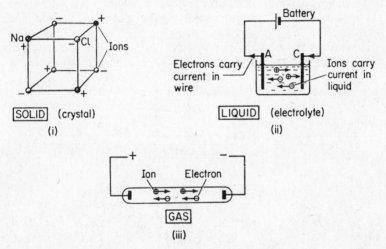

FIG. 1.2. Carriers in electrolyte and gas

solution in a haphazard, or random, motion. At any instant, there are as many positive ions moving one way as there are moving the opposite way. This is also the case with the negative ions. On average, then, there is no *net* drift of electricity along the liquid.

However, when a battery is connected to two separated plates, A and C dipping into the solution, a current is detected, Fig. 1.2 (ii). The electrical pressure difference or potential difference (p. 7) due to the battery causes the positive ions to drift in one direction and the negative ions to drift in the opposite direction. Thus *ions are the current carriers* in salt and acid solutions, or *electrolytes*, as they are known.

Ions also exist in gases. In a tube of air at low pressure, for example, electrons are torn from their atoms when a very high voltage is connected across the air. Positive ions are then formed, Fig. 1.2 (iii). Any atoms to which the electrons attach themselves form negative ions. The carriers of current in the gas are electrons and ions.

Conductors. Insulators

We have already stated that the electrons are particles moving round the nucleus of atoms. In the atoms of *metals*, an electron in the outermost part of the atom is very loosely bound to the nucleus. This electron thus wanders about haphazardly, or randomly, through the metal structure from atom to atom. These electrons are called *free electrons*. All solid conductors have free electrons, particles carrying negative electricity, Fig. 1.3 (i).

Owing to their random motion, at any instant there are just as many free electrons moving one way through a conductor as there are moving the opposite way. The *net* movement of electrons along the conductor is thus zero.

However, when a battery is connected to the ends of the conductor, the 'electrical pressure difference' or potential difference set up by

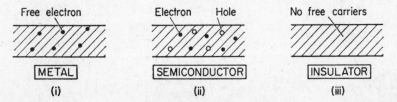

FIG. 1.3. Carriers in metal and semiconductor

the battery causes the electrons to drift in one direction. An electric current now flows. Thus *electrons are the carriers of electric current in metals*.

The speed of the electron drift is a measure of the electric current. This depends on the collisions made by the electrons with the stationary atoms or ions while they move, that is, the current depends on the electrical *resistance* of the metal. Copper is a very good conductor, that is, it has a low resistance. Manganin and Eureka are alloys of copper with a much higher resistance.

According to the electron theory, *insulators* are substances which do not have free electrons inside them. All their electrons are 'bound' to their respective atoms, and are only very slightly displaced under the action of a constant difference of electrical pressure. Sulphur, ebonite, mica, glass, and air are insulators under normal conditions. At very high voltage the insulation breaks down and conduction occurs, as electrons are torn from their atoms.

Holes

As we study in more detail later, there is a class of materials called *semiconductors* which have an electrical resistance between that of a good conductor and an insulator. Germanium and silicon are examples of semiconductor elements. Semiconductors contain some free electrons at normal temperature. The atoms from which they come are left with equal positive charges called *holes*, Fig. 1.3 (ii). The positive charges attract electrons from neighbouring atoms, which in turn have positive charges or holes. When a battery is connected to the semiconductor, holes and free electrons drift through the material. Hole movement is equivalent to the movement of a positive charge equal numerically to that on an electron (p. 199). *In semiconductors, then, the carriers of current are free electrons (−) and holes (+).*

Some Uses of Electrical Particles

Electrical particles of one kind or another are used in a wide variety of useful practical applications.

In the *cathode ray tube* or *television tube*, electrons are liberated from a hot substance and produce light on a coated screen after colliding with it. In *electroplating*, ions carry the metal to be deposited through the particular chemical solution. In *neon sign lighting*, the gas glows when its atoms are struck by electrons and ions are formed to carry the electric current. In *transistors*, electron and hole movement conduct the current. These applications are considered in more detail later.

SUMMARY

1. The nucleus of an atom has a net positive charge and contains most of the mass of the atom; electrons are extremely light, carry negative charges, and are the mobile particles in the atom.

2. An ion is a massive particle which has either a positive or a negative charge.

3. A metal conductor has free electrons inside it, whose drift in one direction constitutes an electric current. An insulator is a substance which has no free electrons inside it. A salt or acid solution contains positive and negative ions. A gas at low pressure contains ions and electrons when a high voltage is connected across it.

4. A semiconductor (such as germanium or silicon) has free electrons and holes (positive charges) at normal temperature.

2: Direct Current (D.C.) Theory

The analogy between a continuous steady flow of water along a tube and a continuous steady flow of electricity along a wire is a useful aid to understanding some of the principles concerning measurement of electric current.

Consider a tube AB which has a continuous steady flow of water along it in the direction A to B (Fig. 2.1 (i)). (This flow could be obtained by a pump which maintains a constant difference of water pressure between A and B in a complete water circuit.) The *current* of water is the quantity of water *per second* passing any section S.

FIG. 2.1. Current analogy

Thus, if 25 cc passes S in 5 sec the current = 25/5 = 5 cc per sec. If 50 cc passes the section S in 5 sec, the current = 10 cc per sec. It is twice as fast as before.

The practical unit of quantity of electricity is a *coulomb* (about 6×10^{18} as much as the quantity of electricity on an electron). From the water analogy, if 15 coulombs of electricity flow past the section T of the wire MN of Fig. 2.1 (i) in 3 sec, the electric current 15/3 = 5 coulomb per sec. The current is the same at all points of the wire if the flow of electricity along it is steady. Generally, if Q is the quantity of electricity flowing past a section of a wire in t sec, the current I is given by

$$I = \frac{Q}{t} \tag{1}$$

When Q is in coulombs and t in seconds, then I is in *amperes*, A. 1 A is a rate of flow of 1 coulomb per sec. It corresponds to a flow of about 6×10^{18} electrons per sec past a given section of a wire carrying that current. Radio valves and transistors may carry currents of the order of thousandths of amperes, or *milliamperes* (mA). A 120-watt electric lamp carries a current of $\frac{1}{2}$ A when used on the mains. Electric fires may carry currents of about 8 A when used.

From (1), it follows that

$$Q = I \times t, \tag{2}$$

6

which is a formula for Q when I and t are given. Thus if a current of 2 A flows for 1 minute or 60 sec, the quantity of electricity flowing past a particular section of the circuit in that time $= 2 \times 60 = 120$ coulombs.

Potential Difference

If an object is raised above the ground to a point X, the object is said to have *potential energy*, Fig. 2.2 (i). It derives this energy from the work done by the person or machine who lifted it to X. When the object is now released, it falls to a point Y where it has a lower potential energy, and thus gives up or releases energy. The energy given up is the difference in the potential energy at X and Y. It could be usefully

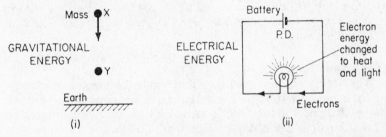

FIG. 2.2. Gravitational and electrical energy

used to raise other objects, for example, by means of attached ropes and pulleys.

The case of potential energy just considered is that of a mass in the earth's *gravitational field*. In an analogous way, a quantity of electricity has potential energy in an *electric field*. Here, electricity will move from one point in the electric field to another where it has a lower energy, and it will then release an amount of energy equal to the difference. We can see this happen when an electric fire or an electric lamp is switched on. The terminals of the mains voltage supply always have a difference of potential energy, or, as it is called, a *potential difference*, p.d., and electricity (electrons) flows continuously through the fire or lamp metal filament from one terminal to the other, Fig. 2.2 (ii). As it does so, energy is released in the form of heat and light. For a similar reason, electric lamps will light up when connected to torch batteries. The energy in the lamp comes from the chemical energy in the battery.

The Volt. Magnitudes of P.D.

The magnitude of potential difference, or p.d., is defined by reference to the amount of energy released when electricity flows between two points. The unit of p.d. is the *volt*, V. One volt is defined as *the p.d. between two points if 1 joule of energy is released when 1 coulomb moves between the points*. It then follows that if 2 coulomb move between two points having a p.d. of 100 volts, then 200 joules are released. Generally, therefore, if Q coulomb move through two points having a p.d. of V volts, the energy W released is given by

$$W = QV \text{ joules}$$

The magnitudes of p.d. vary from very low to very high values. the p.d. across the terminals of a dry (Leclanché) cell is about 1·5 V; the p.d. across a lead-acid accumulator is 2 V and across a 'Nife' accumulator is 1·3 V. In this country the mains p.d. (a.c.) is usually 240 V. These values contrast with the much higher ones of generators at large power stations which may be 11,000 V or 11 kilovolts (kV), and this may be stepped-up to 132 kV or 264 kV. A machine used in nuclear energy experiments has been designed to produce a p.d. of 7,000 million volts.

Ohm's Law

When one, two, three and then four similar accumulators are con-nected in turn to a wire whose temperature remains constant, experiment shows that the current flowing increases each time proportionately. Thus if a p.d. of 2 V maintains a current of 0·5 A in a length of wire, a p.d. of 4 V maintains a current of 1·0 A, a p.d. of 6 V maintains a current of 1·5 A and a p.d. of 8 V maintains a current of 2·0 A.

This was first found by Ohm in 1820. *Ohm's law* states:

The ratio of the p.d. (V) between the ends of a conductor to the current (I) flowing in it is always a constant, provided the physical conditions of the conductor such as its temperature remains unchanged.

Thus, at constant temperature,

$$V \propto I$$

or

$$\frac{V}{I} = \text{constant}$$

Resistance R

If a p.d. of 12 V is applied to a wire X, a current of 2 A may flow. If the same p.d. is then applied to another wire Y, a smaller current of 1 A may flow. The wire Y has thus *greater resistance* to current flow than X. *The ratio V/I is defined as the resistance of a conductor*. Its unit is the *ohm*, Ω. In this case, therefore, the resistance, R, of X = 12 V/2 A = 6 Ω. The resistance, R, of Y = 12 V/1 A = 12 Ω.

Connecting wire is made of pure copper, which has a very low resis-tance. The (copper) leads from the mains plug in a home to a television set may have a resistance of a small fraction of an ohm. *Resistance wire* is made of alloys of copper such as Constantan or Eureka; they have a much higher resistance than pure copper (see p. 20). *Radio resistors* are made from powdered carbon whose resistance may vary from tens of ohms to millions of ohms.

Conductance is the inverse of resistance, or $1/R$. Its unit is the *siemen*, symbol S. Thus the conductance of a 10Ω resistor is $1/10$ or $0 \cdot 1$ S.

Relations between *I*, *V*, *R*

Since $R = V/I$ from previous, it follows that $I = V/R$, $V = I \times R$. These are important formulae, and when they are used R must be expressed in ohms (Ω), V in volts (V), I in amperes (A).

$$I = \frac{V}{R}, \quad V = IR, \quad R = \frac{V}{I}$$

Smaller current units are the *milliampere* (mA) $= 1/1000$ A and the *microampere* (μA) $= 1/10^6$ or 10^{-6} A. Currents of the order of milliamps and microamps are obtained in transistors.

Smaller p.d. units are the *millivolt* (mV) $= 1/1000$ V and the *microvolt* (μV) $= 1/10^6$ or 10^{-6} V.

Larger units than the ohm for resistance are the *kilohm* (kΩ) $= 1000 \Omega$ and the *megohm* (MΩ) $= 1$ million (10^6) ohms. A smaller unit is the *microhm* ($\mu\Omega$) $= 1/10^6$ or 10^{-6} ohm.

EXAMPLES

1. Calculate the current in a resistance of $\frac{1}{4}$ MΩ if the applied potential difference is 250 volts.

$$I = \frac{V}{R} = \frac{250}{250,000} = \frac{1}{1,000} \text{ A} = 1 \text{ mA}$$

2. Find the potential difference between the ends of a 5,000-ohm wire if the current in it is (*a*) **3 mA**, (*b*) 3 μA.

(*a*) $V = I \times R = \dfrac{3}{1,000} \times 5,000 = 15$ volts.

(*b*) $V = I \times R = \dfrac{3}{10^6} \times 5,000 = \dfrac{15}{1,000}$ volts $= 15$ mV.

Rheostats

A *rheostat* is a variable resistance for adjusting smoothly the current in a circuit. A *tubular rheostat* is shown in Fig. 2.3 (i). A rotary rheostat or *potentiometer* ('pot') is widely used in radio (Fig. 2.3 (ii)). Resistance wire is wound between terminals A and B. In the tubular rheostat, the resistance in a circuit joined to D and A is varied smoothly by moving S along a brass bar ED.

Potentiometers ('pots') may be wire wound or have a carbon circular track, Fig. 2.3 (ii). The total resistance may vary from 100Ω to $50,000 \Omega$ (50 kΩ) for wire-wound potentiometers. The contact S is changed by rotating H with a spindle, thus altering the length of resistance material between D, A.

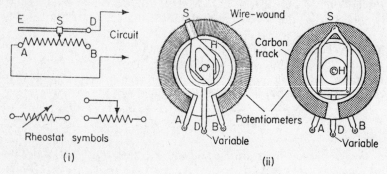

Rheostat symbols

(i)   (ii)

FIG. 2.3.   Rheostat and Potentiometers

Potential Divider

A rheostat or potentiometer also provides a simple means of varying smoothly the p.d. applied to a circuit or apparatus. It is then used as a *potential divider*.

Fig. 2.4 shows how a p.d. of 12 V from an accumulator D is connected to a rheostat so that any p.d. from zero to 12 V may be obtained

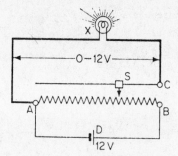

FIG. 2.4.   Potential divider

for an apparatus X such as a lamp. D is connected across the whole of the resistance wire between the terminals A and B. X is connected between the 'slider' terminal C and A. From $V = IR$, it follows that $V \propto R$ when I is constant. Thus the p.d. across any part of the wire is proportional to its resistance, which in turn is proportional to the *length* of the wire. Hence when S is moved to C, the whole p.d. of 12 V is applied to X. If S is moved half-way between A and B, only half the p.d. across the wire, or 6V, is applied to X. If S is moved to A, no p.d. is applied. Thus a variation of p.d. is smoothly obtained by moving S.

Resistance in Series and in Parallel

(a) The combined resistance R of R_1, R_2, R_3, *in series* is obtained by adding them all together (Fig. 2.5 (i)). Thus,

$$R = R_1 + R_2 + R_3 \tag{1}$$

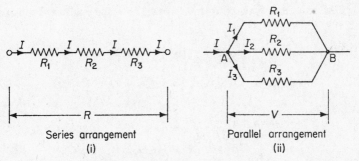

FIG. 2.5. Series and parallel resistors

(b) When each of the three resistances is connected to the same two points, A, B (Fig. 2.5 (ii)), they are said to be *in parallel*. The equivalent resistance R is then given by the formula

$$\frac{1}{R} = \frac{1}{R_1} + \frac{1}{R_2} + \frac{1}{R_3} \tag{2}$$

To prove this, let I_1, I_2, I_3 be the currents in R_1, R_2, R_3 respectively, and I the main current outside the branches, as shown. Experience shows that no electricity accumulates at a junction such as A. Hence $I = I_1 + I_2 + I_3$.

Now $I = V/R$, where V is the p.d. between A and B, if R is the single resistance which can replace the parallel combination without any change of the current I. Also, $I_1 = V/R_1$, $I_2 = V/R_2$, $I_3 = V/R_3$.

As $I = I_1 + I_2 + I_3$,

$$\therefore \quad \frac{V}{R} = \frac{V}{R_1} + \frac{V}{R_2} + \frac{V}{R_3}$$

$$\therefore \quad \frac{1}{R} = \frac{1}{R_1} + \frac{1}{R_2} + \frac{1}{R_3}$$

If I is the current in the main circuit, the p.d. between A and B in the parallel arrangement is calculated from $V = IR$, where R is the *total* resistance obtained from (2). We thus imagine that the main current flows through a resistance R.

EXAMPLE

In the circuit shown in Fig. 2.6 calculate:

   (*a*) the resistance between A and C,
   (*b*) the p.d. between A and B,
   (*c*) the current in the 2-ohm branch.

(*a*) The resistance between A and C = 4·8 Ω + the equivalent resistance of 2- and 3-Ω in parallel.

The latter is given by $\dfrac{1}{R} = \dfrac{1}{2} + \dfrac{1}{3}$, from which $R = \dfrac{6}{5} = 1\!\cdot\!2\ \Omega$ (1)

∴ resistance between A and C = 4·8 + 1·2 = 6 Ω.

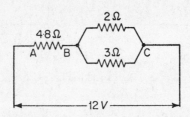

FIG. 2.6. Calculation

(*b*) The p.d. between A and B = $I \times R = I \times 4\!\cdot\!8$ V, where I is the main current.

But $I = \dfrac{\text{p.d. between A and C}}{\text{resistance between A and C}} = \dfrac{12}{6} = 2\ \text{A}$ (2)

∴ p.d. between A and B = 2 × 4·8 = 9·6 V   (3)

(*c*) The current I in the 2-ohm branch

$$= \frac{V}{R} = \frac{\text{p.d. between B and C}}{2}.$$

Now the p.d. between B and C
   = $I \times R$, where R is the equivalent resistance,
   = 2 × 1·2 = 2·4 V from (1) and (2) above.

$$\therefore I = \frac{2\!\cdot\!4}{2} = 1\!\cdot\!2\ \text{A} \qquad (4)$$

Note. (i) The p.d. between B and C = 12 V − p.d. between A and B
     = 12 − 9·6 = 2·4 V from (3).

(ii) The current in the 3-ohm branch

$$= \frac{\text{p.d. between B and C}}{3} = \frac{2\!\cdot\!4}{3} = 0\!\cdot\!8\ \text{A}.$$

Ammeter and Voltmeter Positions

An *ammeter*, *A*, is an instrument used for measuring current. It has to be placed directly in that part of the circuit through which the current passes. It must therefore have a low resistance, so as not to

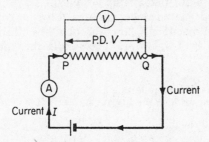

Fig. 2.7. Resistance by voltmeter-ammeter

disturb the condition that existed in the circuit before its entry. The current is constant everywhere in Fig. 2.7.

A *voltmeter*, V, is an instrument used for measuring the p.d. between two points, such as P and Q in Fig. 2.7. Unlike the ammeter, it must be placed in *parallel* with the circuit between the two points. The resistance of *V* must be high compared to the resistance of the circuit between P and Q. The p.d. between the two points then remains practically unaltered (see also p. 16).

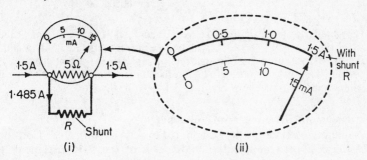

Fig. 2.8. Conversion to ammeter

Conversion of Milliammeter to Ammeter

An instrument sensitive enough to measure milliamperes is called a *milliammeter*. Many commercial instruments are made directly as milliammeters. In one make of instrument the coil has a resistance of 5 Ω and the maximum current which can be measured is 15 mA. It is thus described as a '0–15 mA' instrument. It can be adapted to read higher maximum currents such as 1·5 A, in which case the range is extended to 0–1·5 A. To do this, a suitable resistor *R* is added *in parallel* with the coil, Fig. 2.8 (i). *R* is called a *shunt*, for a reason we shall now see.

Consider the circuit shown in Fig. 2.8 (i). The effect of adding *R* in parallel is to make part of the current of 1·5 A pass through the milliammeter and the remainder through *R* itself. The correct magnitude of *R* is such that 15 mA flows through the milliammeter when the current outside at X is 1·5 A. The needle then deflects full-scale, Fig. 2.8 (ii).

The calculation for *R* is as follows:
Since the current through the instrument = 0·015 A,

∴ the current through *R*

$$= 1·5 - 0·015 = 1·485 \text{ A} \tag{1}$$

We need the p.d. (*V*) between the ends of *R* in order to calculate its resistance.

To obtain *V*, consider the *top* branch. This has a resistance of 5 Ω, the milliammeter resistance.

Hence the p.d. here is given by:

$$V = I \times R = 0·015 \times 5 = 0·075 \text{ V}$$

$$\therefore \text{ shunt resistance } R \text{ required} = \frac{V}{I} = \frac{0·075}{1·485} \text{ from (1)}$$

$$= \frac{5}{99} \text{ or } 0·0505 \text{ Ω}$$

The shunt resistance *R* must be very much smaller than 5 ohms, since most of the current (1·485 A) has to be diverted through *R*. Only a small current (0·015 A) must pass through the instrument. If the meter has to be adapted to measure currents up to 0·75 A the student should verify for himself that the shunt resistance now required is 5/49 or 0·102 ohm.

Conversion of Milliammeter to Voltmeter

A milliammeter can easily be adapted to act as a *voltmeter*. Consider first the p.d. between the terminals A, B of the 0–15 mA meter of 5 ohms resistance when the maximum current of 15 mA is flowing,

Then

$$\text{p.d. } V = IR = 0·015 \times 5 = 0·075 \text{ V}$$

Thus when the instrument is reading 15 mA on its scale it also indicates that the p.d. between the terminals is 0·075 V. If we now forget for a moment that we are dealing with an instrument which measures current, it can be seen, since $V \propto I$ when *R* is constant, that the same 0–15 scale on the instrument can be used to indicate voltages applied to A and B from 0–0·075 V. Thus, for example, if an unknown p.d. applied to A and B causes the needle of the instrument to move to the 10th division on the scale, the p.d. is equal to 10/15 of 0·075 V, i.e. 0·05 V.

Similarly, a 240 μA instrument of resistance 500 ohms can act as a *voltmeter* measuring up to 120 mV with a full-scale deflection, since

$$V = IR = \frac{240}{10^6} \times 500 = 120 \text{ mV}$$

Suppose, now, that the 15 mA instrument of 5 ohms resistance is required to be used as a voltmeter reading to 3 volts with a full-scale deflection. Since the current through the instrument has to be 15 mA for a full-scale

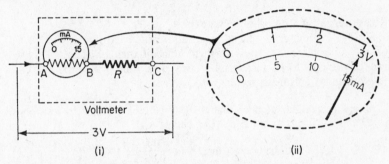

Fig. 2.9. Conversion to voltmeter

deflection it follows, from $V = IR$, that R must be increased in order that IR should equal 3 volts. It should therefore be remembered that a resistance must be added *in series* to convert a milliammeter to a voltmeter. Fig. 2.10(i) shows the series resistance R required. The terminals of the voltmeter are now A and C. To find the magnitude of R, we know that a current of 15 mA flows through ABC when the applied p.d. is 3 volts.

$$\therefore \text{ resistance A to C} = \frac{V}{I} = \frac{3}{0·015} = 200 \ \Omega$$

$$\therefore \text{ series resistance, } R, \text{ required} = 200 - 5 = 195 \ \Omega$$

If a voltmeter reading to 150 V is required for an experiment, the milliammeter can be converted for use on this range by adding a series resistance of 9,995 Ω. This result should be verified by the student. 150 V replaces 3 V in the above example, and the subsequent calculation is exactly the same.

Milliammeter as Ohm-meter

A moving-coil meter can also be adapted to act as an *ohm-meter*. Fig. 2.9A shows the 'ohms scale' calibrated to read resistance directly, as in a multimeter instrument. On switching to 'resistance' on the dial of the instrument, a battery at the back is connected to the coil. A rheostat (pot) inside is then adjusted so that 'zero' resistance is read when the leads are connected together. When the leads are now placed across the terminals of a resistor, its value is read directly from the position of the pointer on the ohms scale, Fig. 2.9A.

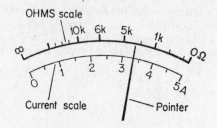

FIG. 2.9A. Ohm-meter

Measurement of P.D. with Voltmeters

Since a voltmeter is placed in parallel with part of a circuit, it will usually divert some current from the circuit through itself. This will reduce the p.d. to be measured. Thus care must always be exercised in choosing a voltmeter to measure p.d.

As an illustration, suppose that a 100 V-battery is joined to resistors of 6,000 and 4,000 Ω in series, Fig. 2.10. Then

$$\text{p.d. between A and X} = \frac{6,000}{10,000} \times 100 \text{ V}$$

$$= 60 \text{ V} \tag{1}$$

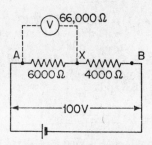

FIG. 2.10. Effect of voltmeter on p.d.

Suppose, now, that a moving-coil voltmeter of resistance 66,000 ohms is connected to A and X in order to measure the p.d. between these points. The effective resistance, R, between A and X is now no longer 6,000 Ω. It is given by

$$\frac{1}{R} = \frac{1}{6,000} + \frac{1}{66,000}$$

since the resistance of the voltmeter is in parallel with 6,000 Ω. Thus

$$\frac{1}{R} = \frac{11 + 1}{66,000}$$

i.e. $$R = 5,500 \text{ Ω}$$

Conditions in the circuit have thus changed with the introduction of the voltmeter across AX, since the resistance across AX has been appreciably reduced.

The total resistance between A and B with the voltmeter connected

$$= 5{,}500 + 4{,}000 = 9{,}500 \ \Omega$$

$\therefore$ the p.d. between A and X

$$= \frac{\text{resistance between A and X}}{\text{resistance between A and B}} \times 100 \ \text{V}$$

$$= \frac{5{,}500}{9{,}500} \times 100 = 58 \ \text{V (approx.)} \tag{2}$$

Thus, measured by this voltmeter, the p.d., is 58 V. The true p.d., that is, before the instrument was connected, is 60 V, from (1).

Suppose, however, that a voltmeter of resistance of 300,000 Ω resistance was used to measure the p.d. between A and X.

In this case the effective resistance between A and X is given by

$$\frac{1}{R} = \frac{1}{6{,}000} + \frac{1}{300{,}000}$$

i.e. $\qquad\qquad R = 5{,}880 \ \Omega \text{ (approx.)}$

$$\therefore \text{ p.d. between A and X} = \frac{5{,}880}{9{,}880} \times 100 \ \text{V} = 59{\cdot}5 \ \text{V} \tag{3}$$

by the same method as above.

This is a closer result to the p.d. between A and X before the introduction of the voltmeter than (2). It can now be seen that the higher the resistance of a voltmeter, the more accurately will it measure the p.d. between A and X. An 'ideal' voltmeter in this respect would be one with an infinitely large resistance.

It is a general rule that a voltmeter should have a high resistance compared to that between the points to which its terminals are connected. If this is not so, the reading on the instrument for the p.d. is inaccurate. A voltmeter of 66,000 Ω resistance is therefore very suitable for measuring the p.d. across a 100-Ω resistor, but unsuitable for measuring the p.d. across a 6,000-Ω resistor, as shown above.

Ohmic Conductors

An appliance such as a magnetic relay or an electric lamp will function efficiently only if the resistance of the wire used has the appropriate value. A resistance of moderate value can be determined roughly by connecting it in series with a battery B and a rheostat S, and measuring the current I with a suitable ammeter A and the p.d. V with a suitable voltmeter V, Fig. 2.11 (i). After adjusting S to obtain several values of current and p.d., the value for R is found each time from $R = V/I$ and the average calculated.

Fig. 2.11 (ii) shows the results obtained when I is plotted against V for the case of a length of manganin resistance wire and for the tungsten-filament of an electric lamp. In the former case, the $I - V$ graph, called a *characteristic curve*, is a straight line OY passing through the

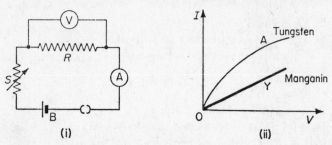

(i)   (ii)

FIG. 2.11. Variation of R with V

origin. Thus the resistance value is independent of the p.d. applied. Manganin wire hence obeys Ohm's law (p. 8) and is therefore called an 'ohmic conductor'. In the case of the lamp filament, its resistance (V/I) varies with the applied voltage V along a curve OA. Its resistance increases because the temperature rises with increasing voltage.

Rectifiers. Non-ohmic Conductors

If a copper disc is oxidised on one of its faces, a cuprous oxide/copper junction is formed, Fig. 2.12 (i). Experiment shows that although

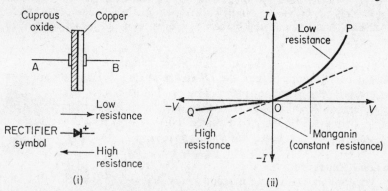

(i)   (ii)

FIG. 2.12. Non-ohmic conductor

the temperature of the disc remains constant, it behaves differently when the voltage V applied is *reversed*.

When a battery is connected so that the cuprous oxide side A is at a higher potential than the copper side B, a current of several milli-amperes flows, Fig. 2.12 (i). As the p.d. V is varied, a curve OP is obtained, Fig. 2.12 (ii). When the battery is reversed, however, a very small current flows. A curve OQ is then obtained. The characteristic $(I-V)$ curve QOP shows that the oxidised disc does not obey Ohm's law. It has a low resistance, in fact, in the direction cuprous oxide to copper, but a high resistance from copper to cuprous oxide.

This type of characteristic $(I-V)$ curve is typical of a class of devices called *rectifiers*. A rectifier characteristic is obtained for the junction between two impure semiconductors, which is another example of a solid rectifier (p. 205). A diode radio valve, which has a glass envelope, is also a rectifier (p. 187). Rectifiers do not obey Ohm's law and are hence called 'non-ohmic' conductors. Non-ohmic conductors are widely used in industry.

Resistivity

Experiments show that the resistance R of a wire is directly proportional to its length l and inversely-proportional to its area of cross-section a. This means that (i) if the resistance of 100 cm of Eureka wire is 5·0 ohms, the resistance of a length of 200 cm of the same wire is 10·0 ohms, (ii) the resistance of 100 cm of Eureka wire of half the diameter or gauge is *four* times the value of 5·0 ohms, or 20·0 ohms, since the area of the circular cross-section is proportional to the *square* of the radius or diameter.

Thus, for a given material, $R \propto l/a$, or

$$R = \frac{\rho l}{a} \tag{1}$$

where ρ is a constant for a given material known as its *resistivity* (formerly called 'specific resistance').

If $l = 1$ cm and $a = 1$ cm^2, then $R = \rho$, from (1). Thus the resistivity may be defined as the *resistance of a piece of material of length* 1 cm *and area of cross-section* 1 cm^2. The simplest shape of such a material is a cube of side 1 cm, or a 'unit cube'. It is incorrect to associate resistivity with a volume. A volume of 1 cm^3, for example, could be a solid of cross-sectional area $\frac{1}{2}$ cm^2 and length 2 cm. This would have a resistance $R = \rho l/a = \rho . 2/\frac{1}{2} = 4\rho$ (*not* ρ).

From (1), $\rho = R . a/l$. The unit of ρ in SI units is thus

$$\frac{\text{ohm} \times \text{m}^2}{\text{m}} = \text{ohm} \times \text{m} \, (\Omega \, \text{m})$$

Hence the resistivity of copper at normal temperature is written as $1 \cdot 7 \times 10^{-8} \, \Omega \, \text{m}$ in SI units; the resistivity of manganin is $48 \times 10^{-8} \, \Omega \, \text{m}$.

The resistivity of a wire can be calculated by measuring its resistance R and its diameter d. Thus suppose the length of some resistance wire is

0·80 m, its diameter is 0·42 mm and the resistance R is 1·84 ohms. The area of cross-section $a = \pi r^2 = \pi \times 0·21^2 \times 10^{-6}$ m². Hence, from $\rho = R \cdot a/l$,

$$\rho = \frac{1·84 \times \pi \times 0·21^2 \times 10^{-6}}{0·80} \; \Omega\,m$$

$$= 32 \times 10^{-8}\,\Omega\,m.$$

Variation of Resistance with Temperature

Experiments show that *pure metals*, such as copper or tungsten, increase in resistance as their temperature rises, Fig. 2.13 (i). At moderate temperatures, the resistance R_t at $t°C$ is related to the resistance R_0 at $0°C$ by $R_t = R_0(1 + \alpha t)$, where α is a constant of the material known as its *temperature coefficient*. The temperature coefficient is the fractional increase in resistance from $0°C$ of a length

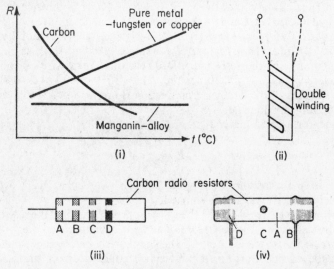

FIG. 2.13. Types of resistors

of material when its temperature is raised 1 deg. C. Its magnitude for most pure metals is about 0·004 per deg. C. Copper windings in large commercial transformers become very hot when working, and their resistance then alters appreciably. Cooling arrangements are therefore provided.

Carbon and most non-metals decrease in resistance as their temperature increases. Fig. 2.13 (i) shows roughly the variation of resistance R with temperature t for carbon.

Alloys. Most alloys increase in resistance as their temperature increases, but not to the same extent as pure metals. Manganin (alloy of copper, manganese, and nickel) and Eureka (alloy of copper and nickel) have very low temperature coefficients, and are consequently used as the material for standard resistances, such as those in the P.O. box, Fig. 2.19 (ii). Nichrome is an alloy of high resistance used for electric fire elements, because it does not oxidise at high temperatures.

Coils made as 'standard resistances', that is, resistances whose values are known to a high degree of accuracy, are wound doubled on a bobbin, Fig. 2.13 (ii). This virtually eliminates self-inductance of the coil (see p. 105), which is undesirable, leaving the resistance property.

Types of Radio Resistors

The most widely used type of radio resistor is one with a *carbon composition*. This is made by mixing some carbon black with binding material, adding some refractory material so that high temperatures can be withstood, and then baking the mixture in a kiln. They may be made in the form of a ceramic tube containing the mixture, Fig. 2.13 (iii), or in the form of a moulded carbon rod, Fig. 2.13 (iv).

To produce millions of resistors at a reasonable cost for use in radio and communications, the values cannot have great precision. They are rated as 5, 10 or 20% 'tolerance' from the manufacturer's listed value. Their disadvantage is the relatively poor stability and their value alters over a period of time.

The *cracked carbon* resistor has a much greater stability and can be made with a smaller tolerance, 1, 2 or 5%. The resistor is made by 'cracking' a hydrocarbon in the form of a hot vapour so that a thin carbon film is deposited on a ceramic base in the vapour. A spiral groove is then cut into a particular pattern on the film, depending on the magnitude of resistance required.

The *wire-wound resistor* can be made to a much greater precision than the carbon types. Nickel-chromium or copper-chromium wire may be used, and coated for insulation with vitreous enamel. Manganin wire is used for high precision as it has an extremely low temperature coefficient (p. 20), and it has a long life.

Colour Code

A colour code has been adopted for resistance values and for the tolerance. The main colours of the spectrum, red, orange, yellow, green, blue, violet, have digits ranging from 2 to 7 inclusive, and are between black, brown representing 0 and 1 respectively and grey, white at the other end, representing 8 and 9 respectively. Tolerance values are represented by: gold -5%; silver -10%; no colour -20%.

black	brown	red	orange	yellow	green	blue	violet	grey	white
0	1	2	3	4	5	6	7	8	9

The first digit or significant figure of the resistor value is given by the colour of the first band A, Fig. 2.17 (iii), or the body A, Fig. 2.17 (iv).

The second digit or significant figure is given by the colour of the second band B or the tip at the end.

The power of ten to multiply the first two digits (or the number of noughts which follow) is given by the third band C or the spot (dot). If there is no spot, the colour is taken as the same as the body.

The band D at the end provides the tolerance.

EXAMPLES

1. A = orange, B = white, 3 = orange, 4 = silver

resistance = 39,000 Ω or 39 kΩ $\pm$ 10%

2. A = red, B = violet, C = red, D = gold,

resistance = 2,700 Ω or 2·7 kΩ $\pm$ 5%

3. A = brown, B = green, C = green, D = nil,

resistance = 15 $\times$ 10^5 Ω or 1·5 MΩ $\pm$ 20%

E.M.F. and Complete Circuits

E.M.F.

A *battery* is a device which changes chemical energy to electrical energy. If a wire is joined to the terminals of a battery it becomes warm, and, in the case of the fine filament of a suitable light bulb, the wire glows. Thus the electrical energy has been changed to heat energy (see p. 34).

The *total energy per coulomb* available from a cell or other generator of electricity is defined as its *electromotive force*, E. The name 'electromotive force' originated from ideas in the early development of electricity, when it was considered that the battery had a 'force' inside which pushed electricity round a circuit connected to it. E.m.f. E is measured in volts.

It should be noted that the term 'e.m.f.' is used only in connection with a *generator* of electricity. This is a device which changes energy from one particular form to electrical energy. Thus we refer to the 'p.d.' across a resistance wire in a circuit, such as that across a rheostat, and *not* to the 'e.m.f.' across the wire, because it does not generate electricity.

Internal Resistance

When a voltmeter of very high resistance is connected to a cell it may record about 1·5 V, Fig. 2.14 (i). Practically no current flows from the cell and its e.m.f. is about 1·5 V. If a small resistor R, however, is joined to the terminals A and B a current flows through R and the cell, and the voltmeter reading may drop to 0·9 V, Fig. 2.14 (ii).

The same p.d., 0·9 V, is obtained if the voltmeter is joined across R, as shown. Thus the p.d. across the *external resistance* R is 0·9 V. The e.m.f., however, is 1·5 V. Hence (1·5 − 0·9) or 0·6 V is needed to maintain or drive the current inside the cell. Consequently the cell has some *internal resistance*, which we shall denote by the symbol r.

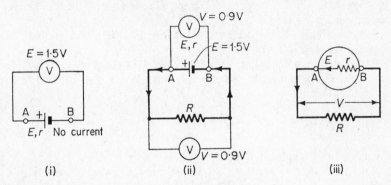

(i)   (ii)   (iii)

FIG. 2.14.   Terminal p.d.

Ohm's Law and E.M.F.

When no circuit or resistance is connected to the terminals of a battery, the latter is said to be on 'open circuit'. The e.m.f. of the battery is its p.d. on open circuit, for example, 1·5 V for the cell in Fig. 2.14 (i).

When a circuit of total resistance R is joined to the terminals A and B of a battery, the latter can be considered electrically as a source of e.m.f. E and an internal resistance r contained between A and B. In Fig. 2.14 (iii), the direction of the e.m.f. is shown by the arrow, and E and r are enclosed to indicate that they are developed inside the cell.

Applying Ohm's law to the complete circuit,

$$\frac{E}{I} = \text{the total resistance of the circuit} = R + r,$$

where I is the current flowing, or

$$I = \frac{E}{R + r} \tag{1}$$

The potential difference (V) at the terminals, A, B (Fig. 12.14) (ii), is the p.d. between the ends of the external resistance, R.

$$\therefore I = \frac{V}{R} \tag{2}$$

Unlike E, which is constant, the terminal p.d. V will vary with the current I and external resistance R.

From (1), $E = I(R + r)$, and from (2), $V = IR$

$\therefore E - V = Ir =$ the potential difference, v, across the internal resistance

$$\therefore E = V + v$$

or, the e.m.f. = the p.d. across the external resistance + the p.d. across the internal resistance.

The terminal p.d. is therefore always less than the e.m.f. (unless the internal resistance is negligible).

It follows from equation (1) that when E is used in any formula the internal resistance, r, must be involved. It can also be seen from the above that

$$r = \frac{E - V}{I}$$

Examples on Complete Circuit

The following examples illustrate circuit calculations with e.m.f. and internal resistance, and should be carefully studied.

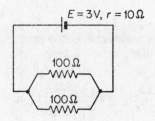

FIG. 2.15. Circuit calculation

EXAMPLES

1. Suppose a dry cell of e.m.f. $1 \cdot 5$ V and internal resistance 4 ohms is connected to a 6-ohm wire. The current flowing, I, is then

$$I = \frac{E}{R + r} = \frac{1 \cdot 5}{6 + 4} = \frac{1 \cdot 5}{10} = 0 \cdot 15 \text{ A}$$

$\therefore$ p.d. across external resistance, 6-ohm wire,

$$V = IR = 0 \cdot 15 \times 6$$
$$= 0 \cdot 9 \text{ V}$$

The p.d. across the internal resistance $= 1 \cdot 5$ V $- 0 \cdot 9$ V $= 0 \cdot 6$ V. As the internal resistance is 4 ohms, the current I inside it $=$ p.d.$/r = 0 \cdot 6/4 = 0 \cdot 15$ A, in agreement with the value previously calculated.

2. A cell has an e.m.f. of 3 V and an internal resistance of 10 Ω. Find the current flowing through the cell and also the p.d. between its poles, (a) when they are joined by two wires in parallel, each of resistance 100 Ω, (b) when they are joined by a wire of negligible resistance (Fig. 2.15).

(a) Let R be the equivalent resistance of the two wires in parallel. Then

$$\frac{1}{R} = \frac{1}{100} + \frac{1}{100}$$

$$\therefore R = 50 \ \Omega$$

$$\therefore I = \frac{E}{R+r} = \frac{3}{60} = 0{\cdot}05 \text{ A}$$

and the p.d. between the poles is given by

$$V = IR = 0{\cdot}05 \times 50 = 2{\cdot}5 \text{ V}$$

(b) Since the wire has negligible resistance,

$$R = 0$$

$\therefore$ total resistance = internal resistance of cell = 10 Ω

$$\therefore I = \frac{3}{10} = 0{\cdot}3 \text{ A}$$

The p.d. between the poles $V = IR = 0{\cdot}3 \times 0 = 0$, an obvious result.

3. Two cells, each having an e.m.f. of 2 V but having internal resistance of 0·3 Ω and 0·2 Ω respectively, are joined in parallel and are connected across a resistance of 0·68 Ω. What current flows through this resistance, and what current is drawn from each cell? (C. & G.)

Let $I =$ the current in the resistance, and I_1, $I_2 =$ the currents drawn from the cells (Fig. 2.16). Then

$$I_1 + I_2 = I \tag{1}$$

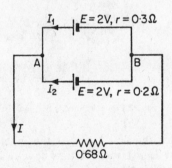

FIG. 2.16. Circuit calculation

The p.d., V, between AB $= IR = I \times 0{\cdot}68$ $\tag{2}$

But V is also the *terminal* p.d. of both cells.

$$\therefore V \text{ for one cell} = E - Ir = 2 - 0{\cdot}3I_1 \tag{3}$$

and for the second cell $V = 2 - 0{\cdot}2I_2$ $\tag{4}$

Equations (1), (2), (3), (4) are sufficient to determine I, I_1, I_2. From (3) and (4),

$$2 - 0 \cdot 2I_2 = 2 - 0 \cdot 3I_1$$
$$\therefore 2I_2 = 3I_1 \tag{5}$$

From (1) and (2),

$$V = 0 \cdot 68I = 0 \cdot 68(I_1 + I_2)$$
$$\therefore 0 \cdot 68(I_1 + I_2) = 2 - 0 \cdot 2I_2 \text{ from (4)}$$
$$\therefore 0 \cdot 68I_1 + 0 \cdot 88I_2 = 2 \tag{6}$$

But $\qquad\qquad\qquad\qquad I_2 = 1 \cdot 5I_1 \text{ from (5)}$

Substituting in (6) for I_2,

$$\therefore 0 \cdot 68I_1 + 1 \cdot 32I_1 = 2$$
$$\therefore I_1 = 2/2 = 1 \text{ A}$$
$$\therefore I_2 = 1 \cdot 5 \text{ A}$$
$$\therefore I = I_1 + I_2 = 2 \cdot 5 \text{ A}$$

Kirchhoff's Laws for Circuits

Kirchhoff gave two laws which enabled the current to be calculated in complicated circuits. They state:

1. The algebraic sum of the currents at a junction is zero.
2. The net e.m.f. in a *closed circuit* is equal to the algebraic sum of the IR products in the circuit.

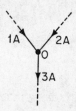

Fig. 2.17. Kirchhoff's first law

Fig. 2.17 illustrates the first law. At the junction O, currents of 1 A and 2 A flow towards it and 3 A thus flow away. If a plus sign is given to a current flowing towards O and a minus to a current flowing away, then

$$+1 \text{ A} + 2 \text{ A} - 3 \text{ A} = 0$$

showing why the first law is true. Thus if I_1 and I_2 are currents flowing towards O and I_3 a current flowing away from O, then

$$+I_1 + I_2 - I_3 = 0, \quad \text{or} \quad I_1 + I_2 = I_3$$

Second Law

The second law applies to a *closed* (or *complete*) *circuit*. As an illustration, consider the circuit in Fig. 2.18.

Step 1. Choose a *closed* circuit, for example, ABCDA.

Step 2. Mark the currents, beginning with I_1 from the battery A. At the junction B, if I_2 flows along BD, then $(I_1 - I_2)$ flows along BC, from the first law.

Step 3. In the closed circuit ABCDA, write down the net *e.m.f.*, which concerns the batteries only. Since they are in opposition,

$$\text{net e.m.f.} = 4 \text{ V} - 1 \text{ V} = 3 \text{ V}$$

Step 4. Write down all the products $I \times R$ in the circuit. *Give a plus sign to a product if the direction of the current is the same as that of the net e.m.f.,*

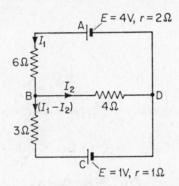

FIG. 2.18. Kirchhoff's laws application

which acts in the direction of ABC since A has a higher e.m.f. than C. Give a *minus* sign to a product if it is in the opposite direction. Thus, considering the resistances this time in the closed circuit ABCDA, we write

$$+6I_1 + 3(I_1 - I_2) + 1(I_1 - I_2) + 2I_1$$

since I_1 flows through the internal resistance of the battery A and $(I_1 - I_2)$ through the battery C.

From the second law,

$$\text{net e.m.f.} = 3 = 6I_1 + 3(I_1 - I_2) + 1(I_1 - I_2) + 2I_1$$

$$\therefore 3 = 12I_1 - 4I_2 \tag{1}$$

Step 5. To obtain I_1 and I_2, we need another equation. Consider, for example, the closed circuit CDBC, which has only one battery at C. Then

$$\text{net e.m.f.} = 1 = -3(I_1 - I_2) + 4I_2 - 1(I_1 - I_2)$$

since the current $(I_1 - I_2)$ flows in the opposite direction to the e.m.f.

$$\therefore 1 = -4I_1 + 8I_2 \tag{2}$$

Solving (1) and (2) we find

$$I_1 = 0{\cdot}35 \text{ A}, \quad I_2 = 0{\cdot}3 \text{ A}$$

Note. If a closed circuit has no battery in it, the net e.m.f. is zero. A current in any particular direction in the circuit can then be given a + sign, in which case a current flowing in the opposite direction has a − sign.

Wheatstone bridge. Measurement of Resistance

The most accurate method of measuring resistance is by a *Wheatstone bridge* network. This consists of four resistances, P, Q, S, R, with a battery B joined to one pair of junctions a, c and a sensitive galvanometer G to the

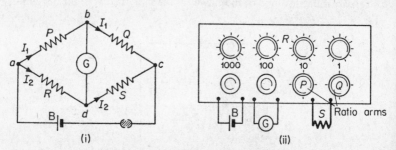

FIG. 2.19. Wheatstone bridge and P.O. box

other junctions, b, d, Fig. 2.19 (i). When the resistances are varied so that no current flows in G, an electrical 'balance' is obtained. In this case

$$\frac{P}{Q} = \frac{R}{S}$$

This is proved as follows:

Since no current flows in G, the current I_1 in P = the current I_1 in Q. Also, the current I_2 in R = the current I_2 in S. Now, the actual potential of b = the actual potential of d because no current flows in G. Thus the p.d. between a and b = the p.d. between a and d. Hence, from $V = IR$,

$$I_1 \times P = I_2 \times R \tag{i}$$

Further, the p.d. between b and c = the p.d. between d and c. Thus

$$I_1 \times Q = I_2 \times S \tag{ii}$$

Dividing (i) by (ii),

$$\therefore \frac{P}{Q} = \frac{R}{S}$$

Thus $S = R \times (Q/P)$ and hence if R and the ratio Q/P are known, the fourth resistance can be calculated.

Dial P.O. Box

The Post Office designed a practical form of Wheatstone bridge for resistance measurement. It contains terminals specifically labelled for the battery, B, galvanometer, G, and unknown resistance, S, and two keys for the battery and galvanometer respectively, Fig. 2.19(ii). The magnitudes of the ratio arms, P and Q, and the variable resistance R are registered on dials. The battery key must be depressed before the galvanometer key so as to establish the current first. The magnitude of the unknown resistance S is given by $S = R \times Q/P$ when a balance is obtained.

The procedure is illustrated by the following:

(*a*) Make $P = 10$ ohms, $Q = 10$ ohms, and vary R until the nearest possible balance is obtained. Suppose $R = 15$ ohms causes the needle in G to deflect one way, and $R = 16$ ohms causes a deflection in the opposite direction.

Then, since

$$S = R \times \frac{Q}{P} = R \times \frac{10}{10} = R$$

this implies that S is between 15 and 16 ohms.

(*b*) Now make $P = 100$ ohms, $Q = 10$ ohms. Suppose $R = 158$, and 159 ohms produce deflections of the needle in opposite directions. Since $S = R \times 10/100 = 1/10$th of R, S is between 15·8 and 15·9 ohms.

(*c*) Finally, make $P = 1,000$ ohms, $Q = 10$ ohms. Suppose $R = 1,582$ ohms when a balance is obtained.

Then $S = 10/1,000 = 1/100$th of $R = 15·82$ ohms.

The reason for the term 'ratio arms' can now be understood. When a balance is obtained, $S = R \times$ the ratio Q/P. The numbers 10, 100, 1,000 for Q and P give simple ratios, 1, 1/10, and 1/100 when the procedure already explained is adopted.

Potentiometer Measurement of E.M.F.

When a moving-coil voltmeter is connected to the terminals of a cell, the reading does not give an accurate value of the e.m.f. because some current flows from the cell.

Fig. 2.20 illustrates an accurate method of comparing the e.m.f.s of cells. It is called a *potentiometer method*. A long uniform wire AB is joined to an accumulator S, which provides a constant current. One cell of e.m.f. E is then connected with its positive pole to A and its negative pole to a point such as F on the wire through a galvanometer G. A current then usually flows through G, as shown. This is because the e.m.f. E (a constant p.d.) may then be *greater* than the p.d. between A and F on the wire. If the contact with F is removed and contact with D is made, the deflection in G may then be in the opposite direction. In this case E is *less* than the p.d. between A and D on the wire.

At some point C between F and D, no current flows in G. Hence E = the p.d. between A and C on the wire. If the cell is removed and a second cell of E_1 is used in its place, a balance may now be found at another point C_1 on the wire. Then E_1 = the p.d. between A and C_1.

$$\therefore \frac{E}{E_1} = \frac{\text{p.d. between A and C}}{\text{p.d. between A and } C_1}$$

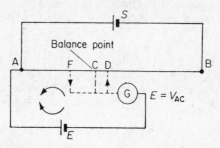

FIG. 2.20. Potentiometer

But the p.d. between the ends of a wire is proportional to its resistance when the current is constant, and the resistance is proportional to the *length* of the wire.

$$\therefore \frac{E}{E_1} = \frac{l}{l_1}$$

where l is the length of AC and l_1 is the length of AC_1. Thus the ratio E/E_1 of two cells may be compared from the ratio of the balance-lengths. Further, if E_1 is the e.m.f. of a *standard cell*, which is accurately known, the unknown e.m.f. can be calculated from $E = E_1 \times (l/l_1)$.

It should be noted that no current flows from the cell of e.m.f. E or E_1 at a balance. Consequently the p.d. at the terminals of the cell is *accurately* the e.m.f. value in each case.

SUMMARY

1. $I = Q/t$. $I = V/R$. $V = IR$. $R = V/I$.

2. The rheostat may be used as a potential divider by connecting a battery to its two 'outer' terminals.

3. In series, $R = R_1 + R_2$; in parallel, $1/R = 1/R_1 + 1/R_2$.

4. The range of a milliammeter may be extended by adding a resistance in parallel and it is converted to a voltmeter by adding a resistance in series.

5. For accurate measurement of p.d. a voltmeter must have a high resistance compared to the resistance between the two points to which it is connected.

6. E.m.f. = p.d. across external resistance (R) + p.d. across internal resistance (r).

7. $I = \dfrac{E}{R+r} = \dfrac{V}{R}$; $r = \dfrac{E-V}{I}$.

8. Kirchhoff's laws: (i) The algebraic sum of the currents at a junction is zero. (ii) In a closed circuit, the net e.m.f. is equal to the algebraic sum of the IR products in that direction.

9. $R = \rho l/a$ — resistivity ρ in 'Ω m'. Pure metals increase in resistance when their temperature rises, carbon then decreases in resistance, and alloys such as manganin have only very slight change in resistance.

EXERCISE 2

Ohm's Law Calculations

1. A current of 2 A is flowing in a wire. What is the quantity of electricity passing a given point in it in (a) 10 minutes, (b) 10 hours?

2. Calculate the current in μA flowing in a wire if 7·2 coulombs flow past a given point in 10 hours.

3. Calculate the p.d. across a resistance of 20 ohms if a current of 3·2 A is flowing in it.

4. The current in a resistor is 1 mA and the p.d. across it is 2·5 V. What is the value of the resistance? What is the current flowing in it if a p.d. of 50 millivolts is applied to it?

5. Two resistances of 5,000 and 10,000 ohms are connected (a) in parallel, (b) in series. Calculate the combined resistance in each case.

6. Two resistances, 10 and 15 ohms respectively, are joined in parallel, and a coil of 14 ohms resistance is placed in series with the combination. (a) Calculate the total resistance of the arrangement. (b) If a p.d. of 100 V is applied across the latter, find the current in each of the three resistances and the p.d. across the parallel combination.

7. A milliammeter has a resistance of 2 ohms and a range of 0–12 mA. Calculate the shunt resistance required to extend the range to 0–1 A.

8. A micro-ammeter has a range of 0–240 μA and a resistance of 500 ohms. (a) What range of voltage could this instrument measure directly? (b) Calculate the series resistance required to convert it into a 0–120 V instrument.

9. What resistance must be placed in parallel with an eleven-ohm coil in order to make the combined resistance ten ohms?

10. Three resistance wires, 5, 4, 10 ohms respectively, are connected in parallel in an electric circuit. If the current in the 4-ohm branch is 20 mA, calculate the currents in the other branches.

11. Explain how a rheostat can be used as (a) a variable resistance, (b) a potential divider. Draw and label a sketch illustrating how the variation of resistance of a lamp with voltage may be obtained.

12. What is the essential difference between an ammeter and a voltmeter? What requirements must they fulfil in relation to the circuit in which they are used in order that accurate measurements should be made?

13. Two resistances of 50,000 and 100,000 ohms are connected in series across a 120-volt supply. Calculate the p.d. across each resistor. A moving-coil voltmeter of resistance 100,000 ohms is connected in turn across each resistor. What is the reading on the instrument in each case?

14. Two resistances of 15 and 30 ohms respectively are connected together in parallel, and a resistance of 10 ohms is placed in series with the combination in an electric circuit. If the p.d. across the 10-ohm resistor is 30 V, find the current in the 15-ohm resistor and the p.d. across the whole arrangement.

Resistivity

15. The resistivity of copper is $1 \cdot 7 \times 10^{-8}\,\Omega$ m. Calculate the resistance of 10 metres of the wire if its area of cross-section is 5×10^{-7} m^2.

16. A current of $1 \cdot 5$ A is flowing along a wire of length $3 \cdot 5$ m and diameter of $0 \cdot 3$ mm. If the p.d. between the ends of the wire is 6 V, calculate the resistivity of the wire.

17. Explain upon what factors the resistance of a metal wire depends. A 10-ohm coil is constructed of manganin wire, $0 \cdot 71$ mm diameter. If the resistivity of manganin is $48 \times 10^{-8}\,\Omega$ m, calculate the length of wire used.

18. The resistance of the wire used for a telephone line is 34 ohms per km when the weight of the wire is 60 kg per km. If the resistance of the material is $1 \cdot 7 \times 10^{-8}\,\Omega$ m, what is the cross-sectional area of the wire? What would be the resistance of a loop to a subscriber 8 km from the exchange if wire of the same material but weighing 240 kg per km was used?   (*C. & G.*)

E.M.F. and Circuits

19. The e.m.f. of a cell is 2 V and has an internal resistance of 2 ohms. If an external resistance of 18 ohms is connected to the poles, calculate the terminal p.d.

20. What is the internal resistance of a cell of e.m.f. $1 \cdot 5$ V which maintains a current of 1 A through an external resistance of $1 \cdot 1$ ohms?

21. Explain what is meant by the terms 'e.m.f.', 'terminal voltage', 'internal resistance' and 'polarisation' when used in respect of a dry cell of the Leclanché type. How many cells, each having an e.m.f. of $1 \cdot 5$ volts and an internal resistance of $0 \cdot 2$ ohm, would be required to pass a current of $1 \cdot 5$ amps through a resistance of 40 ohms?   (*C. & G.*)

Potentiometer

22. Describe how the e.m.f. of a cell is measured by means of a potentiometer. Why is this a more accurate method than measuring the p.d. of the cell on open circuit by a moving-coil voltmeter?

23. Explain fully how a potentiometer is used (*a*) to compare two resistances of the same order, (*b*) to calibrate a voltmeter.

24. The p.d. between the terminals of a cell on open circuit was measured by means of a potentiometer, and a balance was obtained at $95 \cdot 7$ cm. The terminals of the cell were then connected to a 2-ohm resistance coil, and the p.d. between the terminals now gave a balance-point at $83 \cdot 4$ cm. Calculate the internal resistance of the cell.

25. The p.d. across a standard 10-ohm coil was measured by means of a potentiometer when an unknown current flowed in the coil. The balance-point was found to be at $75 \cdot 8$ cm. When a standard cell of $1 \cdot 0186$ volts was used the balance-point was at $54 \cdot 2$ cm. Calculate the unknown current.

26. Describe briefly, with a sketch, a dry cell of the Leclanché type. A dry cell supplies a current of 100 milliamps, when connected across a resistance of 9 ohms, and a current of 50 milliamps when connected across a resistance of 23 ohms. Assuming that the internal resistance of the cell remains constant, what is the e.m.f. of the cell? (*C. & G.*)

Miscellaneous Questions

27. State Ohm's law

Calculate the potential difference across terminals XY in Fig. 2A, when the current in the 25-ohm resistor is 40 mA.

A battery of internal resistance 10 ohms is used to supply this circuit and in order to give the calculated potential difference across XY a 20-ohm resistor in series with the battery is needed. What is the e.m.f. of this battery? (*C. & G.*)

28. Why are some materials better conductors of electricity than others?

Explain why insulating materials eventually break down under excessive voltage stress.

What effect has temperature upon the insulation resistance and breakdown voltage?

Name two electrical materials suitable for use at 100°C. (*C. & G.*)

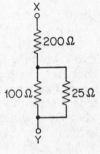

FIG. 2A

29. Explain the principle for the measurement of resistance by means of a bridge circuit and derive an expression from which the unknown resistance can be calculated. What factors determine the accuracy of the measurement?

In a Wheatstone Bridge measurement an unknown resistor is found to balance with 278 ohms in the adjustable arm, the ratio arms being 100-ohm and 200-ohm resistors. When the measurement is repeated with the same circuit but with the 200-ohm resistor replaced by 500 ohms the balancing arm is found to be 685 ohms. The 100-ohm and 500-ohm resistors are known to be accurate, but the 200-ohm resistor in the first measurement is believed to be inaccurate. Calculate its correct value. (*C. & G.*)

30. Explain the principle of the simple potentiometer when used as a means of comparing e.m.fs. Why is it important that the slide wire should be uniform throughout its length?

A small direct current flow in a 100-Ω resistor. How could the potentiometer be used to measure this current without breaking the circuit?

If the standard cell of 1·018 V gives a balance against half the length of the slide wire, what proportion of the length would correspond to the measurement of 15·3 mA in the 100-Ω resistor? (*C. & G.*)

31. Describe the principle of the Wheatstone Bridge for measuring resistance. Explain why a sensitive, centre-zero galvanometer is used in such a bridge circuit.

A Wheatstone Bridge is set up with equal ratio arms of 100 Ω to measure an unknown resistance X, the adjustable resistance then giving a balance at 85 Ω. When one of the ratio arms is replaced by a larger resistance Y the adjustable resistance gives a balance at 160 Ω. Calculate the value of Y.

(*C. & G.*)

3: Electrical Energy and Power

On p. 7, we discussed the relation between p.d. and energy. Here we apply it to a machine and a resistance wire R, Fig. 3.1.

Consider Fig. 3.1 (ii), in which a current of electricity flows from P to T when the resistance wire is connected to the poles of an accumulator, C. The electric potential at P is greater than that at T. This means that a quantity of electricity, Q, at P has a greater energy than the same quantity, Q, at T. Further, as we have seen, energy is liberated when the quantity Q moves from P to T. Now the movement of electricity in the wire is due to the steady drift of electrons, which collide with the atoms of the metal as they move. The energy of the electrons

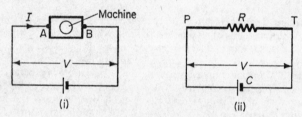

FIG. 3.1. Electrical energy conversion

is given to the atoms, which then vibrate faster, and the temperature of the metal rises. The energy liberated by the movement of electrons thus reappears entirely in the form of *heat* in the wire.

Energy Produced

As stated on p. 7, the volt is defined as the p.d. between two points A and B if 1 joule of energy is liberated when 1 coulomb moves from A to B. Thus if Q coulombs move from A to B in Fig. 3.1(i), where the p.d. is V volts, the energy W supplied to the machine is given by

$$W = QV \text{ joule}$$

Since $Q = I \times t$, where I is the current in amperes and t is the time in seconds (p. 6), then

$$W = IVt \text{ joule}$$

Thus if an electrical machine is supplied with 3 A for 10 min or 600 sec and the p.d. from the supply is 200 V, the energy taken from the supply $= IVt = 3 \times 200 \times 600 = 360{,}000$ joules.

If a suitable electric motor is supplied with this amount of energy, most of it is converted into mechanical energy and the rest as heat and other forms of 'wasted' energy. Again, if accumulators are recharged by this amount of energy, some is converted into chemical energy and the rest wasted as heat. However, if an element of an electric fire or electric cooker of resistance R is connected to A and B, then all the energy is converted into heat. This is the case shown in Fig. 3.1 (ii). Hence, for the resistor R,

$$\text{heat, } H = IVt \text{ joule}$$

But $V = IR$.

$$\therefore \text{ heat, } H = I^2Rt = \frac{V^2t}{R} \text{ joule}$$

If the heat is required in calories, the conversion unit 4·2 joules = 1 calorie (approx.) is used, for example, heat = $I^2Rt/4\cdot2$ calories.

Power

The *power* of any machine is defined as the *rate at which energy is used or liberated.* Thus, generally,

$$\text{power, } P = \frac{W}{t} = \frac{QV}{t} = \frac{IVt \text{ joule}}{t \text{ sec}}$$

$$\therefore P = IV \text{ watts}$$

since 1 watt (W) is defined as the rate of working at 1 joule per sec. Thus an electrical machine which uses 4 A and has a p.d. of 240 V across it has a power = $4 \times 240 = 960$ W. An electronic device which uses a steady current of 5 milliamp and has a steady p.d. of 10 V across it has a power consumption of $(5/1,000) \times 10 = 50/1,000$ W = 50 milliwatt (mW).

In the case of an electric lamp or electric fire where the filament or element has a resistance R, the power P is also given by

$$P = I^2R = \frac{V^2}{R}$$

Thus a 240 V - 60 W lamp has a current I flowing in it given, from $P = IV$, by

$$60 = I \times 240$$

$$\therefore I = \frac{60}{240} = \frac{1}{4} \text{ A}$$

Hence the filament resistance

$$R = \frac{V}{I} = \frac{240}{\frac{1}{4}} = 960 \ \Omega$$

The *kilowatt* (kW) = 1,000 W and is a practical unit of power. The *Kilowatt-hour* (kWh) is a commercial unit of *energy* which is a Board of Trade unit; it is the energy used in 1 hour when the power is constant at 1 kilowatt. Thus if 6–100 W and 8–150 W lamps are used continuously for 2 hours,

$$\text{energy used} = \frac{6 \times 100 + 8 \times 150}{1,000} \text{ (kW)} \times 2 \text{ (h)}$$

$$= 1 \cdot 8 \times 2 = 3 \cdot 6 \text{ kWh}$$

Power Rating of Resistors

Radio resistors and rheostats or potentiometers have a 'power rating' specified by the manufacturer. This is the maximum power which can be safely dissipated. If a greater power is developed in the resistor it will be seriously affected. A 10 kΩ-$\frac{1}{2}$ W radio resistor, for example, can safely dissipate a maximum power of $\frac{1}{2}$ W. Thus the maximum safe current, I, is given by

$$P = I^2 R = I^2 \times 10,000$$
$$\therefore \tfrac{1}{2} = I^2 \times 10,000$$

$$\therefore I = \sqrt{\frac{1}{20,000}} = \sqrt{(50 \times 10^{-6})} = 7 \times 10^{-3} \text{ A}$$

The maximum safe current is thus 7 mA. If a higher current is likely to flow, a resistor with a higher power rating should be used. It is best to double the estimated power dissipation if the resistor is needed to last for some time. For example, if the heat dissipation is likely to be $\frac{1}{2}$ W, it is preferable to use a 1 W resistor and not a $\frac{1}{2}$ W resistor. Resistors rated at over 2 W should be mounted so that the board or panel is not burned.

Energy in Battery Charger Circuits

Batteries are charged from the a.c. mains by using a rectifier, which changes the a.c. to d.c. voltage. A basic charging circuit is shown in Fig. 3.2. It contains a 12 V accumulator whose e.m.f. has fallen to 11·8 V, a rheostat R for obtaining the recommended charging current, an ammeter A, and a d.c. supply of 100 V. If the required charging current is 3 A, then, since 11·8 V acts in *opposition* to the 100 V supply,

$$I = 3 = \frac{100 - 11 \cdot 8}{R + 0 \cdot 1}$$

where 0·1 Ω is the internal resistance of the battery. Hence

$$3(R + 0 \cdot 1) = 88 \cdot 2$$

from which
$$R = 29 \cdot 3 \ \Omega$$

The energy supplied from the 100 V source $= IVt = 3 \times 100$ watts $\times 2$ hours $= 600$ watt-hours, assuming the charging current was constant at 3 A for 2 hours. The energy wasted in the total resistance

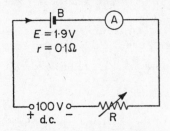

FIG. 3.2. Charging of battery

$= I^2(R + r)t = 3^2 \times 29\cdot4 \times 2 = 529$ watt-hours (approx.). Thus the energy used in restoring the chemicals in the battery $= 600 - 529 = 71$ watt-hours.

Efficiency

The *efficiency*, η, of any circuit or machine is defined by the relation:

$$\eta = \frac{\text{Output power (power delivered by machine)}}{\text{Input power (power supplied to machine)}} \times 100\%$$

Consider the case of a battery or generator of e.m.f. E and internal resistance r supplying power to an apparatus or circuit whose total resistance is represented by an external resistance R. If the current flowing is I, then, if V is the p.d. across R,

input power $=$ power from generator $= IE$;

output power $=$ power developed in $R = IV$

$$\therefore \text{ efficiency, } \eta = \frac{\text{output power}}{\text{input power}} = \frac{IV}{IE} = \frac{V}{E} = \frac{IR}{I(R + r)} = \frac{R}{R + r} \quad (1)$$

This result shows that if r is very small compared with R, as in the case of an accumulator, for example, the efficiency is near 100%. This is because so little energy is wasted in r. On the other hand, if the internal resistance r of the generator is high, the efficiency is low when R is small compared to r. The efficiency of power supplies for apparatus such as oscillators or amplifiers or transformers must be as high as possible for economy. Fig. 3.3 (i) shows how the efficiency varies with the external 'load' R. As R becomes larger, the efficiency tends towards 100% theoretically.

Maximum Power

Maximum efficiency is not always the prime consideration in circuits. One case is the output stage of a radio receiver. This must be designed to deliver maximum *power* to the loudspeaker (see p. 268), so that the loudest sound is produced.

Suppose the loudspeaker has an equivalent resistance R when joined to a power generator of e.m.f. E and internal resistance r. Then

$$\text{power developed in } R, \ P = IV$$

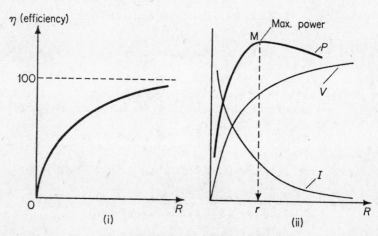

FIG. 3.3. Efficiency and Power variation

Now $I = E/(R + r)$, and hence I decreases as R increases, Fig. 3,3 (ii). The p.d. $V = IR = ER/(R + r)$, and hence increases as R increases, as shown. The product, IV, has a peak or maximum at M, as shown by multiplying the corresponding values or ordinates of the two curves.

Measurement, and theory, show that *the value of R for maximum power is r, the internal resistance.* Thus if a generator has an internal resistance of 2,000 ohms, it will deliver maximum power to an external resistance or 'load' of magnitude 2,000 ohms. In this case the load is said to be the *optimum load*. The efficiency, which is given by $(R/R + r)$, is then $\frac{1}{2}$ or only 50%, as $R = r$. But we are here concerned to obtain maximum power delivery and not maximum efficiency.

Loudspeaker coils have resistances of the order of 10 ohms, say. They need to be supplied with maximum power from a radio or other circuit to produce the loudest sound. Transistors which may supply them with power are 'generators' with an internal 'resistance' of a hundred ohms, say. We therefore need to step-up the loudspeaker resistance to reach optimum load, and this is discussed later (p. 268).

Power Gain. The Decibel

If the power supplied to part of a radio circuit or an apparatus is 100 mW and the output power, or power obtained, is 800 mW, the *power gain* is the ratio 800 mW/100 mW or 8.

A rise in power of the intensity of a sound note from say 1 mW to 10 mW is judged by the ear to be the same as a rise in intensity from 10 mW to 100 mW. The *ratio* of the powers, 10, is the same in each case. Further, a rise in intensity from 1 mW to 100 mW, a ratio of

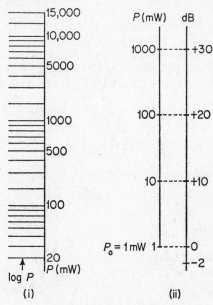

FIG. 3.4. Logarithmic changes

100, appears about twice as loud as a rise from 1 mW to 10 mW, a ratio of 10. Now $\log_{10} 100 = 2$ and $\log_{10} 10 = 1$. Consequently the ear responds to sound intensity variations on a 'logarithmic' basis.

The *decibel* (dB) is a unit of gain or loss in power (or other quantity) on a *logarithmic* basis, using the base 10. It is widely used as a unit in telecommunications or acoustics. Here the enormous range of power changes or frequency changes is reduced to a more compact range of decibels by taking logarithms. This is illustrated in Fig. 3.4 (i) for a power range of 20 mW to 15 W.

The decibel is defined as follows: If a power (or other quantity) changes from a level P_1 to a level P_2, then

$$number\ of\ decibels\ \text{(dB)}\ change = 10 \log_{10} \left(\frac{P_2}{P_1}\right)$$

Thus a power gain from 1 mW to 100 mW = $10 \log_{10} (100/1)$ dB = $10 \times 2 = 20$ dB. A gain from 100 mW to 200 mW = $10 \log_{10} (200/100) = 10 \log_{10} 2 = 10 \times 0.3010 = 3$ dB (approx.).

A power *loss* or *attenuation* from 300 mW to 100 mW

$$= 10 \log_{10} \left(\frac{100}{300}\right) = -10 \log_{10} \left(\frac{300}{100}\right)$$

$$= -10 \log_{10} 3 = -4.8 \text{ dB (approx.)}$$

Fig. 3.4 (ii), illustrates the gain or loss in decibels of a power P, using a power P_0 of 1 mW as a reference (zero dB) level.

When a number of networks are connected together so that the output of one is fed to the next, and so on, the overall gain or loss in power in dB is obtained by simple addition or subtraction. Thus suppose the input at one end is 1 mW and three such networks produce successively power changes of $+20$ dB, -15 dB and $+30$ dB. The output power P is then greater than the input by

$$+20 - 15 + 30 = 35 \text{ dB}$$

$$\therefore \quad 10 \log_{10} \left(\frac{P}{1 \text{ mW}}\right) = 35$$

$$\therefore \quad P = 1 \text{ mW} \times 10^{3.5} = 6{,}990 \text{ mW}$$

Amplifier gain. 3 dB Change

If the input power to an amplifier is P_i and the output power is P_0, the power gain $A = P_0/P_i$. Suppose the input resistance of the amplifier is r_i, the load resistance in the output circuit is R_L; the a.c. input voltage and current are V_1, I_1 respectively; and the a.c. output voltage and current are V_0, I_0 respectively. Then, since power = V^2/R,

$$\text{power gain, } A = \frac{P_0}{P_i} = \frac{V_0{}^2}{V_1{}^2} \cdot \frac{r_i}{R_L}$$

In terms of current,

$$A = \frac{I_0{}^2 R_L}{I_1{}^2 r_i}$$

$\therefore$ gain in decibels = $10 \log A = 20(\log V_0 - \log V_1)$
$$- 10(\log R_L - \log r_i)$$
$$= 20(\log I_0 - \log I_1) + 10 (\log R_L - \log r_i)$$

If the input resistance r_i and the output resistance are equal and the output resistance is matched to the load, then $R_L = r_i$. Hence from above,

$$\text{gain in decibels} = 10 \log_{10} \frac{P_0}{P_i} = 20(\log V_0 - \log V_i)$$
$$= 20(\log I_0 - \log I_i)$$

∴ dB change in power = 2 × dB change in voltage *or* current

Fig. 3.5 shows values of power and voltage change on a decibel

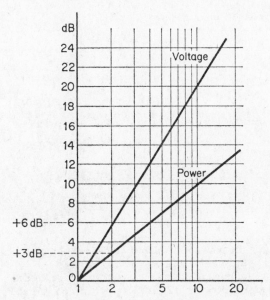

FIG. 3.5. Decibel changes

or dB scale. The dB scale is a 'logarithm scale'.

If the power in an amplifier decreases to one half, then

decibel change = $-10 \log_{10} 2 = -10 \times 0.3010 = -3$ dB (approx.)

A '3 dB change' is often used in discussing the power change in radio circuits, for example, when the frequency of the input is varied (see p. 162). From $P \propto V^2$ and $P \propto I^2$, it follows that a drop in voltage from V to $V/\sqrt{2}$ or 0.7 V (approx.), or a drop in current from I to $I/\sqrt{2}$ or 0.71 (approx.), both represent a decrease of 3 dB in power ratio when the input and output resistances are equal.

EXAMPLE

Define the *decibel* and explain why it is convenient for use in transmission problems.

The input level to an amplifier is $+24$ dB relative to $1\ \mu V$ and the amplifier has a gain of 30 dB. If the input and output impedances of the amplifier are equal and the output is matched to the load, calculate the input and output voltages. (*C. & G.*)

The power in equal resistances is proportional to V^2, where V is the voltage.

$$\therefore \text{ power ratio in dB} = 10 \log_{10}\left(\frac{V_2^2}{V_1^2}\right) = 20 \log_{10}\left(\frac{V_2}{V_1}\right)$$

$\therefore$ input voltage V_1 is such that

$$20 \log_{10}\left(\frac{V_1}{1\ \mu V}\right) = 24$$

$$\therefore \log_{10}\left(\frac{V_1}{1\ \mu V}\right) = 1 \cdot 2$$

$$\therefore V_1 = 1\ \mu V \times 10^{1 \cdot 2} = 1\ \mu V \times 16 = 16\ \mu V \tag{1}$$

Output voltage V_0 is (30 dB + 24 dB) or 54 dB above $1\ \mu V$,

$$\therefore V_0 = 1\ \mu V \times 10^{2 \cdot 7} = 500\ \mu V \text{ (approx.)} \tag{2}$$

SUMMARY

1. Energy change $= QV = IVt$, unit is a *joule*.

$$\text{Power} = IV = \frac{V^2}{R} = I^2 R, \text{ unit is a } watt$$

2. The maximum power is developed in the load of a d.c. circuit when the load is equal to the internal resistance of the battery.

3. Resistors are rated in power, which must not be exceeded.

4. The change in decibels (dB) from a power P_1 to a power P_2 is given by $10 \log_{10}(P_2/P_1)$. A decrease of 3 dB corresponds to a drop in power of one-half. With matched input resistance and output load, a 3 dB drop is also obtained for a voltage or current drop of $1/\sqrt{2}$ times.

EXERCISE 3

What are the missing words in the following statements 1–4?

1. The joule is a unit of . . . ; the watt is a unit of . . .

2. Watts × . . . = joules.

3. A logarithmic unit of power rise or fall is the . . .

4. The total power per unit current supplied by a battery is called its . . .

5. In charging a battery, a current of 3 A flows through a resistor of 20 Ω. Calculate the power dissipated.

6. Can a 12 V battery be safely connected to a resistor of 100 Ω–1 W?

7. Can a current of 10 mA be safely carried by a 1 kΩ–$\frac{1}{4}$ W resistor?

8. The input signal to an amplifier fluctuates from 10 mV to 1 V. What is the fluctuation in dB?

9. The input power to an amplifier rises by (i) 3 dB, (ii) 10 dB from 20 mW in each case. What is the new power in each case?

10. A motor takes 6 A at 110 V. Calculate its power in kilowatts and in h.p. (Assume 1 h.p. = $\frac{3}{4}$ kW.)

11. A lamp takes 50 watts from 100 V mains. Find (a) the current flowing through it, (b) the resistance of the filament, (c) the energy it uses in one hour.

12. 250,000 joules of energy are generated in $\frac{1}{4}$ hour in a conductor carrying a current of 12·5 A. What is the resistance of the conductor?

13. A 100-watt lamp is used normally on a 240 V mains. What is the resistance of the filament?

14. An engine of 150 h.p. drives a dynamo which delivers 220 A and maintains a p.d. of 450 V between its terminals. Find the efficiency of the arrangement. (Assume 1 h.p. = 750 W.)

15. A 2 V battery of negligible internal resistance is connected to wires of 1, 2, 4 ohms resistance, respectively, joined in parallel. Calculate (a) the heat in joules produced in the 2-ohm wire after $\frac{1}{2}$ minute, (b) the ratio of the heats produced in the wires in a given time.

16. A motor takes 6 A from a 240 V main. Calculate the h.p. developed if 80% of the electrical energy is converted into mechanical energy. (750 watt = 1 h.p.)

17. A factory, A, is supplied with electricity from a power station, B. The dynamo at the latter delivers the electrical energy at 220 volts, but owing to the resistance of the leads from A to B the available p.d. at the factory is 200 volts when the current is 25 amp. Calculate (i) the percentage of power dissipated in the leads, (ii) the resistance of the leads.

18. A generator of e.m.f. 10 V and internal resistance 100 ohms is connected to a resistance R. (a) Draw graphs showing the variation with R of the current, p.d. across R, and power in R, taking values of R from 50–150 Ω in steps of 10 Ω. (b) State the value of R for which maximum power in it is obtained, and the magnitude of the latter.

19. The p.d. across a length of 1·6 km of telephone wire, having a cross-sectional area of 22×10^{-4} cm^2 is 6 volts when a current of 50 milliamp is passing through the wire. What is the resistance of a cube, having 1 cm sides, of the material forming the wire? What would be the required area of the conductor if the power loss in the wire, when carrying the same current, is to be reduced to 0·15 watt? (C. & G.)

20. Define the *decibel* and give reasons why its use is convenient for transmission problems.

The input signal to an amplifier varies between 23·5 mW and 1·25 W. Express each power in dB relative to 1 mW and state the fluctuation in the level of the signal in dB. (C. & G.)

21. Calculate the maximum permissible current for the following resistors.
    (i) Carbon: 20 kΩ–$\frac{1}{2}$ W
    (ii) Wire-wound pot: 100 kΩ–15 W.
    (iii) Carbon: 1 kΩ–$\frac{1}{4}$ W.
    (iv) Wire-wound: 200 Ω–1 W.

22. A battery of 12 V and internal resistance 4 ohms is joined to wires of 3 and 6 ohms in parallel. Find the power dissipated in each of the wires and in the internal resistance.

23. Why is heat produced when a current is passed through a resistance? Give an expression from which the amount of heat generated can be calculated.

A small oven used to keep an oscillator at a raised temperature has two separate 100-ohm resistors as heating elements, each operated independently from a 50-volt d.c. supply. The first is permanently connected across the supply. The second is repeatedly switched on and off. It is always 'on' for one minute, but in order to give temperature adjustment in the oven, the time during which it is 'off' can be set to any required value.

Calculate the time per switching cycle during which the heater is 'off', if the average rate of power dissipation by the oven over a long period is 30 watts. (*C. & G.*)

24. Distinguish between the terms *power* and *energy*.

A 50-volt secondary battery used to supply power to two bays of equipment gives on discharge only 60% of the energy that is required to charge it to its initial condition. The first bay requires 8 amperes at 50 volts. The second bay requires 10 amperes at 40 volts and an 8-ohm 40-volt lighting load is also connected in parallel with this bay. A resistor is connected in series with the total 40-volt load so that this load can be supplied from the 50-volt battery.

Calculate the electrical energy required to charge the battery to replace the charge drawn from it in supplying the whole load for one hour. Assume that the battery voltage is constant at 50 volts throughout the discharge period. (*C. & G*).

4: Electrostatic Principles. Capacitors

Friction Produces Charges

A plastic pen-holder or a balloon attracts light pieces of paper after
they are vigorously rubbed. This power of attraction was known
thousands of years ago, and the rubbed materials were said to be
electrified or *charged*. Unlike current electricity, which deals with
electricity which is moving, we are here concerned with static electricity
because the rubbed materials are *insulators*. Static charges are also
produced on insulated *metals* in instruments such as electron micro-
scopes, television receiver or camera tubes, and radio valves. A
competent knowledge of Electrostatics, as the subject is called, is
essential for understanding how many electronic devices function.

Positive and Negative Charges

Experiment showed that rubbed materials possessed either of two
kinds of charges, which were called *positive* and *negative*. We now know
that some electrons are rubbed off from the outer parts of the atoms.
Thus when a polythene rod is rubbed with a duster, electrons pass
from the duster to the rod. The duster is then positively charged
(*electrons have negative charges*, see p. 1). The rod, having gained some
electrons, is now negatively charged. Experiment shows that *like charges
repel, unlike charges attract*.

Induced Charges

If a negatively-charged rod R is brought near to an insulated metal
plate P, electrons (negative charges) in the metal are repelled from A to
B, where A and B are the two sides or faces of P, Fig. 4.1 (i). B then
has a negative charge and A an equal positive charge. The latter charges

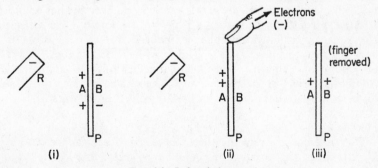

FIG. 4.1. Induced charges

45

are called *induced* charges as they are not acquired by direct contact with the charged rod R.

When the metal P is touched by the finger, electrons repelled by R now leak away to the earth through the body, which is a conductor, Fig. 4.1 (ii). When the finger is removed, P is left only with a positive charge. This is confirmed by experiment. P is said to acquire the positive charge by the process of *induction*.

Force between Charges. Permittivity and Relative Permittivity

When the magnitudes Q_1, Q_2 of two small charges and their distance d apart are varied, experiment shows that the force F between the charges is proportional to the product Q_1Q_2 and inversely-proportional to d^2. Thus

$$F \propto \frac{Q_1Q_2}{d^2}$$

The magnitude of F varies with the nature of the medium in which the charges are situated. When Q_1 and Q_2 are in coulombs and d is in metres, then

$$F = \frac{Q_1Q_2}{4\pi\varepsilon d^2} \text{ newtons}$$

where ε is a constant for the medium. The latter may be a vacuum, air, water, or any other insulating medium. ε is called the *permittivity* of the medium.

The permittivity of a vacuum, ε_0, is a constant which has a numerical value of $1/(36\pi \times 10^9)$ or 8.85×10^{-12} in m.k.s. units; its unit is farad/metre (p. 52). This may also be taken as roughly the permittivity of air. When the air space between two separated metals carrying charges is filled with an insulator such as mica, for example, the force between the charges is reduced about one-sixth. The permittivity ε of mica is thus six times that of air. The *relative permittivity*, ε_r, of a medium is defined as the ratio $\varepsilon/\varepsilon_0$, where ε is the permittivity of the medium. Unlike permittivity ε, ε_r is a ratio or number and has no units. Relative permittivity is also called *dielectric constant*. The dielectric constant of paraffin-waxed paper is about 2, that of mica is about 6 and that of water is about 80. The force between the ions (charges) of sodium and chlorine keeps them together to form common salt (sodium chloride) in the solid state. When water is added to salt the force reduces 80 times and so the salt 'dissolves' in the water.

Electric Fields

Electric fields are regions where an electric force can be detected. Electric fields exist in air all round charged metals inside a television tube or a radio valve, for example.

The electric force or stress in a field can be represented by lines called electric *flux*, whose appearance and density depend on the direction and strength of the particular field. Fig. 4.2 (i) shows a few typical lines round a positive charge Q. The lines occur everywhere in space and not just in the plane of the paper. The arrows on them show the movement of a positive charge in the field.

Screening

When an *earthed* metal plate or gauze is placed between the charge Q and a point B as in Fig. 4.2 (ii), no flux is obtained round B. Hence there is no field round B. We say that the earthed metal M *screens* B from the influence of the electric charge Q.

Screening is explained as follows. The positive charge Q attracts the electrons in the metal M to the side C facing it. The positive

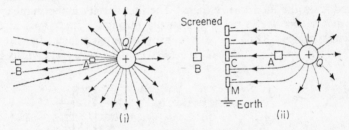

FIG. 4.2. Electric fields and screening

charge left on the side D farther away is neutralised by electrons which flow from the earth to M. Consequently there is no charge on the side D facing B and hence no lines of force round B.

To avoid the effect of strong electric fields in high-voltage laboratories, electrical instruments are tested inside earthed 'cages'. These screen the instruments from external fields. A boiler suit and headgear, with metal wire distributed throughout inside, have been worn by engineers engaged in testing live high-voltage cables. Standing on well-insulated supports, the engineer is then electrically screened by the metal 'cage' round him.

Fig. 4.2 (ii) shows the electric lines of flux between a charged sphere L and a metal gauze M which is connected to the earth. There is an induced negative charge on M.

Fig. 4.3 (i) shows the electric field between a positively-charged plate A and an earthed plate F, with a grid G of parallel wires between them. When the negative charge on G is increased, no lines or field is then obtained at F, Fig. 4.3 (ii). The effect of the positive charge at F is then neutralised by that due to the negative charge (see also p. 211).

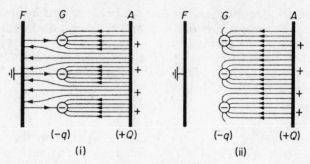

FIG. 4.3. Electric fields

Flux Density. Electric Intensity

The *strength* or *intensity* of an electric field at various points can be judged from the *flux density* there. The flux density is the number of lines per square metre passing normally through a small area at the particular place. Thus the flux density at A is greater than at B, Fig. 4.4 (i); see also Fig. 4.2 (i). Flux density is also known as the

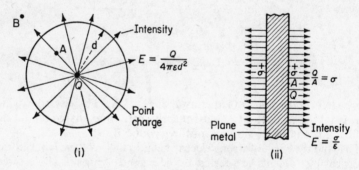

FIG. 4.4. Flux density and electric intensity

electric induction in the medium and is given the symbol D. Its units are 'coulombs per square metre'. If we suppose Q lines spreading all round a small charge of Q coulombs in a medium, then, imagining a sphere of radius d metres round the charge,

$$\text{flux-density, } D = \frac{Q}{\text{area}} = \frac{Q}{4\pi d^2} \tag{1}$$

The strength or intensity, E, at a point in an electric field is defined as the *force per coulomb* at that point. Thus if a small test charge of

q coulomb is placed d metres from a small charge of Q coulombs, then, from p. 46,

$$\text{force on charge } q, \; F = \frac{Qq}{4\pi\varepsilon d^2} \text{ newtons}$$

$$\therefore \text{ force per coulomb} = E = \frac{F}{q} = \frac{Q}{4\pi\varepsilon d^2} \text{ newton per coulomb} \qquad (2)$$

From (1) and (2), it follows that $D = \varepsilon E$ or $E = D/\varepsilon$.

If a charge Q is spread uniformly all over the surface of a small metal *plane*, instead of concentrated at a point as before, then we imagine Q lines of flux normal to the plane on one side, Fig. 4.4 (ii). Close to the plane all the lines pass through an area A. Hence the flux-density D just outside the plane is Q/A. The electric intensity, E, here is given, from (1), by

$$E = \frac{D}{\varepsilon} = \frac{Q}{\varepsilon A} = \frac{\sigma}{\varepsilon}$$

where $\sigma = Q/A = $ *charge-density* on the surface of the plane.

Potential Difference

When electrons are liberated inside a television tube, they are urged to move towards the screen by insulated metals inside, which have high voltages and carry charges. The electrons *gain energy* in moving through the electric field inside the tube, and this is changed into heat and light energy when they strike the screen.

When electric current was discussed on p. 7, it was shown that electrons moving through a wire with a p.d. V volts gain an amount of energy QV joules where Q is the total charge carried in coulombs. If electrons move through empty space, instead of a metal, the energy gained is likewise QV joules, where V is the p.d. in volts and Q is the charge carried in coulombs.

EXAMPLE

An electron of charge $e = 1.6 \times 10^{-19}$ coulomb and mass $m = 9.1 \times 10^{-31}$ kg is liberated with zero velocity inside a cathode ray tube. It is then accelerated in the electric field between two metals which have a p.d. of 1,000 V. Calculate the maximum velocity reached.

The energy gained by the electron in moving between the two plates

$$= QV = 1.6 \times 10^{-19} \times 1,000 \text{ joules}$$

The kinetic energy of the electron on arrival at the second plate

$$= \tfrac{1}{2}mv^2 \text{ joules} = \tfrac{1}{2} \times 9.1 \times 10^{-31} \times v^2 \text{ joules}$$

where v is the velocity in metre per second. Since there is no opposition to the motion of the electron in the evacuated cathode ray tube,

$$\therefore \frac{1}{2} \times 9{\cdot}1 \times 10^{-31}v^2 = 1{\cdot}6 \times 10^{-19} \times 1{,}000$$
$$\therefore v = \sqrt{3{\cdot}5} \times 10^{14}$$
$$= 1{\cdot}9 \times 10^7 \text{ m per sec (approx.)}$$

Electric Intensity and Potential Gradient

Since the potential varies when we move from one point A in an electric field to another point B, we say that a *potential gradient* exists between A and B. By definition, the *potential gradient = (p.d. between A, B)/(distance between A, B)*. A potential gradient thus exists in the space between two parallel metal plates 5 cm apart when they are joined to the terminals of a 200 V battery. In this case

$$\text{potential gradient} = \frac{200 \text{ V}}{5 \text{ cm}} = 40 \text{ V per cm} = 4000 \text{ V per m}$$

If the plates are moved nearer so that they are 2 cm apart, the potential gradient = 200 V/2 cm = 100 V per cm. This is a higher potential gradient than before.

The potential gradient round a point in an electric field is a measure of the electric intensity E there. We can understand why this is the case by imagining a small charge moved a short distance against E, which is defined as the 'force per coulomb' (p. 48). If a considerable amount of work is then done, the intensity is high and the potential energy change is high. The p.d. per centimetre or potential gradient is then high. Conversely, if only a small amount of work is done, the intensity is low and the potential gradient is low. A potential gradient is similar to an 'electric hill'; the steeper the gradient, the more work is done in moving a charge through a given distance, that is, the electric intensity E is high in this case.

Relation between E and Potential Gradient

The exact relationship between E and the potential gradient at a point in an electric field is a simple one. Suppose a small charge q is moved a short distance d in the direction of E. Then, numerically,

$$\text{work done} = \text{force} \times \text{distance} = Eq \times d$$

But the energy change $= q \times V$, where V is the p.d. over the short distance d.

$$\therefore Eq \times d = q \times V$$
$$\therefore E = \frac{V}{d}$$

But V/d is the *potential gradient*. Thus, numerically, $E =$ potential gradient. Consequently the unit of E is often expressed in *volts per metre,* the unit of potential gradient. When calculating the magnitude of the force on a charge in the field the result is in *newtons*, as the following example illustrates.

EXAMPLE

Find the force on, and hence the acceleration of, an electron of charge $e = 1 \cdot 6 \times 10^{-19}$ coulomb and mass $m = 9 \cdot 1 \times 10^{-31}$ kg liberated in a radio valve between two metals 2 mm apart which have a p.d. of 100 V.

$$\text{Electric intensity, } E = \text{potential gradient} = \frac{100 \text{ V}}{2 \times 10^{-3} \text{ m}}$$

$$= 50{,}000 \text{ V per metre}$$

$$\therefore \text{ force on electron} = E \times e = 50{,}000 \times 1 \cdot 6 \times 10^{-19}$$

$$= 8 \times 10^{-15} \text{ newtons}$$

$$\therefore \text{ acceleration} = \frac{\text{force}}{\text{mass}} = \frac{8 \times 10^{-15}}{9 \cdot 1 \times 10^{-31}} = 9 \times 10^{15} \text{ m per sec}^2$$

This enormous acceleration is due to the high numerical value of the electron charge in relation to its mass. The electron thus soon gains a high velocity, which may be 3% of the speed of light, for example.

CAPACITORS

A *capacitor* is an arrangement for storing a quantity of electricity. Millions of capacitors are manufactured annually for use in radio, television and telecommunication circuits. Basically, a capacitor consists of two metal plates separated by an insulating medium such as air, paraffin-wax impregnated paper or mica, for example. The medium is called the *dielectric* of the capacitor.

Charging and Discharging Capacitors

A capacitor such as A, B in Fig. 4.5 (i), becomes charged when a p.d. is applied to the plates, for example, by a battery. In this case electrons are urged to move from plate A to plate B so that a current flows. The plate B then has a negative charge and A has a positive charge. This sets up an opposing p.d to the e.m.f. E of the battery, and when the p.d. becomes equal to E no more electrons flow. The plates now have equal charges, Q say, and are fully *charged*. They are discharged by disconnecting them from the battery and joining them by a wire, Fig. 4.5 (ii). The electrons then return from B to A, so that both plates soon have no charge on them. We shall see later that the inclusion of a high resistance in the circuit will slow down the electron flow during charge or discharge of the capacitor.

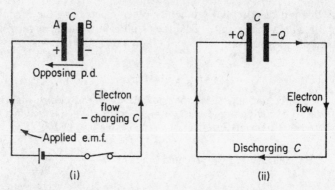

FIG. 4.5. Charging and discharging capacitor

Capacitance

Experiments show that Q, the quantity of electricity stored in a capacitor, is directly proportional to V, the applied p.d. or supply e.m.f.

$$\therefore \frac{Q}{V} = C$$

where C is a constant called the *capacitance*. The greater the capacitance, the more charge will be stored when a given p.d. is applied to the plates.

When Q is in coulombs and V in volts, then C is in *farads*, F. The farad is found to be to be too large a unit for practical capacitors. A smaller unit is the *microfarad*, μF, which is one-millionth or $1/10^6$ F or 10^{-6} F. An even smaller unit is the *picofarad*, pF. This is $1/10^{12}$ or 10^{-12} F. The *nanofarad* is $1/10^9$ or 10^{-9} F.

The following formulae should be remembered:

$$C = \frac{Q}{V} \tag{1}$$

$$Q = CV \tag{2}$$

$$V = \frac{Q}{C} \tag{3}$$

The units must be farads (C), volts (V), coulombs (Q).

EXAMPLE

Find the charge on a $0{\cdot}1\,\mu F$ capacitor when a p.d. of 200 volts is applied to it. What p.d. has been applied to this capacitor if it stores a charge of 5 microcoulomb?

1st part. $Q = CV = \dfrac{0 \cdot 1}{10^6} \times 200$ coulomb

$= 20$ microcoulomb

2nd part. $V = \dfrac{Q}{C} = \dfrac{\frac{5}{10^6}}{\frac{0 \cdot 1}{10^6}} = 50$ volts.

Combined Capacitors

(a) *Parallel.* Suppose C_1 and C_2 are two capacitors in parallel and a p.d. V is applied, Fig. 4.6 (i). The charges $Q_1 Q_2$ on each are then:

$$Q_1 = C_1 V, \qquad Q_2 = C_2 V$$

If C_1 and C_2 were replaced by a single capacitor without affecting their total charge, this would have a capacitance C and a charge Q equal to $(Q_1 + Q_2)$, Fig. 4.6 (ii).

$$\therefore Q = Q_1 + Q_2$$
$$\therefore CV = C_1 V + C_2 V$$
$$\therefore C = C_1 + C_2$$

C is the combined or total capacitance of C_1 and C_2. Generally, all the capacitances are added together to find their combined capacitance

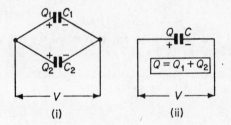

FIG. 4.6. Capacitors in parallel

when they are in parallel. Hence 2, 3 and $4\,\mu\text{F}$ in parallel have a total capacitance of $9\,\mu\text{F}$.

(b) *Series.* The capacitance C of two capacitors C_1, C_2 in series, is given by

$$\frac{1}{C} = \frac{1}{C_1} + \frac{1}{C_2}$$

We can prove this by considering a battery of p.d. V connected across both C_1 and C_2, Fig. 4.7 (i). The electron flow from A to E makes the charges *equal* on both plates, Q say. The other plates B and D then have equal char ges by induction (p. 45).

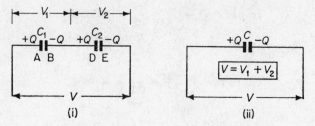

FIG. 4.7. Capacitors in series

If the two capacitors between A and E are replaced by a single capacitor C without affecting their charges, then the charge on C is also Q. This is the charge obtained by shorting the terminals A and E in Fig. 4.7 (i) and the capacitor terminals in Fig. 4.7 (ii). Thus C is the combined or total capacitance of C_1 and C_2 in series.

The p.d. V_1 across $C_1 = Q/C_1$ and the p.d. V_2 across $C_2 = Q/C_2$. The total p.d. V is given by

$$V = V_1 + V_2$$

$$\therefore \frac{Q}{C} = \frac{Q}{C_1} + \frac{Q}{C_2}$$

$$\therefore \frac{1}{C} = \frac{1}{C_1} + \frac{1}{C_2}$$

EXAMPLE

In Fig. 4.8 (i), find (a) the total capacitance, (b) the p.d. across the 3 μF capacitor, (c) the charge on the 2 μF capacitor.

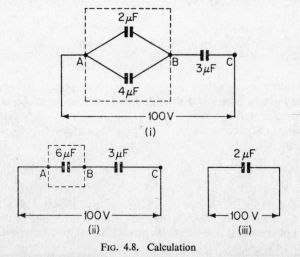

FIG. 4.8. Calculation

(a) The combined capacitance of the 2 μF and 4 μF in parallel = 6 μF. The arrangement is therefore equivalent to the circuit in Fig. 4.8 (ii). The combined capacitance, C, of the 6 μF and 3 μF capacitors is hence given by

$$\frac{1}{C} = \frac{1}{6} + \frac{1}{3} = \frac{3}{6}, \text{ so } C = 2\,\mu F$$

(b) To find the p.d. across the 3 μF capacitor, consider the equivalent capacitor of 2 μF (Fig. 4.12 (iii)).

The charge on it Q

$$= CV = \frac{2}{10^6} \times 100 = 200\,\mu C$$

This is also the charge on the 3 μF capacitor of diagram (ii) since we are dealing with a series circuit.

$$\therefore \text{ p.d. across capacitor} = \frac{Q}{C} = \frac{\dfrac{200}{10^6}}{\dfrac{3}{10^6}} = 66\tfrac{2}{3}\text{ V}$$

(c) To find the charge on the 2 μF capacitor in diagram (i) we require to know the p.d. across A and B, V_{AB}.

Now $\qquad\qquad V_{AB} = 100 \text{ volts} - V_{BC}$

$$= 100 - 66\tfrac{2}{3} = 33\tfrac{1}{3}\text{ V}$$

where V_{BC} is the p.d. across B and C.

$\therefore$ the charge on the 2 μF capacitor,

$$Q = CV = 2 \times 33\tfrac{1}{3} = 66\tfrac{2}{3}\,\mu C$$

Energy in Capacitor

When a capacitor is discharged, a spark often passes across the two plates, accompanied by sound and some heat. Now light, sound and heat are forms of energy. The charged capacitor had thus some energy stored in it. Rows of inter-connected large capacitors have been used to provide high currents and energy by discharging them.

We can calculate the energy stored if we assume that a battery of p.d. V is joined to the capacitor plates, Fig. 4.9. Before connecting the battery, the charge on the capacitor is zero and the p.d. across it is zero. As soon as the battery is connected, charge flows on to the plates and its p.d. rises proportionately since the charge on a capacitor is directly proportional to its p.d. When the capacitor is fully charged it then has a charge Q and a p.d. V. The charge Q has moved, on the average, through a p.d. which is *half* the sum of the p.d. (0) at the beginning and that (V) at the end, that is, through a p.d. of V/2.

Now the energy stored in the capacitor is equal to the work done in moving the charge Q through the average p.d. between its plates, $V/2$ (see p. 8).

$$\therefore \text{ energy, } W = Q \times \frac{V}{2} = \frac{1}{2}QV$$

From $Q = CV$, then, also,

$$W = \tfrac{1}{2}CV^2 = \frac{Q^2}{2C}$$

The energy W is in joules when Q is in coulombs, C is in farads and

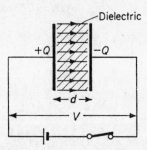

FIG. 4.9. Energy in capacitor

V is in volts. Thus a $2\,\mu$F-capacitor charged by a 100 V battery has an amount of energy W given by

$$W = \frac{1}{2}CV^2 = \frac{1}{2} \times \frac{2}{10^6}\,(\text{F}) \times 100^2\,(\text{V}) = \frac{1}{10^2} \quad \text{or} \quad 10^{-2}\,\text{joules}$$

The energy of a charged capacitor may be considered stored in its dielectric, or in the electric field between its plates. The *energy density*, or energy per unit volume, is the total energy divided by its volume. This can be shown to be equal to $\varepsilon E^2/2$ or $D^2/2\varepsilon$ joules per metre^3.

Capacitance Formula

As we have seen, the simplest capacitor consists of two flat plates with an insulating medium between them. Practical capacitors have a variety of forms, as seen shortly. Basically, however, they are a form of parallel-plate type of capacitor.

Suppose the plates have a common area A, the thickness of the medium or *dielectric* completely filling the space between them is d, and its permittivity is ε (p. 46). If the plates are given a p.d. V and acquire a charge, Q, then intensity of the field between plates,

$$E = \frac{V}{d} = \text{potential gradient}$$

Now from p. 49, the flux-density D in the medium $= \varepsilon E = Q/A$.

$$\therefore \varepsilon \frac{V}{d} = \frac{Q}{A}$$

$$\therefore \frac{Q}{V} = \frac{\varepsilon A}{d}$$

$$\therefore C = \frac{Q}{V} = \frac{\varepsilon A}{d}$$

In this formula, C is in *farads*, if A is the area in square metres, d is in metres, and $\varepsilon = \varepsilon_r \varepsilon_0 = 8.854 \times 10^{-12} \varepsilon_r$, where ε_r is the relative permittivity or dielectric constant of the medium (p. 46).

EXAMPLES

1. Calculate the capacitance between two parallel plates each of area 100 cm^2 and 2 mm apart in air. What charging current would cause the p.d. across this capacitor to rise at a uniform rate of 2 volts per microsecond?

(*C. & G.*)

Area $A = 100 \text{ cm}^2 = 100/10^4 \text{ metre}^2 = 100 \times 10^{-4} \text{ metre}^2$

and $\qquad d = 2 \text{ mm} = 2/1{,}000 \text{ metre} = 2 \times 10^{-3} \text{ metre}$

Using $\varepsilon_0 = 8.85 \times 10^{-12}$, the capacitance C is given by

$$C = \frac{\varepsilon_0 A}{d} = \frac{8.85 \times 10^{-12} \times 100 \times 10^{-4}}{2 \times 10^{-3}} \text{ F}$$

$$= 44 \times 10^{-12} \text{ F (approx)} = 44 \text{ pF}$$

The charge per microsecond,

$$Q = CV = 44 \times 10^{-12} \times 2 \text{ coulomb}$$
$$= 88 \times 10^{-12} \text{ coulomb}$$
$$\therefore \quad \text{current } I = Q \text{ per } second = 88 \times 10^{-12} \times 10^6$$
$$= 88 \times 10^{-6} \text{ coulomb per sec}$$
$$= 88 \times 10^{-6} \text{ ampere} = 88 \text{ } \mu A$$

2. Define the unit of capacitance. Give expressions, with units, for (*a*) the capacitance between two parallel plates separated by a dielectric, (*b*) the energy stored in a charged capacitor.

Each of two separate capacitors consists of two parallel plates with effective area 150 cm^2 spaced 2 mm apart. The dielectric in the first capacitor has a permittivity of 2·3, and in the second capacitor 4·5. Calculate the capacitance of each individual capacitor.

What is the capacitance when the two capacitors are connected: (*c*) in parallel, (*d*) in series? If in (*c*) the capacitors are charged to a p.d. of 100 V, how much energy would be stored in them? (*C. & G.*)

(*a*) $\qquad\qquad\qquad\qquad C = \frac{\varepsilon_r \varepsilon_0 A}{d} \text{ F}$

where A is in square metre and d is in metre.

(b) $$\therefore C_1 = \frac{8 \cdot 85 \times 10^{-12} \times 2 \cdot 3 \times 150 \times 10^{-4}}{2 \times 10^{-3}} \text{ F}$$

$$= \frac{8 \cdot 85 \times 2 \cdot 3 \times 15}{2} \text{ pF} = 153 \text{ pF}$$

Also, $$C_2 = \frac{153 \times 4 \cdot 5}{2 \cdot 3} = 300 \text{ pF}$$

(c) $$C = C_1 + C_2 = 453 \text{ pF}$$

(d) $$C = \frac{C_1 C_2}{C_1 + C_2} = \frac{153 \times 304}{459} = 103 \text{ pF}$$

$$\text{energy} = \tfrac{1}{2}CV^2 = \tfrac{1}{2} \times 453 \times 10^{-12} \times 10^4 \text{ J} = 2 \cdot 3 \times 10^{-6} \text{ J}$$

(see p. 56).

Capacitor Microphone

The capacitor (condenser) microphone is a form of microphone used commercially. Basically, it has a metal-foil diaphragm A, stretched very tightly and mounted close to a back plate B, which has grooves or holes cut in it, as shown, Fig. 4.10. The separation between A and B is of the order of only 0·02 mm.

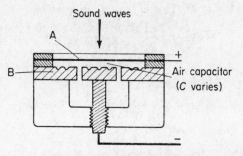

FIG. 4.10.   Capacitor Microphone

A constant charge is maintained on the plate by a battery of about 100 V, with a very high resistance of hundreds of megohms in series. When sound waves are incident on the diaphragm A, the latter vibrates. The separation d between the capacitor plates then varies, and alters C (p. 57). From $V \propto C$, the voltage across the plates then alters, and so an alternating voltage of the same frequency as the sound waves is obtained. This is passed to an amplifier

Practical Capacitors. Multiplate Capacitor

We now consider practical capacitors. The *mica capacitor* is a multiplate or stacked capacitor. One form has two sets of metal foil A and B, carefully insulated from each other, with mica as the dielectric between them, Fig. 4.11 (i). Mica is a high-grade dielectric, that is, the losses in the dielectric are small, and its relative permittivity or dielectric constant ε_r is about 6.

Fig. 4.14 (ii) shows how a multiplate capacitor is built up. The capacitor in Fig. 4.14 (i) has twice the capacitance of capacitor 1 between the top plate and the next plate to it. The capacitor in Fig. 4.14 (ii) has four times the capacitance of capacitor 1. Generally, if n is the number

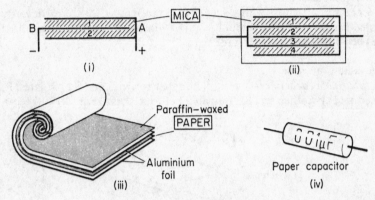

Fig. 4.11. Types of Capacitors

of spaces or dielectrics between the plates of a multiplate capacitor, and $\varepsilon_0 = 8 \cdot 85 \times 10^{-12}$, the capacitance C is given by

$$C = \frac{n\varepsilon_r\varepsilon_0 A}{d} \text{ F}$$

where ε_r is the dielectric constant, A is the area of each plate in square metres, and d is the distance between successive plates in metres. The whole assembly is sealed into a bakelite or plastic case.

The *silver–mica* capacitor has a thin layer of silver coated on the opposite faces of the mica. This eliminates the presence of air between the mica and the 'plate' of the capacitor. The capacitor is very stable and has extremely small losses to frequencies of 200 MHz or more.

Paper Capacitor ·

The paper capacitor has a dielectric of paper impregnated with paraffin wax or an oil. The papers can be rolled between two plates of aluminium foil and then the assembly can be sealed into a cylinder of relatively small volume, Fig. 4.11 (iii), (iv). The paper capacitor is cheap, it can be made in a wide range of capacitance from $0 \cdot 001 \, \mu\text{F}$ to $1 \, \mu\text{F}$, and is widely used in low and medium frequencies, from 50 Hz to 1 MHz, for example. Its main disadvantage is the relatively high power losses in the dielectric. To increase its stability and diminish the power loss, the paper is now replaced by a thin layer of *polystyrene*.

Silver–ceramic

Certain ceramics have a high relative permittivity or dielectric constant, ε_r. They can be made into a capacitor of small size but high capacitance by silvering the outside surface of a thin hollow ceramic tube, and attaching wire terminals.

Ceramic capacitors with values of ε_r between 6 and 90 are particularly noted for their excellent stability and low losses, and are therefore used in very-high-frequency circuits.

Variable Capacitor

A *variable capacitor* is a multiplate capacitor with one set of plates, F, fixed and the other set, M, movable between them, Fig. 4.12. M can

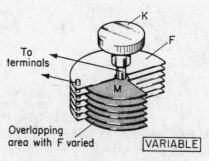

FIG. 4.12.   Variable Air Capacitor

be rotated between F by means of a knob K. The plates F and M may be semicircular or of other shapes. Fig. 4.13 represents three positions of F and M when viewed from above. The principle concerned is

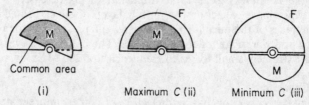

FIG. 4.13.   Variation of common area

simply that the capacitance, C, of a parallel-plate capacitor varies with the area, A, of overlap.

The *variable air capacitor* is used in receiver sets for tuning to the frequencies of radio stations. The maximum capacitance is then about

0·0005 μF. The main advantage of air is that it has extremely low energy losses (a vacuum is a 'perfect' dielectric in this respect). The dielectric strength of air, however, is relatively low. The plates must therefore be well spaced and insulated to prevent voltage 'breakdown' between the plates (p. 62). On this account the variable air capacitor is relatively bulky.

Shape of plates. The frequency of the wave to which the variable capacitor is tuned is proportional to $1/\sqrt{C}$, where C is the capacitance used (see p. 158). Thus the wavelength λ, which is inverse proportional to the frequency, is directly proportional to $\sqrt{C}$. With the fixed plates semicircular and the variable plate shaped in a special manner, the *square* of the angle of rotation θ can be made directly proportional to the area A of overlap. In this case, since $C \propto A$, $\lambda \propto \sqrt{C} \propto \sqrt{A} \propto \theta$. Thus the wavelength is proportional to the angle of rotation. This type of capacitor is called a *square-law* capacitor on account of the shape of the plates.

Another shape of plates, in which the movable plate is semicircular and the fixed plate is shaped, produces a *log law* capacitor. In this case, the angle of rotation is proportional to log λ, where λ is the wavelength. Thus, like the decibel system (p. 39), many stations of widely different wavelength can be grouped conveniently together. Log law capacitors are widely used. *Ganged capacitors,* which consist of several identical variable capacitors beside each other with the movable plates all on one shaft, are log law types. *Trimmer capacitors* are provided as a fine adjustment to equalise all the capacitances. They are of the order of pF. A trimmer capacitor may be a variable air capacitor or an adjustable mica-air dielectric. In the latter case a slight shift of mica will affect the total capacitance.

Electrolytic Capacitors

Electrolytic capacitors are widely used. Basically, they are made by passing a direct current between two aluminium plates immersed in an

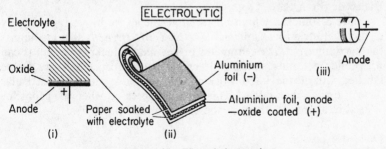

FIG. 4.14. Electrolytic capacitor

electrolyte consisting of ammonium borate solution. Electrolysis takes place, and a very thin film of aluminium oxide is formed on the positive plate, the anode, Fig. 4.14 (i). This film acts as an insulator. It now constitutes the *dielectric* between the two plates of a capacitor, one of which is the positive aluminium plate and the other the electrolyte.

The capacitance C is inversely proportional to the distance, d, between the plates. In the present case d is the thickness of the film of aluminium oxide. It is so small in practice that C becomes very large. An electrolytic capacitor may thus have a capacitance of $200\,\mu F$ in the same space as that occupied by a $2\,\mu F$ paper capacitor. This is an advantage. The electrolytic capacitor is used in radio circuits where a very large capacitance is required. It is cheaper than the other types of capacitors mentioned.

A 'dry' electrolytic capacitor is now made. This is done by rolling paper soaked in the electrolyte between two aluminium foils, Fig. 4.14 (ii). The anode aluminium foil is oxide coated. The whole assembly may be sealed into a metal can, Fig. 4.14 (iii).

A most important point about electrolytic capacitors is that they can only be used in a circuit where the potential of the anode (see above) is *always positive* relative to the other plate. If the potential of the anode becomes negative the aluminium oxide film breaks down. The makers are careful to mark clearly the terminal of the anode of the electrolytic capacitor, usually in red or by a $+$ sign near to it. The capacitors are widely used to provide the large capacitance needed in filtering the ripple in power supply circuits (p. 190) or in decoupling a resistance to prevent a.c. feedback (p. 218). In either case the p.d. acts in one direction when the circuit is working, and a small current flows to maintain the oxide film.

Electrolytic capacitors have considerable dielectric losses. They are not used above a frequency of 10 kHz. Their voltage rating, that is, the maximum voltage which must not be exceeded for dielectric breakdown, depends on the size.

Dielectric Strength

Under a sufficiently high potential gradient, the insulating property of any dielectric breaks down. The *dielectric strength* of a medium is the maximum p.d. per centimetre or per metre thickness which it can withstand, without breaking down. Practical capacitors are hence labelled with the maximum working voltage, above which the particular dielectric will break down. This must be observed when the capacitor is used in a circuit, otherwise the capacitor will be useless.

Dielectric Losses

When alternating voltage is applied to a capacitor, experiment shows that some power is absorbed by the dielectric (see p. 180). These 'dielectric losses', as they are termed, may be considered due to 'dielectric hysteresis', which is analogous to magnetic hysteresis, discussed later on p. 104. The loss of power is important in radio circuits.

Here the alternating voltages concerned may be going through several million cycles per second.

Air has practically no dielectric losses. It is almost a perfect dielectric in this respect. The variable capacitor used for tuning is an air capacitor. A paper dielectric has high losses, but it is inexpensive, and has a fairly large capacitance in relation to its volume. A mica dielectric is a high-grade capacitor in the sense that it has much lower losses than a paper capacitor, but it is more expensive. It has the disadvantage that it cannot be rolled. Electrolytic capacitors have considerable energy losses, relatively very much greater than any other form of capacitor.

Other Capacitances. Self-capacitance

In any coil of wire, as shown in Fig. 4.15 (i), P and the next turn Q

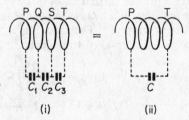

FIG. 4.15. Self-capacitance of coil

constitute two pieces of metal separated by air. Consequently, there is a capacitance C_1 between P and Q. This is the case for the other turns Q, S and T, as shown by C_2 and C_3. The combined capacitance, C, of all these capacitors is known as the 'self-capacitance' of the coil. It is shown in parallel with the coil in Fig. 4.15 (ii) and its value is usually very low and of the order of pF.

Stray-capacitance

A resistor R of practically any shape has some capacitance C, which depends on its geometrical form. C is known as the 'stray-capacitance'. It is represented in parallel with R in Fig. 4.16 (i) and is of the order of pF.

Aerial Capacitances

There are many kinds of aerials, but their common feature is that of a wire such as AB insulated from the earth (Fig. 4.16 (ii)). Each point on the wire constitutes one plate of a capacitor, the other being the earth. C_1, C_2, C_3 represent some of the 'distributed capacitance' of the aerial. The inserted variable air capacitor C may be termed, in contrast, the 'loading' capacitance of the aerial.

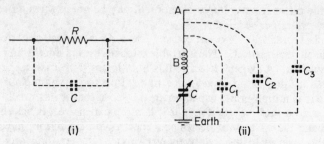

FIG. 4.16. Capacitance of resistor and aerial

Charging with C-R in Series

If a capacitor C is charged by pressing a key K in a circuit with a battery, Fig. 4.17 (i), a flow of current takes place (p. 51). The current continues until the opposing p.d. across the plates becomes equal to E, the e.m.f. of the battery supply. The capacitor is then fully charged. All this takes place in an interval of time depending on the resistance in the circuit.

It is possible to slow up the rate at which the capacitor becomes

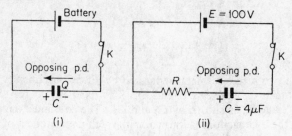

FIG. 4.17. Charging capacitor

charged by placing a high resistance, R, of the order of megohms in series with it (Fig. 4.17 (ii)). When K is now depressed, the charge, Q, rises much more slowly to its maximum value.

Typical charging curves, showing how Q increases with time when C is $4 \mu F$ are shown in Fig. 4.18. The vertical axis represents Q in μC (microcoulombs) and the horizontal axis t in seconds. The capacitance $C = 4 \mu F$ is the same for all the curves, but $R = 3$ MΩ in (1), 2 MΩ in (2), and $\frac{1}{2}$ MΩ in (3). When the capacitor is *fully* charged there is no current in the circuit and the p.d. across it is equal to the e.m.f. of the applied battery. Suppose $E = 100$ volts. Then the final or maximum charge on the capacitor,

$$Q_m = CV = \frac{4}{10^6} \times 100 = 400 \mu C$$

As C and the applied voltage are the same for each of the curves, the charge on the capacitor rises to the same maximum value of $400\,\mu\text{C}$.

Time Constant. If the three curves are examined it is clear that (1) represents a slower rate of charging the $4\,\mu\text{F}$ capacitor than either (2) or (3). Curve (3), corresponding to $C = 4\,\mu\text{F}$, $R = \frac{1}{2}\,\text{M}\Omega$, shows that the charge on the capacitor rises to its maximum value more rapidly than when $C = 4\,\mu\text{F}$, $R = 2\,\text{M}\Omega$, or when $C = 4\,\mu\text{F}$, $R = 3\,\text{M}\Omega$.

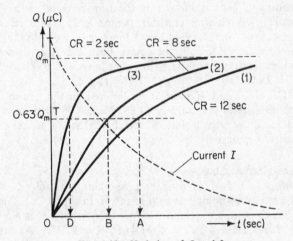

Fig. 4.18. Variation of Q and I

A mathematical study of a circuit with a battery of e.m.f. E applied to C and R in series shows that (a) the charge Q on C grows with time t according to an 'exponential' law, (b) the charge on the capacitor reaches 63% of its maximum value after a time equal to CR seconds, where C is the number of farads and R is the number of ohms. The proof of these statements is beyond the scope of this book. The variations of Q with t shown in Fig. 4.18 are exponential curves.

Fact (b) stated above forms a very useful method of comparing the rate of charging capacitors when a resistance is included in series with it. Take the case of $C = 4\,\mu\text{F}$, $R = 3\,\text{M}\Omega$ (1). Then

$$CR \text{ sec} = \frac{4}{10^6} \times 3 \times 10^6 = 12 \text{ sec}$$

For $C = 4\,\mu\text{F}$, $R = 2\,\text{M}\Omega$ (2),

$$CR \text{ sec} = \frac{4}{10^6} \times 2 \times 10^6 = 8 \text{ sec}$$

For $C = 4\,\mu\text{F}$, $R = \frac{1}{2}\,\text{M}\Omega$ (3),

$$CR\,\text{sec} = \frac{4}{10^6} \times \tfrac{1}{2} \times 10^6 = 2\,\text{sec}$$

Thus the charge on the capacitor rises to 63 per cent of its maximum (fully charged) value in 12 sec for (1), in 8 sec for (2), and in 2 sec for (3). The capacitor is thus charged at the fastest rate for circuit (3), and at the slowest rate for circuit (1).

The product $CR\,\text{sec}$ is known as the *time-constant* in a C and R series circuit. A high time-constant means a slow rate of charging. The charge-curves (1), (2), (3) in Fig. 4.18 are labelled with their respective time-constant values. If they have been carefully drawn and a horizontal line is drawn from T to intersect them where $\text{OT} = 0.63\,Q_m$, then $\text{OD} = 2$ sec, $\text{OB} = 8$ sec and $\text{OA} = 12$ sec.

After $2CR$, $3CR$ and $4CR$ sec from the instant the circuit is made, the charge on C rises respectively to 86, 95 and 99% of its maximum (final) value. Thus after a time of about $5CR$ sec, a capacitor can be considered fully charged.

Voltage and Current Changes

The *voltage* across C is directly proportional to Q. It therefore rises from zero at a similar rate to that shown in Fig. 4.18. The *current* I in the circuit is always given by $I = V/R$, where V is the voltage across R. Suppose $E = 100$ V, $C = 4\,\mu\text{F}$, $R = 2\,\text{M}\Omega$. At the instant of switching on ($t = 0$), the charge on C and the voltage across C are zero. Hence, since R and C are in series, the voltage across R is 100 V. Thus the current I on switching on is given by

$$I = \frac{100}{2 \times 10^6} = 50\,\mu\text{A}$$

As the voltage across C rises, the p.d. V across R decreases since $V = (100 - \text{voltage across } C)$. Thus the current decreases continuously to zero, as the following example also illustrates.

EXAMPLE

An uncharged capacitor (C) in series with a resistor (R) is connected to a constant voltage supply (V). Why does the voltage across the capacitor rise slowly? Sketch a curve of voltage against time. What is the meaning of *time-constant* for the circuit?

A capacitor of 10 μF is charged through a series resistor from a 100-V battery. What value of resistor will give a time constant of 0·1 seconds? For this circuit calculate the current flowing: (*a*) at the instant of switching on, (*b*) after a time equal to the time constant, (*c*) after a long period of time.

(*C. & G.*)

First part. Briefly the voltage across C rises slowly because the resistance R reduces the current charging C.

Let R = the resistance in ohms. Since CR is the time constant,

$$\therefore 10 \times 10^{-6} \times R = 0.1$$

$$\therefore R = \frac{0.1}{10 \times 10^{-6}} \, \Omega$$

$$= 10,000 \, \Omega = 10 \, \text{k}\Omega$$

(a) When $t = 0$, there is no voltage across C. Hence voltage V across $R = 100$ V.

$$\therefore I = \frac{V}{R} = \frac{100}{10,000} \, \text{A} = 10 \, \text{mA}$$

(b) When $t = CR$ sec, voltage across $C = 0.63 \times 100$ V $= 63$ V (approx.). Thus voltage V across $R = 100 - 63 = 37$ V.

$$\therefore I = \frac{V}{R} = \frac{37}{10,000} = 3.7 \, \text{mA}$$

(c) After a long time,

$$I = 0$$

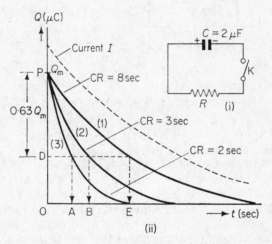

Fig. 4.19. Discharging C through high R

Discharge of C through High Resistance

The discharge of a charged capacitor C can be slowed and varied by using different high resistances R in series, Fig. 4.19 (i). Fig. 4.19 (ii) shows how the charge Q diminishes with time t when $C = 2\,\mu\text{F}$, $R = 4\,\text{M}\Omega$ (curve 1), $C = 2\,\mu\text{F}$, $R = 1\frac{1}{2}\,\text{M}\Omega$ (curve 2), and $C = 2\,\mu\text{F}$, $R = 1\,\text{M}\Omega$ (curve 3). The product CR when C is in farads and R

is in ohms is the *time-constant* in seconds. It represents the time taken for the charge to decrease by about 63% of its initial value Q_m. Thus, in Fig. 4.29, OA represents 2 sec, OB represents 3 sec and OE represents 8 sec. The fastest discharge corresponds to the smallest value of the time-constant. We shall see later that a combination of capacitor-resistor in some radio circuits requires a particular value of time-constant (p. 317).

The *voltage* V across C follows the same variation with time as the charge Q, since $V \propto Q$. The *current* I in the circuit $= V/R$ and hence varies in the same way as V.

Pulse Voltage and *C–R* Circuit

A *pulse voltage* is an abrupt variation of voltage repeated at definite time intervals. It may be obtained from certain radio circuits and is utilised in conjunction with a capacitor-resistor (*C–R*) combination in television and computer circuits.

Fig. 4.20 (i) illustrates a rectangular pulse voltage. It rises to a

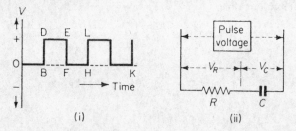

FIG. 4.20. Pulse voltage

maximum BD at an instant B, remains constant for a time BF, then becomes zero at F for a time FH, and repeats this cycle of variations.

In Fig. 4.20 (ii) the pulse voltage V is applied to *C–R* in series. Fig. 4.21 shows the voltage obtained across the two components. The voltage V_C rises along BY to a maximum value, since the voltage V charges the capacitor through R in the time interval BF, Fig. 4.21 (ii). When the pulse voltage becomes zero at F, C discharges through R. Thus V_C falls along YT. The action is then repeated.

The voltage V_R is given by $V_R = IR$, where I is the current at a particular instant. As C becomes charged, the current diminishes. Thus V_R varies along LF in the time BF, Fig. 4.21 (iii). When C discharges, the current diminishes again but in the opposite direction, from M to H. Since $V_C + V_R = V$, the voltage graphs of V_C and V_R add together to form the graph of V, as the reader should verify. V_C provides an 'integrating voltage' and V_R a 'differentiating voltage' for analogue computer circuits.

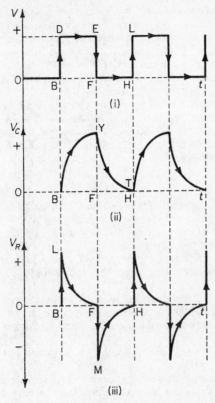

FIG. 4.21. Voltage waveforms

SUMMARY

1. Positive and negative charges have electric fields round them.

2. The field strength or intensity at a place is numerically equal to the potential gradient there.

3. Earth potential is 'zero' by convention.

4. $C = Q/V$, where C is in farads, Q in coulombs, V in volts. A coil of wire has a 'self-capacitance', a resistance wire 'stray-capacitance', an aerial 'distributed capacitance'.

5. In series, $1/C = 1/C_1 + 1/C_2$; in parallel, $C = C_1 + C_2$.

6. (*a*) The capacitance of a parallel-plate capacitor is given by

$$C = \frac{\varepsilon_r \varepsilon_0 A}{d} \text{ F}$$

(*b*) The capacitance of a multiplate capacitor is n times that above, where n is the number of dielectrics. The variable capacitor is usually a 0.0005 μF air capacitor, with one set of movable plates.

(c) The electrolytic capacitor has aluminium as one of its plates and the electrolyte as the other. The dielectric is a very thin film of aluminium oxide between them, which produces a large capacitance. The capacitor can be used only across two points whose p.d. is always in the same direction.

7. The energy of a capacitor = $\frac{1}{2}QV = \frac{1}{2}CV^2$, and is stored in the dielectric. 'Dielectric losses' are greatest for the electrolytic capacitor, and very nearly zero for an air capacitor.

8. The time-constant is CR sec. for the charge and discharge of a capacitor through a resistance, where C is in farads and R is in ohms. When the capacitor is charged the p.d. across it increases and the current in the circuit decreases. When the capacitor is discharged the p.d. falls at the same rate as the current diminishes.

EXERCISE 4

1. Write down the relation between charge Q, p.d. V and capacitance C. What is the charge on a 2 μF capacitor joined to a 100-V battery?

2. Which type of capacitor has (i) the smallest, (ii) the highest dielectric constant or relative permittivity?

3. What is the meaning of *microfarad* and *picofarad*? What values, roughly, may an electrolytic capacitor and a tune control or trimming capacitor have?

4. A charge of 0·2 microcoulomb is obtained on a capacitor of magnitude C when a battery of 100 V is applied. What is the magnitude of C?

5. Describe a capacitor which can be used in 'tuning' and explain its action.

6. From the following capacitors A, B, C, which would you use for (i) 0·1 μF, (ii) 100 μF, (iii) 0·0005 μF:

A air capacitor, B paper capacitor, C electrolytic capacitor?

Which type of capacitor has the greatest loss of energy and which has the least loss of energy?

7. Write down an expression for the *energy* of a capacitor C when a p.d. V is applied. Calculate the energy stored when a 4 μF capacitor is charged by a battery of 100 V.

8. Which formula correctly gives the capacitance of a parallel-plate capacitor: (i) ε_0/A, (ii) εAd, (iii) $\varepsilon A/d$, (iv) $\varepsilon A/d^2$, (v) $\varepsilon A^2/d$? The permittivity of free space is $8 \cdot 854 \times 10^{-12}$ farad/metre. Calculate the capacitance in pF of a parallel-plate air capacitor whose common area is 100 cm^2 and whose plates are 1 mm apart.

9. Calculate the capacitance between two parallel plates each of 200 cm^2 and 1 mm apart in air.

What charging current would cause the p.d. across the capacitor to rise at a uniform rate of 4 volts per microsecond?

10. A 200 V battery is connected to a 4 μF and 1 μF capacitor in series. Calculate the charge on, and p.d. across, each capacitor.

11. A capacitor of 5 μF is connected in parallel with the 1 μF capacitor in Q. 10. Find the p.d. now across the 4 μF capacitor, and the charge on the 5 μF capacitor.

12. Describe a variable capacitor. On what factors does its maximum capacitance depend?

13. What factors determine the capacitance existing between two parallel metal plates? Give a formula from which this capacitance can be calculated.

Two insulated parallel metal plates each of 600 cm² effective area and 5 mm apart in air are charged to a p.d. of 1,000 volts. Calculate (a) the capacitance between the plates, (b) the charge held by the capacitor.

The source of supply is now disconnected, the plates remaining insulated. (c) Calculate the p.d. between the plates when their spacing is increased to 10 mm. (d) Calculate the p.d. when the plates, still 10 mm apart, are immersed in oil of relative permittivity 5·0.   (C. & G.)

14. What is the advantage of electrolytic capacitors? Describe how one is constructed, and state the chief precaution to be observed when it is used.

15. Calculate the time constant of a series circuit in which (a) $C = 0.2 \ \mu F$, $R = 1$ megohm, (b) $C = 0.001 \ \mu F$, $R = 100,000 \ \Omega$. State which capacitor charges at a slower rate.

16. Define the unit of capacitance. Give expressions, with units, for (a) the capacitance between two parallel plates separated by a dielectric, (b) the energy stored in a charged capacitor.

Each of two separate capacitors consists of two parallel plates with effective area 300 cm² spaced 1 mm apart. The dielectric in the first capacitor has a permittivity of 2, and in the second capacitor 6. Calculate the capacitance of each capacitor.

If the capacitors are placed in parallel and charged to a p.d. of 100 V, how much energy would be stored in them?

17. State the relationship between the voltage across a capacitor, the charge it carries and its capacitance. Derive an expression for the energy stored by a charged capacitor.

A parallel-plate capacitor having two plates each of effective area 200 cm² spaced 4 mm apart, is immersed in a tank of oil of relative permittivity 5. Calculate the capacitance.

An identical capacitor, but with air, not oil, as the dielectric, is connected in parallel with the first, the two being then charged in parallel from a 500-V battery. What is the energy stored in the combination? The battery is then disconnected and the oil drained from the tank. Calculate the final potential difference across the capacitors.   (C. & G.)

18. A charged metal ball, 15 cm in diameter, is suspended so that the centre of the ball is 30 cm above a large earthed flat metal plate. Draw the lines of electric force surrounding the ball. A capacitor consisting of two parallel plates, one of which is insulated and one of which is earthed, and spaced 5 cm apart, is charged to a p.d. of 100 volts. Explain what would be the effect on the voltage between the plates if the earthed plate is moved to bring the plates 2·5 cm apart.

19. Why does the capacitance of a capacitor depend on the area of the plates, the separation of the plates, and the type of insulating medium employed? A charge of 1 micro-coulomb is applied to a capacitor consisting of two plates each 40 cm in diameter, spaced 2 mm apart in air. To what voltage would the condenser be charged?   (C. & G.)

20. Discuss briefly the factors which determine the choice of dielectric in the electrolytic, fixed and variable types of capacitors used in a radio receiver.

Quote typical capacitance values for (a) a preset trimming capacitor as used in a tuned radio circuit, and (*b*) an electrolytic capacitor. Mention two uses of an electrolytic capacitor.

What determines the shape of the plates required in a variable tuning capacitor?   (*C. & G.*)

21. What are the relative advantages and disadvantages of paper, as compared with air, as a dielectric? A capacitor is made from three parallel plates separated 0·5 cm from each other, the outer two plates being connected together. What would be the effect on the capacitance of the capacitor if the middle plate were moved to a distance of 0·25 cm from the top plate?

(*C. & G.*)

22. A 1 μF capacitor and a 2 MΩ resistor are connected in series with a 50 V battery. Calculate (*a*) the final charge on the capacitor, (*b*) the initial current in the circuit, (*c*) the current after 2 sec.

23. A 2-megohm resistor, *R*, is connected in series with a 2 μF capacitor, *C*, and the combination connected to a 200-volt battery. Draw to scale the variation with time of (i) the voltage across *C*, (ii) the voltage across *R*, (iii) the current in the circuit, taking times of 0, *CR*, 2*CR*, 3*CR*, 4*CR* sec.

5: Magnetism and Electromagnetism

Magnetism. Repulsion and Attraction

Magnets are used in a wide variety of applications in industry. In telecommunications and radio, for example, they are used in relays, telephones and loudspeakers. Here we shall deal only with the basic principles of magnets.

A pivoted magnet will turn and finally take up a position pointing approximately geographic north–south. The end of the magnet which

FIG. 5.1.   Force between poles

always points northwards is called a *magnetic north* (*N*) *pole*; the other end, which always points southwards, is called a *magnetic south* (*S*) *pole*.

By bringing the N-pole of a magnet slowly towards the N-pole of a pivoted magnet or magnetic needle, and then repeating with two S-poles, experiment shows that *like poles repel*, Fig. 5.1 (i). A N- and a S-pole, however, attract each other, Fig. 5.1 (ii). Hence *unlike poles attract*. This is a fundamental law of magnetism.

Magnetic Materials

Pure (soft) iron, nickel and cobalt are strongly attracted by magnets. They are called *ferromagnetic* substances. [There are substances only weakly attracted by magnets, called *paramagnetic*, and others which settle in equilibrium at right angles to an applied magnetic field, called *diamagnetic*. These will not concern us.] Powerful magnets, both permanent and temporary, can be made from alloys of nickel and cobalt. *Alnico* is an alloy used for permanent magnets. *Mu-metal* is an alloy used for transformer cores. In addition, materials called *ferrites*, made from a form of ferric oxide, are widely used in modern electronics and radio equipment, for example, as aerials in transistor receivers.

Steel is made from iron by adding a small percentage of carbon. The effect is to make a substance which is physically and magnetically much harder than pure iron. The magnetic differences between iron and steel are discussed later, but for the present we may note that (*a*) unmagnetised iron can be made into a magnet much more easily

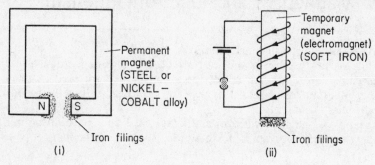

FIG. 5.2. Magnet and Electromagnet

than unmagnetised steel, and (*b*) a steel magnet is much harder to demagnetise than an iron magnet, i.e. it makes a better permanent magnet, Fig. 5.2 (i), (ii). Iron and steel are called, simply, magnetic substances, while brass, wood, and lead are examples of non-magnetic substances.

Magnetic Induction

Magnets may be made by stroking a bar of steel, for example, with a magnet or by placing the steel inside a current-carrying solenoid, a long coil of insulated wire (p. 77). Magnets are also obtained without

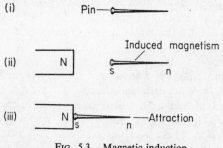

FIG. 5.3. Magnetic induction

actual or physical contact, in which case they are said to be obtained by *induction*.

A simple example occurs when a magnet is moved towards a steel pin, Fig. 5.3. Due to the magnetic effect of the N-pole on tiny magnetised regions or domains inside the steel, the pin becomes magnetised as shown, Fig. 5.3 (ii). Its magnetism is 'induced'. As a result of the attraction by the N-pole on the pole nearest to it, the pin now moves towards the N-pole, Fig. 5.3 (iii). Thus a magnetic material is first magnetised by induction before attraction occurs.

Magnetic Fields

The region where a magnetic force is experienced is called a *magnetic field*. We can easily see the magnetic field pattern due to a magnet or magnets on paper by sprinkling iron filings all round and tapping the paper. The filings become magnetised by induction, and then turn and take up a position along the direction of the magnetic force. The field due to a bar-magnet is *non-uniform*; its magnitude and direction vary from point to point, Fig. 5.4 (i). On the other hand, the field between

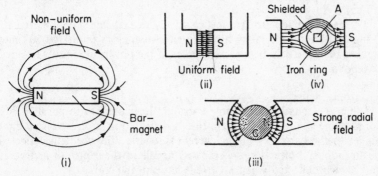

FIG. 5.4.   Magnetic fields

two close poles of a horse shoe-type magnet is *uniform*—the strength and direction of the field is constant at all points, Fig. 5.4 (ii). A strong *radial field* is illustrated in Fig. 5.4 (iii). A soft iron cylinder C becomes magnetised by induction and the lines in the narrow air-gap between the curved poles N, S and C all radiate towards the centre of C. Fig. 5.4 (iv) shows how an object A is shielded from a magnetic field by placing an iron ring round it—the magnetic lines pass through the iron from the N- to the S-pole, and not through the air space at A. The ring thus acts as a 'magnetic shield'. Arrows on magnetic lines always represent the direction of movement of a north pole.

Magnetic fields of different pattern and strength are widely used in industry. As we see later, moving-coil loudspeakers and ammeters, for example, need a strong radial field to function efficiently.

Magnetic Induction.

In the case of an electric field, we imagine lines of electric flux in it (p. 47). Likewise, we imagine lines of *magnetic flux* in a magnetic field. Flux, Φ, is expressed in units called *webers*, Wb. The *flux-density* or *induction*, *B*, at a point is the flux per square metre passing through an area held normally to the lines at that point.

Magnitudes of *B*

Flux density, *B*, is expressed in *teslas, where* 1 *tesla* = 1 Wb *per square metre* (1 Wb/metre²). Thus if the flux passing normally through a ring of area 10 cm² is 0·5 milliwebers or 0·5/1,000 Wb, then, since 10 cm² = 10/10⁴ metre²,

$$\text{flux-density } B = \frac{\text{flux}}{\text{area}} = \frac{0 \cdot 5/1,000}{10/10^4} = 0 \cdot 5 \text{ Wb per metre}^2 \text{ or tesla}$$

This is the order of magnitude of the flux density between the poles of powerful magnets such as those used in a moving-coil instrument (p. 85).

The earth's magnetic field is a relatively weak field. The flux density B in it is about $0 \cdot 5 \times 10^{-4}$ Wb per metre², which is about 10,000 times weaker than the field between the poles of the powerful magnet referred to above.

Electromagnetism

When a current flows along a straight horizontal wire parallel to a compass needle below it, the needle is deflected in a direction at right angles to the wire. When the current is reversed the needle is deflected in the opposite direction. A compass needle at the centre of a circular coil is also deflected when a current flows in the coil.

These simple experiments suggest that there is a magnetic field surrounding a conductor when it carries a current. The *appearance* of the field depends on the shape of the conductor. The pattern of the lines of flux in the neighbourhood can be seen either by using iron filings or a compass-needle. The *direction* of the magnetic field at a point is always in a plane *perpendicular* to the current to which it is due, and this important fact should be remembered for subsequent use. The induction, *B*, in the field at a point depends on the position of the point, the strength of the current and the form of the circuit through which it flows. It is independent of time when these three quantities are fixed. This makes the magnetic effect particularly useful for measuring current. The action of commercial moving-coil instruments depends on the magnetic field set up when a current flows in a conductor (p. 86).

Magnetic Fields due to Current

1. *Straight wire.* The field consists of concentric circles round the wire C, i.e. A is their centre, Fig. 5.5 (i). The direction of the lines of force, or field, are shown by the arrows. The lines exist in planes *perpendicular* to the wire. Fig. 5.5 (i) indicates only one plane. The

magnetic field exists in other planes perpendicular to the wire, through points such as B or C, because the lines of force occur in space all round the wire.

2. *Narrow circular coil.* The magnetic field exists in planes such as

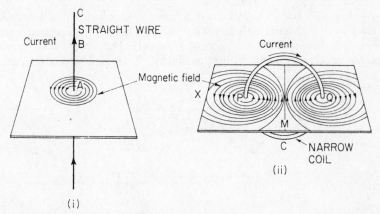

FIG. 5.5.   Magnetic fields

X *perpendicular* to the plane of the coil C, Fig. 5.5 (ii). The lines of force are circular near P and Q, but straighten towards the centre, M, of the coil. (X in Fig. 5.5 (ii) is drawn to bisect the coil.) Over a small

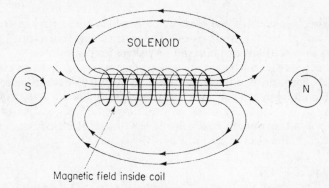

FIG. 5.6.   Field of Solenoid

region in the middle the lines of force are straight and parallel, indicating that the field is constant or uniform there.

3. *Solenoid.* The lines of force are in planes *perpendicular* to those of the circular coils which make up the solenoid (Fig. 5.6). To remember the shape of the magnetic field, note that the solenoid acts like a

bar-magnet when a current flows in it. The ends act as the north and south pole respectively as shown. In the middle of the solenoid the field is uniform. If the length of a current-carrying solenoid is more than ten times greater than its diameter, the field is practically uniform everywhere inside the coil.

4. *Toroid (or endless solenoid)*. A 'toroid', L, is a closed coil usually wound on a circular soft-iron ring, as in Fig. 5.7. Compared with Fig. 5.6, the toroid is an 'endless' solenoid. The lines are complete circles passing through the iron as shown. They pass perpendicularly

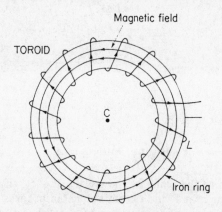

FIG. 5.7. Field of Toroidal coil

through the planes of the circular coils which make up the toroid. There are practically no lines of force outside this coil, as at *C*. The field is thus constant or uniform everywhere inside.

Fig. 5.7 illustrates a *magnetic circuit*, which is analogous to an electric circuit. The iron is analogous to the conductors in the circuit; the magnetomotive force due to the current-carrying coil is analogous to the e.m.f. of the battery used; and the magnetic lines or flux (p. 75) produced in the iron are analogous to the flow of electricity or current produced in the electric circuit.

Direction of Fields

The direction of the lines of force round a current, already inserted in previous diagrams, can be deduced from *Maxwell's corkscrew rule*. This states that:

If a right-handed corkscrew is turned so that its point travels in the direction of the current for a *straight conductor*, then the direction of rotation of the screw is the direction of the circular lines of force round it.

In the case of a *circular conductor*, such as the solenoid or toroidal coil, if the corkscrew is rotated in the current direction, then the direction of travel of its point is the direction of the lines of force. Apply the rule to Figs. 5.5, 5.6, 5.7.

A simple rule for the magnetic effect due to a current-carrying circular conductor is a 'clock rule', illustrated in Fig. 5.6. If the current flows *clockwise* when one end is viewed, then that end acts like a *south* (S) magnetic pole; if it flows anticlockwise, the end acts like a *north* (N) magnetic pole.

Magnetising Force or Intensity

The magnetic field of a solenoid or toroid is used in practice to make magnets. The greater the number of turns per metre length of the solenoid, and the greater the current, the stronger is the magnetising force or intensity. Magnetic intensities, *H*, are thus expressed in *amperes per* metre (A per m). The 'ampere-turns' is the name given to the product *NI* of the number of turns *N* and the current *I*.

The following formula for magnetic intensity, *H*, are proved in more advanced texts, where *I* is in amperes and *l, d, r* are in metres. *Solenoid (or Toroid)*: In the middle of a long solenoid of length *l*,

$$H = \frac{NI}{l} \text{ A/m}$$

Straight conductor, infinitely long:

$$H = \frac{I}{2\pi d} \text{ A/m}$$

where *d* is the perpendicular distance from the point to the conductor. *Narrow Circular Coil*:

$$H = \frac{NI}{2r} \text{ A/m}$$

at the centre of the coil, where *r* is the radius.

To show how the formula is applied for the case of a solenoid, for example, suppose a current of 300 mA is passed through such a coil, with 200 turns wound on a former 10 cm long. Then, using m.k.s. units,

$$I = 300 \text{ mA} = 0.3 \text{ A}, \qquad l = 10 \text{ cm} = 0.1 \text{ metre}, \qquad N = 200$$

$$\therefore H = \frac{NI}{l} = \frac{200 \times 0.3 \text{ (A)}}{0.1 \text{ m}} = 600 \text{ A/m}$$

A current of 3 A would produce a field of 6,000 A/m, which is 10 times as strong. A greater number of windings or turns per metre would also increase the field strength inside the solenoid.

Permeability. Relative permeability

The intensity H is related to the flux-density B in the field by $B = \mu H$, where μ is the permeability of the medium (compare the case of the electric field, where $D = \varepsilon E$ and ε is the permittivity, p. 49).

The permeability of a vacuum or free space is denoted by μ_0, and in the m.k.s. system, $\mu_0 = 4\pi \times 10^{-7}$ henry per metre. For any other medium of permeability μ,

$$\mu = \mu_0 \mu_r,$$

where μ_r is a number known as the *relative permeability*. For air, μ_r is practically 1; for a particular soft magnetic alloy μ_r may be as high as 2000. See also p. 105.

Suppose this alloy is used inside a solenoid which produces a magnetic intensity $H = 600$ A/m. The flux-density or induction B in the iron is then given by

$$B = \mu H = \mu_0 \mu_r H = 4\pi \times 10^{-7} \times 2000 \times 600$$
$$= 1 \cdot 5 \text{ Wb per metre}^2$$

Magnetic Relay

The magnetic effect of a current in a solenoid is utilised in the *magnetic relay*. This component is widely used in telecommunications. It opens and closes electrical circuits during transmission and reception

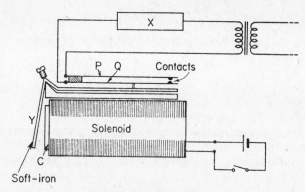

Fig. 5.8. Magnetic relay

of messages. In one form, it consists of a solenoid with a soft-iron core C. This attracts a pivoted soft iron armature Y when a current flows in the solenoid, Fig. 5.8. The movement of Y may then close contacts on springy metals such as P and Q connected to another circuit X, thus passing on the message to this circuit.

Telephone Earpiece

The telephone earpiece is another device which uses the magnetic effect of current. It converts electrical energy due to speech into sound energy again. Basically, it contains (i) a permanent magnet M, (ii) two short solenoids A, of many turns of fine insulated wire, oppositely wound on soft-iron cores B, (iii) a thin Stalloy (nickel-iron) diaphragm D just in front of the cores, Fig. 5.9.

The permanent magnet converts the pole-pieces into magnets, with opposite poles N and S at X and Y as shown. D is therefore attracted. When a *direct* current flows in the coils the magnetic effect

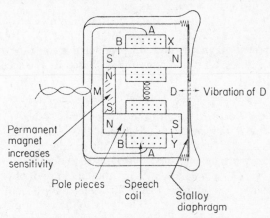

FIG. 5.9.   Telephone earpiece

of the current may strengthen N and S, in which case D moves a little towards them. If the magnetic effect of the current weakens the strength of N and S, then D is released and moves a little away from them. In either case a "click", but nothing further, is heard in the 'phones.

When *alternating* current, a.c. (i.e. one whose direction *reverses* after regular intervals of time), passes into the coils, its magnetic effect alternately strengthens and weakens the N and S poles. Consequently D moves to and fro about its equilibrium position at a rate equal to the number of times per second that the a.c. reverses in direction. This is known as the *frequency* of the a.c. As the diaphragm vibrates it causes the air in contact with it to oscillate at the same frequency. A note is then produced of the same frequency as the alternating current in the coils. The telephone is thus a device for converting electrical energy into sound energy.

Low-resistance 'phones have coils which have only about a few hundred ohms resistance. High-resistance 'phones have coils of much thinner wire which have a resistance of several thousand ohms. The former are more robust and less expensive than the latter. Direct current in the coils diminishes the amplitude of vibration of the diaphragm when a.c. is flowing. It can be eliminated by placing a large capacitor in series with the earphones (p. 134).

Effect of Permanent Magnet

The permanent magnet in the telephone earpiece plays an important part in its action. Without it, the diaphragm is attracted on both halves of the audio-frequency a.c. variation, so that the diaphragm would vibrate at *twice* the frequency of the a.c. When a complex speech current flows in the coils, consisting of many different frequencies, considerable distortion would thus occur.

Further, the pull F on the magnetic diaphragm is proportional to B^2, where B is the flux-density outside the poles (p. 110). Suppose that a permanent magnet is present, producing a constant flux-density of B_0 in the iron core. If a change ΔB is caused by the speech current in the coils, then

$$F \propto B^2 \propto (B_0 + \Delta B)^2 \propto B_0^2 + 2B_0 \cdot \Delta B,$$

neglecting $(\Delta B)^2$ compared with the other terms. When F varies due to changes of ΔB, the variation in pull, since B_0^2 is constant, is proportional to $B_0 \cdot \Delta B$. Thus the larger B_0, the greater is the variation in pull. Hence a permanent magnet increases considerably the *sensitivity* of the earpiece. The material used for the diaphragm, often the alloy Stalloy, should have a high change in flux-density for a small change in magnetising force, so that it responds easily to the variation of current. We say that the material should have a high 'incremental permeability' (p. 105).

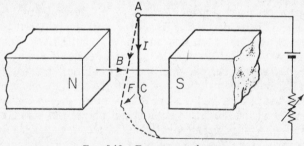

FIG. 5.10. Force on conductor

FORCE ON CONDUCTOR

Interaction between Magnetic Fields

When a length of wire AC is situated perpendicularly to the uniform magnetic field between the poles N, S of a magnet, and a current I is passed into the wire, AC is seen to move in a direction perpendicular to both the field and its length, Fig. 5.10. A *force F*, thus acts on AC.

The existence of the force can be explained by the interaction between the magnetic field of the magnet and that of the current-carrying wire. Fig. 5.11 (i) shows the magnet field; Fig. 5.11 (ii) shows the current

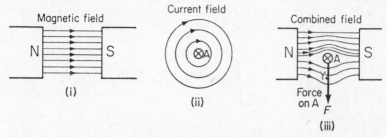

Fig. 5.11.   Interaction of fields

field; Fig. 5.11 (iii) shows the appearance of the combined field; the flux density has increased on the side above A and decreased on the side Y. The wire moves from the increased flux density to the reduced flux density region. The force on the wire thus acts *perpendicular* to both the length of wire and the magnetic field.

Fleming's Left-hand Rule

Fleming gave a useful rule which enables the direction of the force to be quickly found. It states:

If the first three fingers of the **left** hand are held perpendicular to

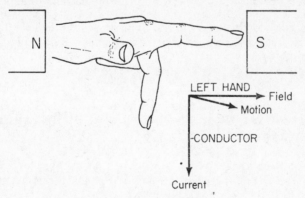

Fig. 5.12.   Fleming's left-hand rule

each other, with the forefinger pointing in the direction of the field and the middle finger in the direction of the current, then the *thumb* points in the direction of motion or *force*, Fig. 5.12.

No force acts on a current-carrying wire which is parallel to the field.

As we now explain, the maximum force occurs when the wire is perpendicular to the field.

Magnitude of Force

When the whole of the length of a wire is perpendicular to a magnetic field, the force F is given by

$$F = BIl \text{ newtons}$$

where l is the conductor's length in *metres*, I, is the current in it in *amps*, and B is the flux density in *tesla* (*weber per m^2*), Fig. 5.13 (i).   Thus

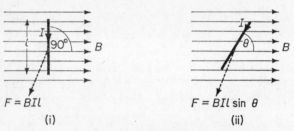

$$F = BIl$$ $$F = BIl \sin \theta$$
(i)   (ii)

Fig. 5.13.   Magnitude of force (*F towards reader*)

a wire 10 cm long, carrying a current of 0·5 A and perpendicular to a field of 80×10^{-3} tesla, experiences a force,

$$F = 80 \times 10^{-3} \times 0.5 \times 10/100 = 0.004 \text{ newton}$$

If the same conductor is inclined at an angle θ to the field, the component of the field perpendicular to the conductor is $B \sin \theta$, Fig. 5.13 (ii). Thus in this case

$$F = BIl \sin \theta \text{ newton}$$

Thus if the above current-carrying wire is placed at 30° to the field, the force on it $= 0.004 \sin 30° = 0.002$ newton. Parallel to the field the force becomes zero.

Torque on Rectangular Coil

A number of useful instruments have a *rectangular coil* in a magnetic field.

Suppose such a current-carrying coil PQRT is situated in the plane of a uniform magnetic field B, Fig. 5.14 (i). The forces F on the vertical sides PQ and RT are each equal to BIl newtons, with the usual notation, and act in opposite directions. There are no forces on PT or QR since these conductors lie parallel to the field. The coil thus *rotates* under the action of the two forces F, Fig. 5.14 (ii). The two equal forces together constitute a 'couple' acting on the coil, and the turning-effect or *torque* of the couple is given by

torque $= F \times$ perpendicular distance between the forces F
$= NBIl \times b$ newton metre,

assuming there are N turns in the coil and its breadth is b. Now $l \times b = A$, the area of the rectangular face of the coil. Thus if A is in metre^2,

$$torque = NBAI \ newton \ metre$$

Fig. 5.14 (ii) shows the flux-density immediately round a section of

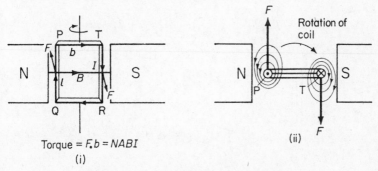

Torque $= F.b = NABI$
(i)

FIG. 5.14. Torque on Rectangular Coil

the vertical conductors PQ, TR, of the coil when it carries a current. TR moves down and PQ moves up, in each case from the dense to the less dense part of the field, and the coil rotates.

As an illustration of the magnitude of the forces and torque on a rectangular coil, suppose such a coil has 30 turns, vertical sides of length 10 cm and horizontal sides of length 4 cm, and carries a current of 2 A when the plane of the coil is situated parallel to a horizontal field of 0·5 Wb per m^2. Then, since 10 cm $= 10/100$ metre and 4 cm $= 4/100$ metre,

1. force on 30 vertical wires $= 30 \times BIl = 30 \times 0.5 \times 2 \times \dfrac{10}{100} =$ 3 newtons; and
2. torque $=$ force $\times$ breadth of coil $= 3 \times \dfrac{4}{100} = 0.12$ newton metre.

Moving-coil Instrument

The most widely used commercial current- and p.d.-measuring instrument contains (i) a rectangular coil of wire PQRT, (ii) a *radial* magnetic field concentrated between the circular poles N,S of a permanent magnet and a concentric soft-iron core, (iii) springs, oppositely wound, which control the rotation of the coil about a vertical axis,

Fig. 5.15 (i). The ends of the coil are joined to the springs and the terminals, A, B, of the instrument are connected to the springs.

When a current I flows in the coil, it is deflected by the couple acting in it, as already explained. The springs exert an opposing couple. Thus the coil comes to rest after rotating through a particular angle θ, Fig. 5.15 (ii). The greater the current I, the greater is the deflection θ.

In its deflected position, the deflecting torque due to the current is balanced by the opposing torque due to the spring. If the latter is

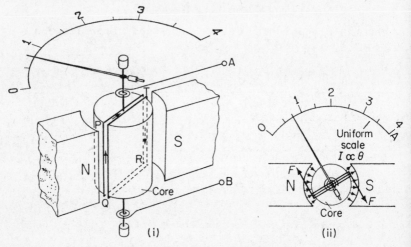

FIG. 5.15. Moving-coil Instrument

elastic, the opposing torque $= c\theta$ newton metre, where c is a constant which depends on the material of the spring and θ is the angle of deflection. The radial magnetic field is an important factor in the action. When the coil comes to rest in its deflected position, *the plane of the coil will always be parallel to the field*. This is the case irrespective of the angle through which the coil is deflected. Consequently, the deflecting torque at any position is $NABI$. Hence, in equilibrium,

$$NABI = c\theta$$

$$\therefore I = \frac{c}{NAB} \cdot \theta$$

$$\therefore I \propto \theta$$

This is a *linear* relation between I and θ. It means that if the angle of rotation of the coil is 10° for a 1 A current, it will be 15° for 1·5 A and 20° for 2 A. The scale is thus a 'uniform' one, that is, equal divisions along it represent equal changes in current. This is a great advantage, both for making sub-divisions on the scale and for reading it accurately.

In contrast, the scale of the hot-wire ammeter tends to obey a law $I^2 \propto \theta$, that is, a square-law scale (p. 123). The scale is thus a non-uniform one—the divisions are crowded at the beginning and wider further along.

Moving-coil instruments can be converted into *ammeters*, which read higher current ranges, by adding suitable low resistors in parallel called 'shunts'. The calculation was explained on p. 14. They can also be converted into *voltmeters* by adding suitable resistors in series (see p. 14). The instrument can also be calibrated as an *ohm-meter* to measure resistance (p. 15).

Very small currents, such as extremely small fractions of a microamp (one-millionth amp), can be measured with a *moving-coil mirror galvanometer*. In this sensitive instrument, the spring is replaced by a long phosphor-bronze wire, from which the coil is suspended; the wire has a very weak control over the deflection so that extremely small currents can be measured. Further, the pointer is replaced by a beam of light, which measures the coil deflection by means of an attached mirror.

Forces between Currents. The Ampere

If a current in the same direction flows through two parallel close wires, experiment shows they attract each other, Fig. 5.16 (i) illustrates the field round the two wires A and B. On one side of A or B the flux

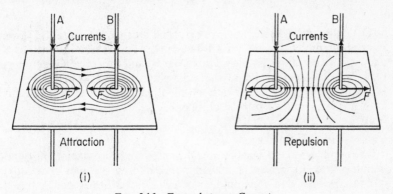

FIG. 5.16.   Forces between Currents

density is increased and on the other side it is reduced. The wires thus move closer to each other (p. 83).

Conversely, if a current flows in opposite directions through A and B, repulsion occurs. Fig. 5.16 (ii) illustrates the flux-density round the wires.

Since the force between two current-carrying wires can be measured to a high degree of accuracy, the *ampere* is now defined as follows:

The ampere is that current which flows in each of two infinitely long straight conductors of negligible cross-section one metre apart in a vacuum when each is repelled by a force of 2×10^{-7} newton.

Principle of Ampere Balance

The ampere balance is used at National Physical Laboratories to measure current accurately. Basically, it consists of two fixed coils A, C with a parallel coil B in the middle attached to one side of a sensitive chemical balance, Fig. 5.17.

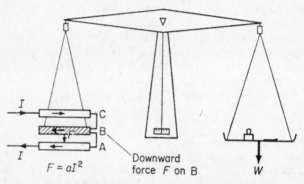

$$F = aI^2$$

Downward force F on B

W

FIG. 5.17.   Ampere Balance

The coils are in series, and are arranged so that the current I flows in opposite directions in C and B but in the same direction through B and A. The coil B is then urged downwards, and the force F is counterbalanced by a weight W on the scale-pan. Since $F = aI^2$, where a is a constant which depends only on the dimensions of the coils and is known, the current I can then be calculated.

Moving-coil Loudspeaker

The moving-coil loudspeaker is widely used for reproduction of sound in radio and TV receivers and in public-address systems. Basically, it consists of a coil F wound on a cylindrical former which has a paper cone diaphragm rigidly attached to it, Fig. 5.18 (i). The coil is situated in the narrow gap between the poles P of a powerful pot magnet M, whose section is shown in Fig. 5.18 (ii). The magnet produces a radial magnetic field. The cone is suspended loosely from a baffle-board.

The coil F is the *speech coil*. When a current flows in F the field of M is normal to every element of the conductor such as a, b, c, d. If Fleming's left-hand rule is applied to every element it can be seen that the force acting on each is in the same direction, in this case out of the page away from the reader. Thus the force on the coil is directed along its *axis*.

When an alternating current (a.c.) of audio-frequency from a radio receiver, for example, flows in F, reversal of current takes place every half cycle. The force on F is thus in opposite directions as the a.c. flows. The cylindrical former and the paper cone therefore *vibrate* along their axis with a frequency equal to that of the a.c. The large mass of air in

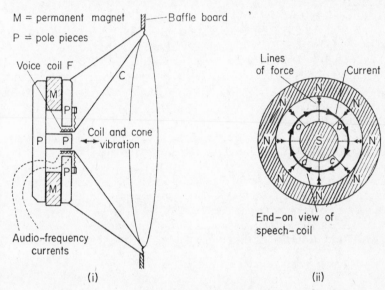

M = permanent magnet

P = pole pieces

Voice coil F

Lines of force

Current

Coil and cone vibration

Audio-frequency currents

End–on view of speech–coil

(i)   (ii)

FIG. 5.18.   Moving-coil loudspeaker

contact with the cone is set vibrating at the same frequency, and a corresponding sound frequency is heard. The loudspeaker is thus a device for converting electrical energy into sound energy. The greater the electrical power supplied to it from the a.c. source, the louder is the sound it emits.

The axial force on the coil *F* at any instant can be simply calculated. Suppose it has 10 turns and a circumference of 20 cm or 0·2 metre, and is situated in a radial field of 0·5 tesla (Wb per metre^2).   Then, from p. 84, for a current of 4 mA,

$$\text{force, } F = Bll = 0.5 \times 10 \times 0.2 \times 4/1{,}000 \text{ newton}$$
$$= 4 \times 10^{-3} \text{ newton}$$

Baffle Board

When the cone moves forward, a compression of air, or pressure rise, occurs immediately in front of it. Simultaneously, a rarefaction of air,

or pressure fall, occurs immediately behind the cone. The wave generated behind the cone is thus completely out of phase with that generated
in front of the cone. (The phase difference is 180° or $\lambda/2$, see p. 120.)
Hence if the wave behind travels round to the front the two waves will
interfere with each other. The sound heard then lacks intensity. This
is particularly the case at low frequencies, or long wavelength. The
wave behind the cone then has time to travel round to the front before
the next vibration of the cone takes place. In this case the sound lacks
bass note intensity.

A *baffle board* is used to overcome this effect. This is a flat board
with a hole in its centre; the speaker is fitted over the hole and attached
to the board so that the cone can vibrate freely. The baffle board
increases the distance between the waves produced by the front and
back of the cone and thus prevents their interference.

Effect of Magnetic Field

The force exerted on the speech coil for a given current is proportional
to the flux density produced by the magnet (p. 89). The speaker
sensitivity is hence increased by using materials such as Alcomax,
which makes a very powerful magnet. This has the advantage of reducing the size of the speaker. It should also be noted that a uniform flux
density is essential in the gap between the N- and S-poles of the magnet;
otherwise the deflection of the coil is not directly proportional to the
current and *distortion* of sound occurs.

SUMMARY

1. Like poles repel, unlike poles attract.

2. B is the flux-density or magnetic induction in the magnetic field. Units:
Wb per m^2 or teslas. H is the magnetising field. Units: A per m.

3. The magnetic field due to current-carrying conductors exists in planes
perpendicular to the plane of the conductor. In a solenoid, $H = NI/l$
A per m (approx.), where N is the number of turns, l is the length in metres,
I is in A.

4. Due to the audio-frequency current in the speech coils of a telephone
receiver, the iron diaphragm vibrates. The permanent magnet increases the
sensitivity.

5. The *force* F on a straight conductor perpendicular to a magnetic
field $= BIl$ newtons, where B is in tesla (Wb per m^2), I in A, l in m.

6. The *torque* on a rectangular coil whose plane is parallel to a magnetic
field $= NABI$ newton metre. $I \propto \theta$ on account of the radial field in the
moving-coil meter.

7. The moving-coil loudspeaker coil is situated in a radial magnetic field.
The sensitivity depends on the field strength. The baffle board prevents
interference between the sound waves in front and those behind the vibrating
cone.

EXERCISE 5

1. State the chief differences between iron and steel. Why are permanent magnets made of steel and an electromagnet made of soft iron?

2. Draw a sketch of the lines of force between a north and a south pole in air. State the effect of introducing a piece of soft iron between them, and illustrate your answer by a diagram.

3. Define the terms *flux* and *flux-density*. How is the induction of a magnetic field defined in terms of the flux there? Draw a sketch of the lines of force in a field of *uniform* induction.

4. Draw sketches of the magnetic flux round a straight wire, a circular coil, and a solenoid, each carrying a current, and show clearly the directions of the current and the magnetic field. State the effect on the flux-density at a point inside the solenoid (*a*) if the current is decreased, (*b*) if the number of turns is increased, (*c*) if soft iron is introduced inside it.

5. Explain fully the action of a simple relay.

6. A bar magnet is suspended horizontally in the centre of a vertical ring of wire which carries a direct current. Sketch the resulting magnetic field in the horizontal plane of the magnet when the axis of the magnet is (*a*) in line with the ring (*b*) at right angles.   (*C. & G.*)

7. Calculate the force on a conductor 5 cm long carrying a current of 2 A perpendicular to a uniform magnetic field of intensity 0·4 Wb per metre^2.

8. A rectangular coil of 20 turns has sides of 5 cm and 2 cm. It is situated with its plane parallel to a uniform magnetic field of intensity 0·2 Wb per m^2 and its longer side perpendicular to the field. Calculate (i) the force on the longer side of the coil, (ii) the torque on the coil in newton metre, if the current flowing is 0·5 A.

9. A moving-coil loudspeaker has a coil of 8 turns each of which has a circumference of 15 cm. If it is situated in a uniform radial magnetic field of strength 0·2 Wb per metre^2, what is the force on the coil when it carries a current of 5 milliamp? Draw a sketch of the radial field with the coil in it.

10. A rectangular coil of area 10 cm^2 and 5 turns is situated in a magnetic field so that its plane is (i) parallel and then (ii) perpendicular to a uniform magnetic field of 0·4 Wb per m^2. Find the torque on the coil in each case when the current is 2 A.

11. 'The *sensitivity* of a moving-coil instrument depends on the elastic forces in the hair spring, as well as other factors. The scale is *uniform* on account of the *radial field*.' Explain the two statements, showing particularly the meaning of the words italicised.

12. A rectangular coil of sides 4 cm by 2 cm and 10 turns is situated in a radial magnetic field of 0·2 Wb per m^2. The movement of the coil is controlled by a spring whose opposing torque is 10^{-6} newton metre per degree of rotation. Find the angle of deflection when a current of 10 mA flows in the coil.

13. Write down a law by which the direction of the force on a conductor carrying a current in a magnetic field can be determined. Illustrate your answer by a diagram.

Calculate the force acting on a conductor 10 cm long carrying a direct current of 10 amperes at right angles to a uniform magnetic field of 10 milliwebers/m^2. Hence find the turning moment on a coil 10 cm square of

500 turns carrying a current of 10 amperes when the plane of the coil is parallel to the above magnetic field. The coil is pivoted on an axis, perpendicular to the direction of the field and in the plane of the coil, on a line joining the midpoints of opposite sides.

What is the turning moment when the coil is rotated by 90° from this position? Explain your answer.   (*C. & G.*)

14. Describe the principle of operation of a modern telephone receiver. Explain why it is necessary to include a permanent magnet and deduce the effect of this on the sensitivity of the receiver.   (*C. & G.*)

15. Describe the principle of operation of the moving-coil milliammeter. Why is it necessary to have a uniform radial magnetic field in the air gap? How is this achieved? If the moving coil is square, with 1-cm sides and 80 turns, the flux density in the air gap being 0·1 Wb/m², find the deflecting torque per milliampere in the coil.

Calculate the angular deflection of the coil per milliampere if the control torque due to the hair springs is 10^{-3} newton metre per degree of coil rotation.   (*C. & G.*)

16. Describe the principle of operation of the moving coil loudspeaker. What factors determine (*a*) the sensitivity, (*b*) the distortion produced by this type of speaker?

The moving coil of the loudspeaker consists of 100 turns in the form of a cylinder 5 cm in diameter. This moves axially along a cylindrical air gap across which is maintained a uniform radial magnetic field of intensity 0·5 Wb/m². Calculate the axial deflecting force on this coil per milliampere of current.   (*C. & G.*)

17. What advantages and disadvantages does a moving-coil type of voltmeter possess as compared with one of moving-iron type? Describe briefly, with a suitable sketch, the action of either type of instrument.

    (*C. & G.*)

18. Making reference, with sketches, to the main principles of operation in each case, explain why a moving-coil d.c. ammeter usually has a uniform scale while a moving-iron d.c. ammeter usually has an irregular scale.

    (*C. & G.*)

19. (*a*) State Fleming's rule for the direction of the force on a conductor carrying a current when it is placed in a magnetic field, and illustrate it by two examples.

(*b*) Draw a sketch of a moving-coil loudspeaker, and explain briefly how it functions.   (*C. & G.*)

20. Give a brief description of the principle of operation of a moving-coil milliammeter. In particular explain the meaning of *control torque*.

A moving-coil meter has a coil 1 cm square containing 100 turns. The coil is pivoted about an axis in the plane of the turns and bisecting two opposite sides. It moves in a radial uniform magnetic field of 2 milliwebers per square metre. Calculate the torque on the coil when a current of 10 mA is flowing in its turns.   (*C. & G.*)

6: Electromagnetic Induction

Induced E.M.F. and Current

When the N-pole of a magnet is suddenly brought near to the end of a long coil or solenoid C, Fig. 6.1 (i) (ii), an electric current flows in C which can be detected by a sensitive microammeter or galvanometer G. This current has been obtained without the aid of a battery. It is called an *induced current*. The e.m.f. to which it is due is known as an *induced*

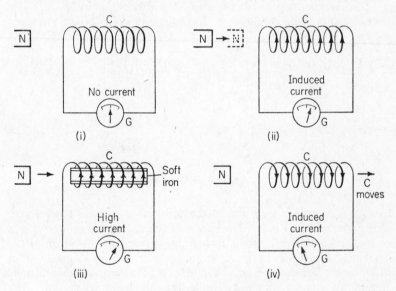

FIG. 6.1.   Electromagnetic induction

e.m.f.. It is set-up by movement of electrons in the wire when the magnet moves. The phenomenon is generally called *electromagnetic induction*.

The following important points can be observed in this simple experiment:

1. The induced current flows *only as long as the magnet is moving*, Fig. 6.1 (i), (ii).

2. The deflection in G is greater the *faster* the magnet is moved towards the coil.

3. For a given speed of approach of the magnet, the induced current in the coil will increase the greater the number of turns, N, of the coil, or the larger the circular area of the turns.

4. If a soft-iron core is placed inside C, as in Fig. 6.1 (iii), a considerable increase in the induced current is obtained.

5. If the magnet is kept still, and the *coil* C is moved to and fro, an induced current is again obtained, Fig. 6.1 (iv). If the magnet and coil are moved both together at the same speed, however, no induced current is observed.

Generally, then, an induced e.m.f. and current are obtained only when there is *relative motion* between the coil and magnet.

Current direction by Lenz's Law

Lenz gave a useful law for determining the direction of the induced current in a closed circuit. It states:

The direction of the induced current in a circuit is such that it opposes the motion or change producing it. In the case of Fig. 6.2 (i), the induced

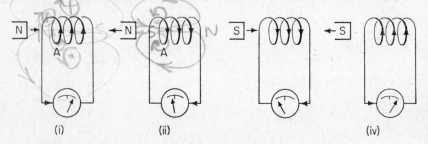

Fig. 6.2. Lenz's law

current is in such a direction in the coil that it opposes the forward movement of the N pole. The end A of the coil therefore acts as a N pole (like poles repel), which in turn means that the direction of the current is anti-clockwise there (from our rule for the magnetic effect of a current flowing in a circular coil). In (ii) A acts as a south pole. It then attracts the receding N pole, thus opposing its motion. The induced current is therefore clockwise. In (iii), A acts as a south pole and in (iv), as a north pole for a similar reason. The directions of the induced currents are therefore as shown.

Lenz's law can be explained from the Principle of the Conservation of Energy. In Fig. 6.2 (i), for example, suppose the induced current flowed clockwise, instead of anticlockwise as shown. The end A of the coil would then act as a S-pole and attract the N-pole of the magnet. This would make the magnet move faster towards A, and would therefore induce a stronger pole. In turn, this would increase the speed of the magnet, and so on. Hence the electrical energy in the circuit and the kinetic energy of the magnet would both increase, although no source of energy is available. This is impossible, from the Principle of the Conservation of Energy. Thus the current flows *anticlockwise*, as shown in Fig. 6.1 (i). The movement of N towards the coil is now opposed, so that work is done in moving N. The energy provided in this way re-appears as electrical energy in the coil.

Flux Linkage. Faraday's Law

Faraday used the idea of magnetic flux, described on p. 75, to explain electromagnetic induction. Suppose the N-pole of a magnet is at X near the coil C, Fig. 6.3. A definite number of lines of flux then pass through the face of the coil or *link* the coil, as shown. While N moves to Y near the coil, the magnetic flux linking the coil increases. When N

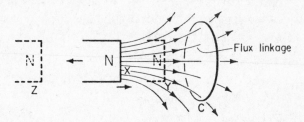

FIG. 6.3. Flux linkage

is stationary at Y, the flux linking C no longer changes. If N now moves back from Y to Z, the flux linking C decreases. Faraday's (or Neumann's) law states that: *The induced e.m.f. is proportional to the rate of change of the flux linking the coil or circuit.*

In particular cases, the *flux linkages* can be calculated. Suppose a coil of N turns each of area A square metres is placed in a uniform magnetic field of B teslas (weber per square metre) so that all the flux passes normally through the face of each turn. The flux Φ linking one turn is then AB Wb (webers); the total flux linkage $= N\Phi = NAB$ Wb. From Faraday's law, if t represents the time in seconds to make a flux change from Φ_1 to Φ_2, then the induced e.m.f. E is given by

$$E = -N \times \frac{\text{flux change in Wb}}{\text{time to make change in sec}} \text{ volts} \qquad \text{(i)}$$

$$= -N \frac{\Phi_2 - \Phi_1}{t}$$

In calculus notation, $E = -N \dfrac{\Delta\Phi}{\Delta t}$ volts

where $\Delta\Phi =$ flux change per turn in Wb, $\Delta t =$ time change in sec, $d\Phi/dt =$ the rate of change of Φ.

It may be noted from (i) that, substituting units,

$$\text{one volt} = \frac{\text{one turn} \times \text{one weber}}{\text{one second}}$$

$$\therefore \ 1 \ \text{weber} = 1 \ \text{volt-second}$$

as 'one turn' is dimensionless. Thus instead of 'webers', the unit of 'volt-sec' may be used for flux, Φ.

As an illustration of calculating induced e.m.f., suppose a coil of 80 turns is in a field of 0·020 tesla (0·02 Wb per m²) so that the flux links all the turns normally, and the flux-density is reduced to 0·005 tesla in 0·05 sec. Then if the area of the face of the coil is 3 m²,

$$\text{change in flux linkage} = N \cdot \Delta\Phi = 80 \times 3 \times (0\cdot02 - 0\cdot005)$$
$$= 3\cdot6 \ \text{Wb}$$

$$\therefore \ \text{average e.m.f.,} \ E = \frac{3\cdot6}{0\cdot05} = 72 \ \text{V}$$

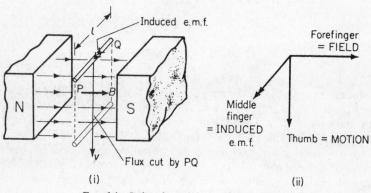

Fig. 6.4. Induced e.m.f. in straight conductor

Induced E.M.F. in Straight Conductor

When a *straight conductor* moves through a magnetic field and 'cuts' lines of flux, an induced e.m.f. is obtained along the conductor. This is the basis of *generators* producing high voltages such as 11,000 V at electrical power stations. These consist basically of long straight conductors in series, rotating at a constant speed in a uniform strong magnetic field.

Suppose a conductor PQ of length *l* metres moves perpendicularly to the lines of flux in a uniform magnetic field of *B* tesla at a velocity of *v* metre per sec, Fig. 6.4 (i). Then, in one second, the flux cut, Φ, is given by

$$\Phi = B \times \text{area swept} = B \times lv$$
$$\therefore \ E = Blv \ \text{volts}$$

If the conductor moves at an angle θ to the field, then, since the component of the velocity normal to the field is $v \sin \theta$, $E = Blv \sin \theta$ volts in this case.

As an illustration, suppose a conductor of length 40 cm moves with a constant velocity of 4 metres per sec normally to a magnetic field of $B = 0.20$ weber per metre^2. Then, since 40 cm = 0.4 metre

$$E = Blv = 0.20 \times 0.4 \times 4 = 0.32 \text{ V}$$

Fleming's Right-hand Rule

The direction of the induced e.m.f. (or current) in a straight conductor is conveniently obtained from Fleming's *right*-hand rule. This is applied as follows:

If the first three fingers of the *right* hand are held mutually at right angles, with the forefinger pointing along the field and the thumb along the direction of motion of the conductor, then the *middle* finger points along the direction of the induced e.m.f. and current.

Fig. 6.4 (ii) illustrates the rule. If the conductor is inclined at an angle other than 90° to the field, the direction of the component of the field perpendicular to the wire is taken. If the conductor is parallel to the field, or moves parallel to the field, Fleming's rule cannot be applied—no induced e.m.f. is obtained in these cases.

Electrodynamic Microphones. Moving-coil

Electrodynamic microphones are widely used. One form, shown in principle in Fig. 6.5 (i), is the *moving-coil microphone*. This has a coil C made from aluminium tape, and situated in a powerful radial magnetic field between the pole pieces N, S of a magnet M. A light diaphragm D is attached to C.

When sound waves are incident on D, the coil moves to and fro at the same frequency in the radial magnetic field. As can be seen from the section of the coil C in the diagram, the wire cuts the flux lines or field perpendicularly as it vibrates. Thus an induced e.m.f. is obtained from the ends of the coil. This has the same frequency as the sound waves and is passed to an amplifier. The action of the coil in the radial field is exactly opposite to the case of the moving-coil loudspeaker (p. 88).

The output from the microphone is very small, for example, 100μV. Amplification is therefore necessary. The whole arrangement is in an air-tight box, but as changes in atmospheric pressure would make the diaphragm move slightly, an 'equalising tube' T is used to connect the cavity behind the diaphragm with the air outside. Absorbent material inside helps to eliminate any reflection of sound waves.

This type of microphone is sensitive and has a good frequency response curve—it is fairly flat from 40 Hz to 15 kHz, which is practically the whole of the audio-frequency range.

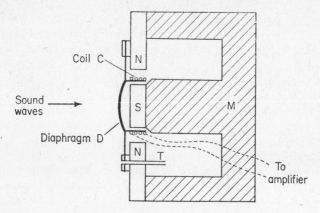

Fig. 6.5. Moving-coil microphone

Ribbon Microphone

The ribbon microphone is another form of electrodynamic microphone. Basically, it consists of aluminium leaf about 2·5 cm long, 6 mm wide and 0·0005 mm thick. The ribbon R is corrugated to provide

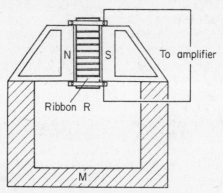

Fig. 6.6. Ribbon microphone

greater flexibility and is clamped between two pole-pieces, N, S, of a magnet M, Fig. 6.6. The magnet must be mounted well below the ribbon on account of its bulk, otherwise it will interfere with waves incident on the microphone.

When sound waves are incident on R, the ribbon vibrates in a direction perpendicular to the magnetic field between N, S. An induced e.m.f. is therefore obtained between its ends, from Fleming's right-hand rule. The e.m.f. is passed to an amplifier.

The frequency response is better than the moving-coil type. This is due to the extremely free undamped movement of the ribbon. The impedance of the ribbon is only about $0.2\ \Omega$ and this is stepped up to a standard value of $30\ \Omega$ by means of a small transformer at the base. The moving mass of the ribbon is only about 0.2 milligram, which compares with 80 milligrams for the moving-coil microphone. The chief use of the ribbon microphone is in high-quality reproduction of music. Unlike the moving-coil microphone, normally it cannot be used outdoors.

Electrodynamic microphones provide a smaller output than the carbon microphone, relatively they are less sensitive, and they are much more expensive. But (i) their frequency-response is generally very good over a wide audio-frequency range, (ii) no steady d.c. battery supply is needed as for the carbon microphone, (iii) they are not subject to background noise and 'hissing' as in the carbon microphone.

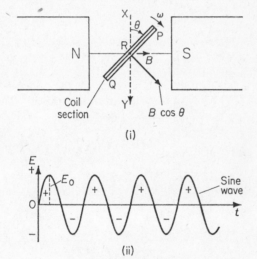

FIG. 6.7.   Simple dynamo

Simple Dynamo

A simple dynamo consists of a rectangular coil rotating at a steady angular velocity ω about a horizontal axis R in a uniform field of flux-density B tesla (Wb per metre^2), Fig. 6.7 (i) shows an end-on view of the rotating coil PQ. As it turns, the coil cuts the flux in the field and an induced e.m.f. is therefore set up in the coil.

At the instant shown, the side of the rectangular coil through P is moving downward. After the plane of the coil passes the vertical XY,

P begins to move upward through the field. Thus the e.m.f. in the coil *reverses* each time its plane crosses the vertical, that is, twice in one revolution. The e.m.f. is thus shown negative for half a cycle in a graph of e.m.f. E against time t, as in Fig. 6.7 (ii).

Magnitude of E.M.F. Sinusoidal E.M.F.

The flux linking the coil at an instant when the plane is inclined at an angle θ to the vertical is given, since $B \cos \theta$ is the field component normal to the turns and $\theta = \omega t$, by

$$N\Phi = NAB \cos \theta = NAB \cos \omega t$$

where A is the area of the coil, N is the number of turns and B is the flux density of the magnetic field, Fig. 6.7 (i). Thus flux-linkage $\propto \cos \theta$. The e.m.f. e is given, from Faraday's law, by the rate of change of the flux-linkage.

$$\therefore e = -\frac{d}{dt}(N\Phi) = \omega NAB \sin \omega t$$

$$\therefore e = E_m \sin \omega t$$

where $E_m = \omega NAB =$ the maximum or peak value of the induced e.m.f. When $\omega (= 2\pi f)$ is in radians per second, A in square metres and B in tesla, then E_m is in volts.

The e.m.f. e is called a *sinusoidal* alternating e.m.f., since its magnitude is proportional to the sine of the angle from the vertical. The variation is a smooth curve, shown in Fig. 6.7 (ii).

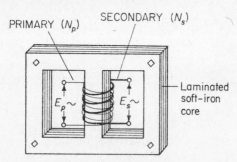

FIG. 6.8.   Iron-cored transformer

Commercial (Iron-core) Transformer

The commercial transformer is a device which changes the magnitude of an alternating (a.c.) voltage or e.m.f. Basically, it consists of a *primary* coil to which the voltage E_p to be changed is applied, and a *secondary* coil from which the new a.c. voltage or e.m.f. E_s is obtained, Fig. 6.8. The copper coils of wire, suitably insulated by enamel for example, are wound round an insulating former and they have a core of soft iron or other suitable magnetic material of low hysteresis loss (p. 104).

The core is made from a stack of thin sheets or laminations, each oxidised so they are all insulated from each other. This reduces eddy current losses of power (p. 102). 'E'- and 'I'-type laminations are used in Fig. 6.8 but 'U'- and 'T'-type are also widely used. The former carrying the primary and secondary windings is mounted over the centre limb C of the iron core. Small transformers are needed in radio receivers. Very large transformers are required in the Grid System, which supplies electricity commercially.

Transformer Action. Turns Ratio

When an alternating e.m.f. of peak or maximum value E_p is connected to the primary P, an alternating current flows in P. The changing current produces a change in flux-density ΔB in the iron in a short time Δt. Hence the change in flux-linkage in the same time with the secondary coil S is $N_s A \cdot \Delta B$, where N_s is the number of turns and A is the area of the coil. But the change in flux-linkage in the primary P in a time Δt is $N_p A \cdot \Delta B$, where N_p is the number of turns in the primary. Hence, since the induced e.m.f. in each coil is proportional to the rate of change of the flux-linkage, it follows that, if S is on open circuit,

$$\frac{E_s}{E_p} = \frac{N_s A \Delta B / \Delta t}{N_p A \Delta B / \Delta t} = \frac{N_s}{N_p}$$

Thus the ratio of the e.m.f.s, E_s/E_p, is equal to the ratio of the number of turns in the respective coils, N_s/N_p. For a *step-up* transformer in which $N_s/N_p = 10/1$, an e.m.f. of 1 V applied to the primary is stepped up 10×1 V to 10 V at the secondary, if it is on open circuit. For a *step-down* transformer in which $N_s/N_p = 1/20$, an e.m.f. of 6 V applied to the primary is stepped down to 6 V/20 or 0·3 V. The transformer transforms alternating e.m.f. or voltage but not direct voltage, since the latter produces no flux changes.

Currents and Losses in Transformer

When the secondary circuit is closed, a current flows in it and exact analysis is complicated. To simplify matters, suppose losses of power are neglected and a current of peak value I_s flows in the secondary. Then, if I_p is the peak value of the primary current,

power in primary = $E_p I_p$ = power in secondary (approx.) = $E_s I_s$

$$\therefore \frac{I_s}{I_p} = \frac{E_p}{E_s} = \frac{N_p}{N_s}$$

Thus the currents in the secondary and primary are *inversely* proportional to the turns-ratio, N_s/N_p. This means that a step-up transformer produces a higher e.m.f. in the secondary than the primary but a lower current. Likewise, a step-down transformer produces a lower e.m.f. in the secondary than the primary but a higher current. Usually, then, a low voltage winding has a much heavier current rating than a high voltage winding.

We shall see soon that there are losses of power in a transformer due to heat produced by circulating or eddy currents in the iron core (p. 103) and to a phenomenon in iron known as 'hysteresis' (p. 104). Leakage or loss of magnetic flux also occurs, since not all the flux linking the primary coil passes through the secondary coil. Interleaving of the primary and secondary windings in sections helps to reduce this loss. Further, heat is produced in both coils due to the flow of current and this is called 'copper losses'. As a result of all this loss of power, the *efficiency* of the transformer, defined as the ratio *output power/input power*, may be as low as 90% for transformers designed to handle a few hundred watts. For transformers of very high ratings, such as 200 kW, the efficiency may be as high as 98%.

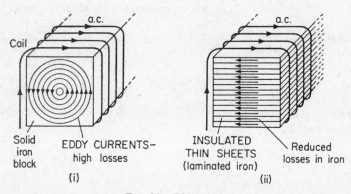

FIG. 6.9. Eddy currents

Eddy Currents

When varying magnetic flux is produced in a metal, an induced current flows. In a solid or a sheet of metal, the currents circulate in various closed paths similar to 'eddies' in water, Fig. 6.9. They are therefore called *eddy currents*. Eddy currents produce heat and they have been utilised in physiotherapy.

Eddy currents are also used to *damp* the movement of the deflected coil in the moving-coil instrument (p. 86) The coil is then brought quickly to rest. This is done by winding the rectangular coil on an aluminium former. As the coil oscillates about its deflected position in the radial magnetic field, the flux cut sets up eddy currents inside the metal former. These oppose the motion of the metal, from Lenz's law (p. 94). Hence the metal and coil come to rest very quickly. Conversely, if the coil is wound on a wooden former, or has no former, the coil oscillates at its deflected position for a time, which is tedious. The coil is then *undamped*.

Electromagnetic machinery such as dynamos or generators have soft-iron cores. Induced or eddy currents in the iron produce heat. As already explained on p. 102, this is a loss of energy. These losses are reduced by using *insulated sheets or laminations* of iron. The eddy currents now circulate in the laminations, and not in a *solid* iron core, which reduces the energy loss. In radio-frequency (r.f.) transformers, where eddy currents would be much greater than in commercial transformers, the losses can be further reduced by making the iron in dust form, impregnated with an insulating compound. *Ferrite cores* have a high resistivity and hence low eddy current losses, and are therefore widely used, as in aerials, for example.

If two coils are very close to each other, and carry high-frequency alternating currents as in the r.f. amplifier stages of radio receivers, for example, magnetic flux from one coil will link with and interfere with the other coil. This is called 'mutual induction' (see p. 111). To prevent mutual induction, the coils are enclosed by cans of copper or aluminium. The r.f. magnetic fields produce eddy currents in the cans, which oppose the flux producing them. In the neighbourhood of the cans the flux is thus appreciably reduced, and hence mutual induction with other coils is minimised. The reduction in flux through a particular coil, however, reduces its inductance (p. 105) and there is also an increase in its effective resistance.

R.F. Resistance. Skin Effect

A conductor carrying a direct current (d.c.) will have the same current per unit area flowing in all parts of its cross-section. For example,

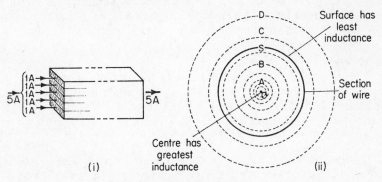

FIG. 6.10. Skin effect

a conductor with a cross-sectional area of 5 mm² and carrying a current of 5A will have 1A flowing in every square millimetre of its cross-section, Fig. 6.10 (i). This is due to the fact that d.c. resistance is inversely-proportional to the area of cross-section (p. 19). When the conductor carries alternating current of high frequencies (r.f.) of the order of 10^6 Hz or greater, however, this uniform distribution of resistance does not hold. The distribution of current alters accordingly.

To explain the effect, suppose a straight conductor of centre O carries an alternating current, Fig. 6.10 (ii). At a particular instant when the current has some value, circular lines of magnetic flux exist both inside the conductor, as at A and B, and outside the conductor as at C and D. Suppose the current reduces to zero. The flux at D, C, B and A will then all disappear towards the centre O, so that the induced or 'back' e.m.f., which opposes the current change, is relatively high at the centre. The flux passing through B, however, which is farther away from the centre, is the flux *outside* B. The flux change through B is hence less than through O. The 'opposition' to the current change is thus less. It can now be seen that the least flux change occurs at the surface, S, of the conductor when the current disappears. The least opposition to the change of current is thus at the surface.

What has been said about the different flux change in the centre and at the surface applies equally when the current rises again to some value from zero. The greatest flux change or 'back' e.m.f. occurs at the centre. The least flux change or 'back' e.m.f. occurs at the surface. Thus the easiest path of flow of the r.f. current is along the surface or 'skin' of the conductor. On this account it is called the *skin effect*. The effective cross-sectional area of the wire is now much less than its actual area. Hence its r.f. resistance is much greater than its d.c. resistance.

On account of the skin effect, the solid conductor is often replaced by copper tubing in r.f. circuits. To improve the conductivity at very high frequencies wires are often silver-coated. Strands of insulated fine wire, twisted so that they all pass from the centre to the outside section and thus have the same opposition to current, are also used to produce more uniform current distribution and hence less r.f. resistance.

B-H curve

The properties of a magnetic material are usually deduced from its *B–H curve* or *loop*. The curve shows the variation of its magnetic induction *B* when the material is taken through a complete cycle of variation of magnetising field *H*. Fig. 6.11 shows a typical *B–H* curve. It provides the following information:

1. *Hysteresis losses*. Due to internal 'magnetic friction' in the material, the magnetised domains, which are very tiny regions of magnetism inside, do not keep in step with the applied field *H* as they turn. Thus the magnetic induction *B* in the material *lags behind H*. This is called *hysteresis*. The area of the *B–H* loop is proportional to the energy loss per unit volume of the material. In a suitable *transformer core* material, the hysteresis loss of energy must be small (p. 102). Fig. 6.14 shows that soft iron is a better material than steel as a transformer core.

2. *Permeability*. At any value of H, the permeability μ is given by $\mu = B/H$. A suitable transformer core material has a high value of μ. The incremental permeability at H, $\delta B/\delta H$, can also be obtained.

3. *Remanence*. OL is a measure of the 'remanence', or flux-density, B_r,

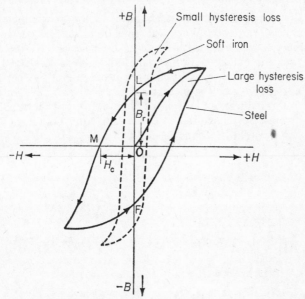

Fig. 6.11. *B-H* curves

remaining when the magnetic field is switched off ($H = 0$). A suitable *permanent magnet* material should have a high value of remanence.

4. *Coercive force*. OM is a measure of the coercive force, H_c, of the material. This is the reverse magnetic field which must be applied to demagnetise the material. A suitable permanent magnet material should have a high value of coercive force.

Self Inductance, *L*

When a current in a coil is varying, a corresponding change occurs in the flux linking the coil. An induced e.m.f. is therefore set up in the coil which is proportional to the rate of change of the current from Faraday's law. This is an e.m.f. which *opposes* the rise or fall of current, from Lenz's law, and is hence often called a 'back' e.m.f. The property of a coil which opposes *changes* in current through it is known as its *self-inductance* or, briefly, its inductance property. It should be carefully distinguished from the opposition of the coil to steady currents, which is the d.c. *resistance R* of the wire of the coil.

From above, the induced e.m.f. of opposition, $e \propto (i_2 - i_1)/t$, where $(i_2 - i_1)$ is the current change from i_1 to i_2 in a time t. In calculus notation, di/dt represents the rate of change of the current in the coil at an instant. Thus

$$e = L\frac{di}{dt}$$

numerically, where L is a constant known as the 'self-inductance' or 'inductance' of the coil. When the rate of change of current is in *amperes per sec* and e is in *volts*, then L is in **henrys** (H). One henry (1 H) is thus the inductance of a coil if an induced e.m.f. of 1 volt is produced when the current in it changes at the rate of 1 A per sec.

If the current in a coil is increased from zero to I amp. in a short time t sec, the induced e.m.f. $= LI/t$ from above. If the flux-linkage increases from zero to $N\Phi$ in this time, then, from Faraday's law, the induced e.m.f. $= N\Phi/t$. Thus $LI = N\Phi$, or

$$L = \frac{N\Phi}{I}$$

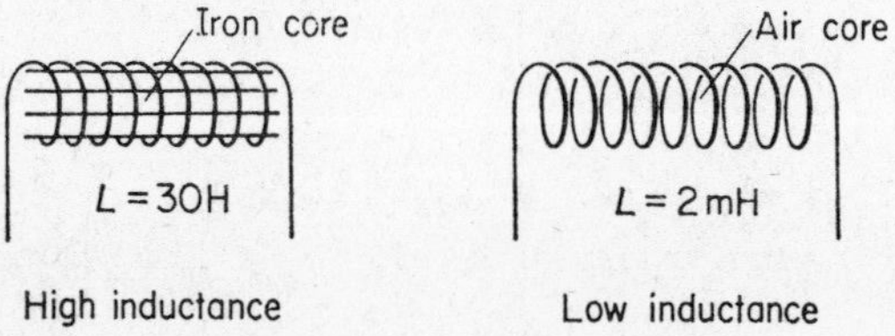

High inductance   Low inductance

Fig. 6.12. High and low inductance

Hence the inductance L can also be defined as the *flux-linkage per ampere*. One henry is thus the inductance of a coil when a current of 1 A produces a flux linkage in it of 1 weber. An iron-cored coil may have an inductance such as 30 H or more, whereas an air-cored coil may have an inductance of the order of millihenries (mH) or less, Fig. 6.12.

In general, it can be seen that the magnitude of L, the self-inductance of a coil, increases with the number of turns N, the area A and the permeability μ of its core, since the flux-linkage then increases. We shall now show that $L = N^2 A\mu/l$.

Suppose a current I flows in the coil and sets up a flux-density B normally to all the turns. Then

$$\text{flux-linkages} = N\Phi = NAB$$

But $$B = \mu H = \mu NI/l$$

where l is the length of the coil (p. 79).

$$\therefore \text{ flux-linkages, } N\Phi = NA\mu H = N^2 A\mu I/l$$

$$\therefore \text{ flux-linkages per amp, } L = \frac{N\Phi}{I} = \frac{N^2 A\mu}{l}$$

The inductance of a coil thus depends on the *square* of the number of turns, as well as on A, μ and l.

Suppose a solenoid has 500 turns wound on a soft-iron core of relative permeability 1000, and an area of 6 cm² or 6×10^{-4} m² and a length of 20 cm or 20×10^{-2} m.   Then, since $\mu = \mu_r\mu_0 = 1000 \times 4\pi \times 10^{-7}$, the inductance L is given by

$$L = \frac{N^2 A \mu}{l} = \frac{500^2 \times 6 \times 10^{-4} \times 1000 \times 4\pi}{10^7 \times 20 \times 10^{-2}} \text{ henries (H)}$$

$$= 1 \text{ H (approx.)}$$

The formula $L = N^2A\mu/l$ was derived on the assumption that all the flux links the coil.   This is nearly true for an iron core.   Without an iron core, there is considerable 'flux leakage', that is, all the flux does not link all the turns.   The amount of flux leakage depends on the geometry of the coil construction.   Charts are available for calculating L from coils of various geometries.

Current Growth in $L-R$ Series Circuit

The inductance of a coil affects the growth of current in a d.c. circuit, such as that containing a magnetic relay for example (p. 80).   As an illustration, suppose a battery of e.m.f. 100 V is connected to a coil

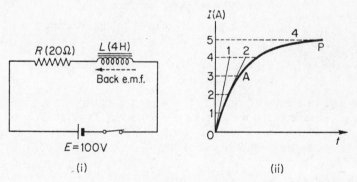

FIG. 6.13.   Current in L-R series circuit

of inductance L of 4 H and resistance R of 20 Ω.   For convenience, we can separate R from L, as shown in Fig. 6.13 (i).

Suppose the circuit is made by pressing the key.   While the current rises from zero, part of the e.m.f. of 100 V is used to maintain the current in R.   The remainder is used to maintain the growth of the current against the opposing or 'back' e.m.f., which is due to the inductance L of the coil. The growth of current can be obtained as follows:

(i) At time $t = 0$ there is no current,
∴ the p.d. across $R = IR = 0$
∴ the p.d. to maintain the growth of current

$$= 100 - 0 = 100 \text{ V} = \text{back e.m.f., } E$$

But $E = L \times$ ampere change/sec $= 4 \times$ ampere change/sec at this instant.

$$∴ 4 \times \text{ampere change/sec} = 100$$
or $$\text{ampere/sec} = 25$$

This is the value of the rate of change of current at $t = 0$, and is represented by the gradient of line (1) in Fig. 6.13 (ii).

(ii) When the current is finally established at P (Fig. 6.13 (ii)), the back e.m.f. $= 0$. The whole of the 100 volts is then used to maintain the steady current through R, and hence the value of this current is $I = 100/20 = 5$ A. Further, as the current is steady, there is no back e.m.f. This corresponds to the broken line (4), whose gradient is zero.

(iii) Suppose now that the current at an intermediate point A is 3 A at some instant. Then

$$\text{p.d. across } R = IR = 3 \times 20 = 60 \text{ V}$$

∴ p.d. to maintain current growth $= 100 - 60 = 40$ V $=$ back e.m.f., E. But

$$E = L \times \text{ampere change/sec} = 4 \times \text{ampere change/sec}$$
$$∴ \text{ampere change/sec} = 40/4 = 10$$

This rate of change of current at A is represented by the gradient of line (2). It is less than the gradient of (1), illustrating that the changing current slows down. The rise of current in the L, R series circuit can be shown to follow an exponential law.

Time-constant

When the inductance L of the coil increases and its resistance R remains the same, the 'opposition' to the growth of current increases. The current then rises more slowly to its maximum or steady value. The effect here is analogous to the case of the capacitor (C) in series with a resistor (R), discussed on p. 64. There it was stated that the charge rises to about 63% of its final value in a time CR seconds, called the *time-constant* of the circuit. In a similar way, calculation shows that the current in the L-R series circuit rises to about 63% of its final value, from the instant of switching on, in a time L/R seconds. The ratio L/R is called the 'time-constant' of the circuit. A coil with greater inductance and less resistance thus makes the current rise relatively slowly.

Similar principles operate when the circuit is broken at contacts after the current has reached a steady value. The current then decreases by 63 % of its value in L/R seconds, where R is the total *circuit* resistance. As R now includes the broken contact resistance, which is very high, the current drops very quickly. This rapid flux change in the coil produces a fairly high voltage across the contacts for the case of a coil with a soft-iron core, as in the magnetic relay. A spark is usually obtained across the contacts, as the insulation of the air is then broken down. To prevent the contacts melting, these are nickel-silver tipped. A large capacitor across the contacts, to absorb the energy here, reduces or 'quenches' sparking.

Energy in Magnetic Field of Inductor

In order to establish a current in an inductor, work must be done against the back e.m.f. while the current rises to its final value. The work done reappears as *energy in the magnetic field of the coil*. As shown below, the magnitude of the energy is $\frac{1}{2}LI_0^2$ joules, where L is the inductance in henries and I_0 is the steady current in amperes. This energy has been drawn from the battery. Once a steady magnetic field is established, no further energy is needed to maintain it since there is now no back e.m.f. Any energy dissipated in the circuit is then attributed to the power loss, I^2R, due to the resistance R in the circuit. If the circuit is broken, the current decreases to zero. The energy of the magnetic field in the coil is then dissipated mainly as heat. This is the origin of the heat produced at the broken contacts of a relay when a spark is obtained (p. 80).

To find the magnetic energy stored in the coil, suppose the coil has an inductance L and the current rises to a final value I_0. At a particular instant t while the current is rising, the back e.m.f. is given by Ldi/dt, where i is the instantaneous current (p. 106). In a further small time dt, the quantity of electricity which has moved against the back e.m.f. is $i \cdot dt$. Thus

$$\text{total energy} = \int_0^{I_0} \left(L\frac{di}{dt} \right) \cdot i \, dt = \int_0^{I_0} L \cdot i \, di = \tfrac{1}{2}LI_0^2$$

When L is in henrys and I_0 is in amps, then the energy $\frac{1}{2}LI_0^2$ is in *joules*.

EXAMPLES

1. A 4 H inductor has a steady current of 5 A flowing through it. The circuit is broken and the current falls to zero in 0·1 sec. Find the energy obtained from the magnetic field and the average value of the induced e.m.f.

$$\text{Energy, } W = \tfrac{1}{2}LI_0^2 = \tfrac{1}{2} \times 4 \times 5^2 = 50 \text{ joules}$$

$$\text{Average e.m.f.} = L \times \text{ampere change per sec} = 4 \times \frac{5}{0\cdot 1} = 200 \text{ V}$$

(Note the relatively high induced voltage which may be obtained across the contacts when a circuit with a high-inductance coil is broken. In some circuits induced voltages of several thousand volts may be produced, so that adequate insulation of the coil and its turns must be provided to avoid electrical breakdown.)

2. A 2 H inductor produces a magnetic flux of 6 milliwebers per turn when carrying a direct current of 3 A. Find (i) the number of turns in the coil and (ii) the energy stored in the field.

(i) From p. 106,

$$L = \text{flux-linkage per ampere}$$

$\therefore$ flux-linkage in coil $= L \times$ current in amperes $= 2 \times 3 = 6$ webers

$$\therefore \text{ number of turns} = \frac{6 \text{ webers}}{6 \text{ milliwebers}} = 1,000$$

(ii) Energy stored,

$$W = \tfrac{1}{2}LI_0^2 = \tfrac{1}{2} \times 2 \times 3^2 = 9 \text{ joules}$$

Energy in Medium. Attracting Force

The energy stored in the coil can also be expressed in terms of the flux-density B of the medium and its permeability, μ (p. 105). A similar case of stored energy occurred for the case of the medium (dielectric) between the plates of a charged capacitor, p. 56. It was stated there that the electrical energy per unit volume of the medium was $D^2/2\varepsilon$, where D was the electric induction and ε was the permittivity of the medium. Similarly, the magnetic energy per unit volume is given by $B^2/2\mu$.

A particular case of a force produced by a magnetic energy change occurs in the telephone earpiece. Here the magnetic diaphragm is attracted continuously by the poles of the neighbouring magnet, so that it vibrates when a speech current flows in the coils (p. 81). The attracting force per unit area of the diaphragm is proportional to the energy in the field round it and is thus proportional to B^2, the square of the flux-density in the medium. A similar result holds for the attractive force of an electromagnet or in the magnetic relay. In the telephone earpiece, however, we are interested in the *variations* of B^2, rather than B^2 itself, as explained on p. 82.

Mutual Induction

When two coils A and B are near each other, magnetic flux due to current in A say will link B. Hence if a change of current occurs in A, an induced e.m.f. is set up in B which opposes the change. This is called *mutual induction*. A similar change of flux in B will set up an induced e.m.f. in A of the same magnitude. The magnitude of the mutual induction will depend on how near the coils are to each other, the medium between them and their respective number of turns and area.

Mutual Inductance

We define the mutual inductance M between two coils A and B in a similar way to self- inductance (p. 106), Fig. 6.14. Thus if an induced

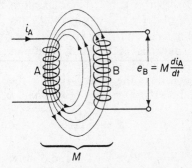

Fig. 6.14.   Mutual inductance

e.m.f. e_B is produced in B by a rate of change of current, di_A/dt, in A, then

$$M = \frac{-e_B}{di_A/dt}$$

The unit of M is a *henry*, the same as for self-inductance. Since $e_B = Nd\Phi_B/dt$ (see also p. 95), it follows that, numerically,

$$M = \frac{Nd\Phi_B}{di_A}$$

Thus M is also the flux linkage change in webers in B due to a current change of 1 A in A. M will hence increase when the two coils are closer together or when they are wound round soft iron.

If the terminals of the second coil, B say, are connected together, then the induced e.m.f. in it, due to a current change in A, will cause a current i_2 say to flow. This current itself produces a 'back' e.m.f. in B whose magnitude is proportional to the rate of change of i_2. In addition, *it produces magnetic flux which links the other coil* A. Consequently, an induced e.m.f. is produced in A by mutual induction. From Lenz's law, this opposes the e.m.f. in A and hence the current in A is reduced.

A different effect occurs when the secondary terminals of a commercial transformer are connected to a load so that a secondary current flows. This produces a reduction in the primary flux linking the soft iron. Thus an increased current is drawn from the primary source in this case, to re-establish the flux.

Maximum Mutual Inductance. Coupling Factor

The maximum mutual inductance between two coils occurs when *all* the flux in one coil links all the turns of the other coil. This is the case for two coils in an iron-cored transformer, which are wound round a common closed soft-iron core. The maximum mutual inductance M_0 is then shown to be $\sqrt{L_1 L_2}$, where L_1, L_2 are the individual self-inductances of the coils A and B (p. 105).

The mutual inductance is less than this maximum, M_0, if the coils are air-cored, and the coupling is said to be 'loose' if only a small amount of flux from one coil links the other. If M is then the magnitude of the mutual inductance, the *coefficient of coupling*, k, is defined by:

$$k = \frac{M}{\sqrt{L_1 L_2}}$$

Values as low as $k = 0.005$ are used in radio practice.

If two coils of self-inductance L_1, L_2 respectively are joined in series, and the flux due to current in each coil is in the same direction as the flux due to mutual induction between the coils, then the total self-inductance $= L_1 + L_2 + 2M$. If the flux due to mutual induction opposes the flux due to self-inductance, then the total self-inductance $= L_1 + L_2 - 2M$. These results can be seen by considering a change of current ΔI. With the flux in the same direction in each coil, for example, the flux change in one coil is $(L_1 \cdot \Delta I + M \cdot \Delta I)$ and in the other is $(L_2 \cdot \Delta I + M \cdot \Delta I)$, making a total flux change per unit current change of $(L_1 + L_2 + 2M)$.

SUMMARY

1. Flux linkage $N\Phi = NAB$ webers (Wb). Induced e.m.f. $\propto$ rate of change of flux linkages (Faraday's or Newmann's law). Direction of induced e.m.f. or current opposes the motion or change producing it (Lenz's law).

2. For a straight conductor moving perpendicular to a field B with constant velocity v, induced e.m.f. $= Blv$, where l is the length. For the simple dynamo, $e = E_m \sin \omega t$, where $E_m = \omega NAB$; this is a *sinusoidal e.m.f.*

3. In an iron-cored transformer, $E_s/E_p = N_s/N_p$.

4. $L =$ flux linkage per unit current. The energy stored by a steady current I_0 in the magnetic field of an inductor $= \frac{1}{2}LI_0^2$. The time-constant for a L–R series circuit is L/R seconds.

5. The area of the B–H loop or curve is proportional to the hysteresis losses in a magnetic material. Other losses in the material are eddy-currant losses, which are reduced by laminating the core or by using materials (ferrites) with a high resistivity.

EXERCISE 6

(Where necessary, use magnetic permeability of free space $\mu_0 = 4\pi \times 10^{-7}$ henry per metre.)

1. State Lenz's and Faraday's laws of electromagnetic induction.

2. Explain, as fully as you can, what takes place when a bar magnet is quickly plunged into the centre of a coil of wire and is slowly withdrawn.

(C. & G.)

3. Explain how eddy currents are set up in the core of an a.c. transformer. Why are such currents objectionable and what steps are taken to reduce their magnitude? (C. & G.)

4. Draw sketches illustrating a step-down and a step-up transformer. Why is steel unsuitable for the core of a commercial transformer? A step-up transformer has 100 turns in the primary and 2,500 turns in the secondary. If the voltage from the latter on open circuit is 400 V, calculate the input voltage.

5. What points of difference are there between the *resistance* and the *inductance* of a coil of wire? Explain the effect on the inductance when a soft-iron core is introduced into the coil.

6. When a current of 1 A in a coil is increased to 3 A, the flux-linkage of the coil increases from 50 milliwebers to 150 milliwebers. Calculate the inductance of the coil.

7. A powerful bar magnet is suspended by threads so that it hangs horizontally. A thick aluminium ring is also suspended with its centre directly in front of the N-pole of the magnet. When the magnet is set swinging to and fro, the ring soon picks up the oscillation. (i) Draw a diagram showing what happens to the ring when the N-pole first moves, (ii) account for the oscillation of the ring.

8. Draw a diagram of a *step-down* and a *step-up* commercial transformer. Explain the relation between the output and input a.c. voltages when the secondary is an open circuit. What happens when the secondary terminals are connected to a load?

9. Which of the following formulae is that of the energy in an inductance L carrying a steady current I: (i) $\frac{1}{2}LI$, (ii) $\frac{1}{2}LI^2$, (iii) $\frac{1}{2}L^2I$, (iv) $\frac{1}{2}L/I$, (v) $\frac{1}{2}L/I^2$. A coil of 4 H and resistance 20 ohms carries a steady current of 2 A: (i) What is evidence that energy is stored in the coil? (ii) How is the energy stored? (iii) What was the origin of the energy? (iv) Calculate the energy stored.

10. A coil of 2 H and 10 ohms resistance is connected to a 20 V d.c. supply. Calculate (*a*) the final steady current, (*b*) the initial rate at which the current rises. Draw a sketch showing how the current varies with time.

11. What is meant by *self-induction* and *mutual induction*? Give an example of each.

12. An a.c. supply of 12 V–24 W is needed from a 240 V mains supply. (i) Draw a sketch of the transformer required, (ii) calculate the current in the primary, assuming no power is wasted. List the ways in which power is wasted in practice.

13. A coil of 100 turns wound round an iron core has an inductance of

0·5 H. What inductance is produced when a coil of 200 turns is wound on another core identical to the first one?

The area of the coil is 40 cm², its length is 10 cm and the permeability of free space is $4\pi \times 10^{-7}$ henries per metre. Calculate the relative permeability of the iron core.

14. With reference to a typical magnetisation (*B–H*) curve explain the meanings of (*a*) relative permeability, (*b*) remanence, (*c*) coercivity.

When an alternating current flows in an iron-cored coil some power is lost. Explain the reasons for this.

What steps are taken in the design of the iron core to minimise core losses?

(*C. & G.*)

15. State Faraday's law of electromagnetic induction. Explain the principle of self-induction in a coil.

A 2-henry inductor carrying a direct current of 4 A produces a magnetic flux of 10 milliwebers. Calculate (*a*) the number of turns on the coil, (*b*) the energy stored in the magnetic field. (*C. & G.*)

16. Explain, and give an example of, electromagnetic induction. Describe the difference between self-induction and mutual induction.

Two separate inductors of 50 and 150 mH respectively are mounted so that there is a mutual inductance of 40 mH between them. What will be the resulting inductance when the two are connected: (*a*) in series aiding, (*b*) in series opposing.

17. Explain the principle of the transformer.

An a.c. supply of 100 volts 2 amperes is required and a 200-volt a.c. supply is available. Explain how the 100-volt supply can be obtained by using a transformer and calculate the turns ratio. What value of series resistor could be used instead of a transformer? Which method would you expect to give the better overall power efficiency and why? (*C. & G.*)

18. What do you understand by the term *magnetic hysteresis*? Draw typical hysteresis loops for (*a*) soft iron, (*b*) hard steel and, making reference to those curves, explain the terms *saturation, permeability, retentivity*, and *coercive force*, indicating how the values of these differ in the case of the two materials. (*C. & G.*)

19. A 10-V battery of negligible internal resistance is switched across a coil of 1-H inductance and 40-ohm resistance. Sketch a curve showing the current/time relationship from the instant of switching on. Write down an expression representing the instantaneous value of the current.

Find (*a*) the initial current, (*b*) the final current.

If a second coil were wound over the first, but insulated from it, what effect would occur in the second coil due to the increasing current in the first winding? At what time relative to the switching-on of the battery would the effect in the second winding be a maximum? Give a reason for your answer. Assume that the terminals of the second coil are open-circuited throughout.

(*C. & G.*)

20. Explain, with the aid of a sketch, the principle of operation of a moving-coil microphone.

State briefly the relative advantages and disadvantages of the moving-coil and carbon-granule microphone with respect to frequency response, sensitivity and reliability. (*C. & G.*)

7: Alternating Current (A.C.) and Circuits

ALTERNATING CURRENT

Sinusoidal A.C.

The simplest (pure) alternating current is known as a *sinusoidal* alternating current. It varies with time as a sine (or cosine) curve. The simple dynamo, discussed on p. 100, produces a sinusoidal voltage. Fig. 7.1 illustrates the sinusoidal variation with time t of a quantity y,

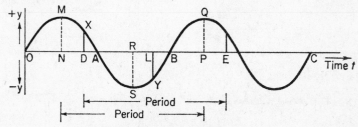

FIG. 7.1. Sinusoidal variation

which may be either current or voltage. Thus an alternating current, for example, increases from zero to a maximum, diminishes to zero and reverses in direction (y negative), grows to a maximum once more in this direction, and then diminishes to zero again. The bob of a pendulum undergoes a sinusoidal variation of displacement in its to-and-fro motion when the swing is small.

Definitions in A.C.

A *cycle* is one complete set of variations, for example, from O to B or from N to P or from D to E.

The *frequency* (f) of a.c. current or voltage is the number of cycles per second.

The *period* (T) is the time taken for 1 cycle. Thus $T = 1/f$.

The *instantaneous value* of a.c. is the value at a particular instant, such as DX or LY. Instantaneous values will be noted by a small italic letter, such as i for current and v for voltage.

The *peak value* of a.c. is the maximum value, such as NM or RS in Fig. 7.1. Peak values will be denoted by a capital italic letter with a subscript 'm' for 'maximum', such as I_m for current and V_m for voltage.

A sinusoidal alternating current can thus be represented by

$$i = I_m \sin \omega t = I_m \sin 2\pi ft$$

Here i is the instantaneous value and I_m is the peak value. Similarly, a sinusoidal a.c. voltage can be represented by (see p. 100)

$$v = V_m \sin \omega t = V_m \sin 2\pi ft$$

Other Wave-forms

Fig. 7.2 shows some waveforms other than the sinusoidal waveform which are met in radio. Although Fig. 7.2 (ii)–(v) appear complicated,

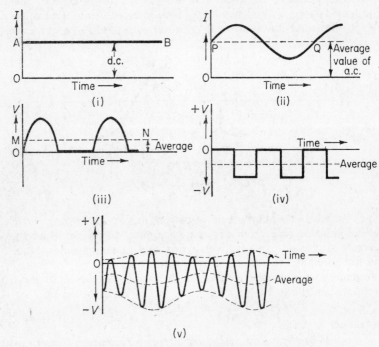

Fig. 7.2. Wave-forms

they can all be analysed into a number of different sinusoidal waves which, added together, produce the particular waveform.

1. In Fig. 7.2 (i) AB represents a direct current or voltage. Its frequency is zero.

2. Fig. 7.2 (ii) shows a varying current which flows in one direction. It has an average represented by the height of the line PQ above the time-axis. The average of the a.c. we have considered previously (Fig. 7.1) was zero over its cycle, since it had negative as well as positive values.

3. The variation shown in Fig. 7.2 (iii) consists only of the positive half-cycles of a pure alternating voltage. This, too, has an average value, as indicated by MN.

4. The voltage wave-form shown in Fig. 7.2 (iv) represents a negative rectangular pulse (see p. 68 for positive rectangular pulse), and the variation has an average negative value.

5. The voltage variation in Fig. 7.2 (v) is not of constant amplitude. It is only slightly positive, and the average value shown follows the variation of the peaks of the negative portion of the curve.

Frequency Values

The frequency of commercial a.c. mains in this country is 50 Hz (1 Hz = 1 hertz = 1 cycle per sec). The frequency of sound waves varies from about 20 Hz to 16,000 Hz or 16 kHz (1 kHz = 1 kilohertz = 1,000 Hz). When sound waves due to speech or music are converted by a microphone to alternating currents of the same frequency, we then have a.c. of sound- or *audio-frequency* (a.f.) range. A useful value for discussion of a.f. alternating current is 1,000 Hz.

Transmission over long distances can take place when the alternating currents in the transmitter are of the order 10^5–10^9 Hz. This range of frequencies is known as a *radio frequency* (r.f.) range. A useful or average figure when discussing r.f. alternating current or voltage is 1 million or 10^6 Hz, called a megahertz and denoted by MHz. 1 MHz is the radio frequency of waves from a station broadcasting on a 300-metre wavelength. For all radio waves, frequency (Hz) × wavelength (metres) = 3×10^8 (approx).

The student should make a point of remembering 50, 1,000 and 10^6 Hz for general discussions of, respectively, mains, audio frequency (a.f.) and radio frequency (r.f.).

Sinusoidal Graph

A sinusoidal graph can be drawn by the method illustrated in Fig. 7.3. In Fig. 7.3 (i), the radius OA of the circle represents the *peak* value, a say, of the alternating current or voltage. The line ON is a fixed line with which OA makes an angle θ as shown. The height AN of A above ON, represented by y, is thus given always by $y/a = \sin \theta$, or $y = a \sin \theta$. Thus y represents a sinusoidal variation with a peak value a.

The graph of y with θ or time t is drawn by supposing that the radius OA moves anticlockwise round the circle at a steady angular speed, that is, the radius turns through equal angles in equal times. Instead of plotting y with time t, we may therefore plot y against θ, the angle of rotation. The result is shown in detail in Fig. 7.3 (ii) when OA occupies eight different positions. One complete revolution represents 360°.

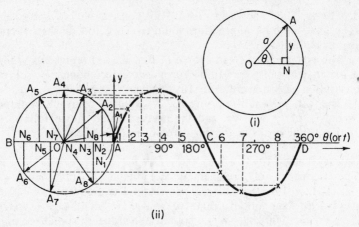

FIG. 7.3. Drawing of a sinusoidal graph

Phase Difference. Lagging and Leading

In a.c. circuit theory we frequently consider two alternating currents or voltages of the same frequency but 'out of step' or out of *phase* with each other. The two variations, x and y say, can be plotted by the circle method just described. Thus in Fig. 7.4, the radii of the two circles represent the respective peak values. OA and OB represents the

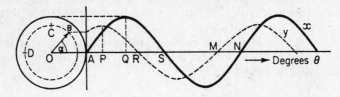

$$PQ = RS = MN = \alpha° = \text{phase angle}$$

FIG. 7.4. Phase difference

respective positions of the rotating radii at some instant. When OB rotates further to OC and y reaches its maximum value (corresponding to P), OA is then an angle α behind it. x reaches its maximum at some time later, corresponding to Q. When OB rotates further to OD (corresponding to R), OA is then still an angle α behind it. x reaches a corresponding zero value some time later, corresponding to S. And so on, as x and y vary.

We express this constant 'out-of-step' behaviour between x and y by saying that x *lags* on y by an angle α, or, what amounts to the same thing, that y *leads* on x by an angle α. This angle α is known as the *phase angle* between x and y. It is constant when they are of the same frequency. It can always be deduced from a graph of the two varying quantities. Thus from the graphs drawn, α is equal to PQ, RS or MN on the scale of degrees.

If OA $= a$, then $x = a \sin 2\pi ft$. If OB $= b$, then $y = b \sin (2\pi ft + \alpha)$, because y leads on x by the angle α. When x and y are 'in step' or *in phase*, then $x = a \sin 2\pi ft$ and $y = b \sin 2\pi ft$. Expressing these results with symbols for voltage, two voltages 90° out of phase can be represented respectively by:

$$v_1 = V_{m_1} \sin \omega t \quad \text{and} \quad v_2 = V_{m_2} \sin (\omega t + 90°)$$

Here v_2 leads v_1 by 90° in phase angle.

Vectors

A *vector* is defined as any quantity which is represented completely by a line having magnitude *and direction*. Velocity, displacement, and force in Mechanics are examples of vector quantities, because one has to specify direction in each case as well as magnitude in order to represent them completely. Temperature has a magnitude but no direction, and is therefore not a vector quantity. *Alternating currents and voltages can be treated as vector quantities.* The phase angle ϕ

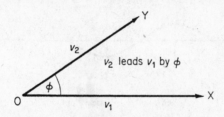

FIG. 7.5. Phasor diagram

between two alternating currents, or two alternating voltages, must therefore always be taken into account.

The magnitude and direction of a vector quantity is represented by a straight line drawn to scale. Suppose that the peak value of an alternating voltage v_1 is 4 V. Then the line OX, drawn 4 cm long on a scale of 1 cm to 1 V, represents v_1, Fig. 7.5. Suppose that the peak value of another alternating voltage v_2 of the same frequency is 3 V. Then the line OY, 3 cm long and inclined at the phase angle ϕ to OX, represents v_2. This simple sketch is known as the *phasor diagram* of v_1 and v_2. It gives all the information required about the two a.c. voltages on the understanding that (i) the lines shown represent their peak values, (ii) ϕ is their constant phase difference, (iii) the lines are imagined to rotate in an anti-clockwise direction in tracing out the variations. In drawing a vector diagram we may start with any direction for representing v_1. But having chosen it, v_2 must be represented by the line drawn at the phase angle ϕ to it.

Phase Difference

The following special cases of phase difference between voltages v_1 and v_2, shown in Fig. 7.6, occur in a.c. circuits. Similar phase differences occur between alternating currents.

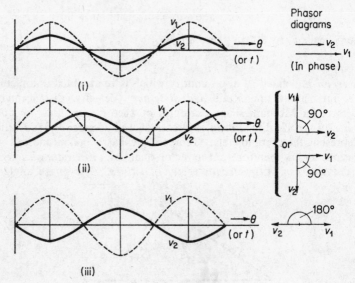

FIG. 7.6. Phase values

It should be noted that in (i) corresponding values, e.g. zero or maxima, occur at the same instant, but in (ii) the maximum of one quantity occurs at the same instant as the other is zero, and vice versa.

Vector Addition

Suppose that the alternating voltages across X and Y in the a.c. circuit shown in Fig. 7.7 are 90° out of phase and of the same frequency. Let V_1, V_2 be the respective peak voltages, and to fix our ideas suppose $V_1 = 3$ volts, $V_2 = 4$ volts. The voltage variation v_{AB}, v_{BC} across AB and BC respectively can then be represented by the graphs in Fig. 7.8 (i), assuming that v_{BC} leads on V_{AB}. The voltage variation, v_{AC}, between A and C is obtained by adding together these two graphs, as shown in Fig. 7.8 (ii). The curve v_{AC} reveals that (i) it has the same frequency as v_{AB} or v_{BC}, (ii) its peak value is 5 volts, and (iii) it leads on v_{AB} by an angle $\theta = 53°$. Thus the peak value of v_{AC} is not the arithmetical sum of V_1 and V_2, because the alternating voltages v_{AB} and v_{BC} are vectors and out of phase with each other.

The following method for *vector addition* can be used:

Draw OP to represent V_1 in magnitude, Fig. 7.8 (iii). Then draw

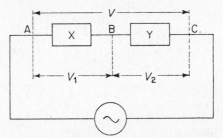

Applied a.c. voltage

FIG. 7.7. Vectors out of phase

OQ to represent V_2 on the same scale, *at the phase angle*, suppose it is 90°, to OP. Now complete the parallelogram which has OP, OQ as two of its sides by drawing the appropriate lines from P and Q. Then *the diagonal through* O represents the magnitude and phase of the peak

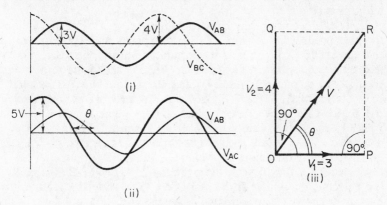

FIG. 7.8. Addition of Vectors

value, V, of the vector sum of V_1 and V_2, i.e. OR represents V, and angle POR, θ, is the phase angle of V relative to V_1.

It can now be seen that the magnitude of the phase angle between V_1 and V_2 will considerably affect their vector sum. It should be realised that we have just discussed a special case of the phase angle namely 90°, which is a common one in a.c. theory. Consequently, OQRP is a rectangle.

To calculate V and θ for this special case, we have:

$$OR^2 = OP^2 + PR^2$$

from Pythagoras' theorem for triangle ORP.

$$\therefore V^2 = 3^2 + 4^2$$

$$\therefore V = \sqrt{25} = 5 \text{ volts}$$

Also, since angle P $= 90°$ in triangle ORP,

$$\tan \theta = \frac{RP}{OP} = \frac{4}{3}$$

$\therefore \theta = 53°$ from the tables

Thus the peak value of v_{AC} is 5 volts and leads by $53°$ on v_{AB}, as shown in Fig. 7.8.

The same information can also be obtained by drawing OQPR to scale, and then measuring OR and the angle POR.

Measurement of A.C. Root-mean-square Value

We now consider the measurement of alternating current and voltage.

By itself, a moving-coil instrument cannot measure a.c. It will record the average value of a.c. as the needle reverses every half-cycle, and this is zero.

A *hot-wire ammeter* may be used to measure a.c. because it utilises the heat produced in a wire. The heat depends on i^2, the *square* of the current (p. 35). Thus heat is produced on both halves of a cycle and the needle will then be deflected. Fig. 7.9 shows the principle of the hot-wire ammeter. Basically, it has a resistance wire AB connected to two terminals T, T, Fig. 7.9. Phosphor-bronze wire CM is attached to the centre C of AB. Thread joined to the wire at M passes round a wheel P, and is kept firmly round P by a spring. When a current, d.c. or a.c., flows in AB, the wire becomes hot and expands. The sag at C is taken up by the thread, which then turns P. A pointer attached to the axle of P now deflects through an angle. Generally, the greater the current, the greater is the deflection. The scale is calibrated by passing in known steady currents. Since the heat produced depends on the square of the current, the scale is non-uniform, as shown.

The heating effect of an alternating current varies throughout the cycle since the current i varies. Thus the pointer deflection gives a measure of *the average of all the values of i^2 taken over a cycle*. This particular value is called the *root-mean-square* (*r.m.s.*) *value* of the alternating current.

As an illustration of the meaning of 'root-mean-square' value, suppose an alternating current, represented in Fig. 7.10, has a current peak, I_m, of 12·0 mA. Suppose we take 200 values of the square of the current from the graph in the period AC, having divided this time into 200 equal parts. Let the sum of these 200 current-squared values be 14,100 mA². Then

$$\text{mean (average)-square} = \frac{14,100}{200}$$

and

$$\text{root-mean-square (r.m.s.)} = \sqrt{\frac{14,100}{200}} = 8\cdot4 \text{ mA}$$

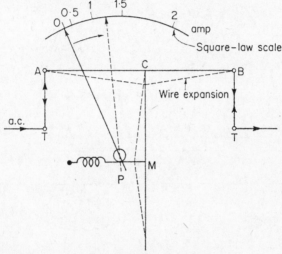

Fig. 7.9.   Hot-wire ammeter

R.M.S. and Peak Relations

The r.m.s. value of an alternating current or voltage depends on its wave-form. Consider the case of a 'sinusoidal current', which is an important waveform. This is a symmetrical curve about the time-axis ABC, Fig. 7.10. The current-squared graph AXBYC has only positive values since i^2 is positive. It is a symmetrical curve, and hence its mean or average value is *half-way* between its peaks and the time axis. In other words,

$$\text{mean-square value} = \tfrac{1}{2}I_m^2$$

$$\therefore \text{ r.m.s. value, } I = \sqrt{\tfrac{1}{2}I_m^2} = \frac{1}{\sqrt{2}} I_m \qquad (1)$$

Thus, to a close approximation,

$$\text{r.m.s. value, } I = 0\cdot71 I_m \qquad (2)$$

or

$$I_m = \sqrt{2}I = 1\cdot41 I \qquad (3)$$

The student should remember the relations (1), (2), (3) for subsequent use. It must be carefully noted that they apply only to the case when the variation of i with time is a sine or cosine curve. With variations other than sinusoidal (see p. 116), the peak values have a different numerical relation with their root-mean-square value to that given in (1) or (2).

The r.m.s. value of any a.c. may also be defined as that value of

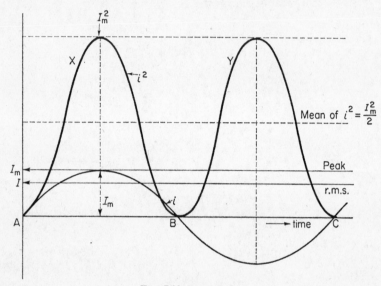

FIG. 7.10 R.m.s. value

direct current which gives the same heating effect per second. Thus suppose I is that value of d.c. Then the heat per second generated by it is I^2R, where R is the resistance of a wire through which it passes. When an alternating current flows through R, the heat generated per second is the average heat developed per second, and this is therefore given by (average of i^2) $\times$ R

$$\therefore I^2 \times R = (\text{average of } i^2) \times R$$

$$\therefore I = \sqrt{\text{average of } i^2}$$

The definitions of r.m.s. value given above for alternating current apply equally well for a sine-wave alternating voltage. Thus (i) the r.m.s. of an alternating voltage is that value of direct voltage which produces the same heat per second in a pure resistance, (ii) the r.m.s. value V is the square root of the average of v^2 taken over the cycle. It follows that $V = 0.71V_m = 0.71V_m$, and $V_m = 1.41V$. The mains voltage in this country is generally 240 V a.c. This is the root-mean-square value. The peak value V_m is given by

$$V_m = 1\cdot41V = 1\cdot41 \times 240 = 340 \text{ volts (approx.)}$$

Capacitors, for example, used on the 240 V a.c. mains must thus be able to withstand a voltage of about 340 volts while working.

Other A.C. Instruments

As we saw in the case of the hot-wire ammeter, an instrument whose needle deflects according to the square of the current or voltage can be used directly to measure a.c. We now discuss briefly the principles of some other instruments used for measuring a.c.

Rectifier Bridge Circuit

Moving-coil meters, known as *multimeters*, are widely used for measuring a.c. and d.c. When the switch on the instrument panel is turned to a.c., metal rectifiers at the back are automatically connected with the meter to form a 'bridge circuit'. A rectifier conducts appreciably in one direction only (p. 18).

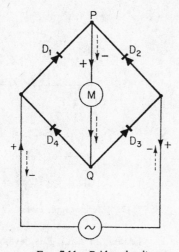

Fig. 7.11. Bridge circuit

Fig. 7.11 shows the principle concerned. It consists of a bridge circuit with four rectifiers D_1, D_2, D_3, D_4 and the instrument M. On the +ve half of an a.c. cycle, only D_1 and D_3 conduct; on the −ve half of the same cycle, only D_2 and D_4 conduct. On *both* halves, however, a current flows in M from P to Q. Thus a reading is obtained on the meter M.

The reading corresponds to the average value of the half-waves of the a.c. voltage applied. If this is sinusoidal, the average value, $V_{av} = (2/\pi)V_m$, where V_m is the peak value. But the r.m.s. voltage, $V = V_m/\sqrt{2}$ (p. 123). Hence

$$V = \frac{1}{\sqrt{2}} \times \frac{\pi}{2} V_{av} = 1 \cdot 11 V_{av}$$

The r.m.s. values are thus about 1/9 or 11% more than the d.c. meter reading, and are easily marked on the meter scale.

Thermocouple Meter

For frequencies higher than about 100 kHz, the accuracy of the rectifier meter falls off seriously. This is due to the shunting rectifier 'capacitance' and to the reactance of the coil. The *thermocouple meter* is widely used at radio frequencies for measuring a.c. currents. The short length of heater element used has negligible inductance and capacitance.

If two unlike metals such as antimony A and bismuth B are joined at their

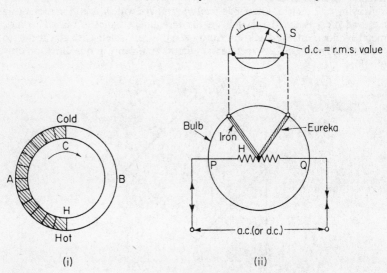

FIG. 7.12. Thermocouple meter

ends, and one junction H is heated, an e.m.f. E is developed in the circuit in the direction ACBH. This is shown diagrammatically in Fig. 7.12 (i). The source of E is the diffusion of electrons which takes place across the junction when one is heated. Its magnitude depends on the nature of the two metals used and the temperature difference between the junctions. The two metals constitute in this case a 'thermocouple'.

The *thermocouple meter* consists basically of a short length of resistance wire PQ, with one junction H of a thermocouple of iron and eureka wire attached to the wire, Fig. 7.12 (ii). When a current flows in PQ, the wire and hence H becomes hot. A d.c. moving-coil instrument S then has a deflection which is related to the temperature of H and hence to the r.m.s. value of the alternating current in PQ. By calibration, r.m.s. values of current can be read directly on S.

A less sensitive instrument is made by separating H from PQ by a glass bead and allowing the heat to reach H by conduction through the bead. A more sensitive instrument is made by placing the heating and the thermo-couple elements inside a vacuum in a small glass bulb, as indicated in Fig. 7.12 (ii). In this case no heat is lost by convection to the surroundings and so H reaches a higher temperature than with air present. For high currents of the order of an ampere, the instrument is made more robust by using air in the bulb.

Moving-iron Repulsion Instrument

A moving-iron repulsion instrument is a robust instrument for measuring a.c. Basically, it consists of a solenoid S with a fixed piece of soft iron F and a movable soft-iron M inside, Fig. 7.13. When a current, d.c. *or* a.c.,

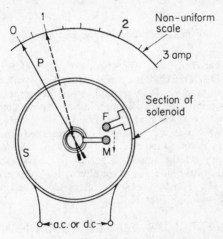

FIG. 7.13.   Moving-iron repulsion meter

flows in S, the magnetic effect magnetizes F and M with like poles facing each other. Thus M is repelled by F. The movement of M deflects a pointer P attached to a wheel, and the angle of deflection, which is controlled by a spring, is a measure of the magnitude of the current. The scale can be made partly linear by shaping the moving iron.

Cathode-ray Oscillograph

The cathode-ray oscillograph (C.R.O.), described on p. 193, can be used to measure the peak value of an alternating voltage. This instrument contains an electron beam, which produces a spot of light S on striking a fluorescent screen, Fig. 7.14 (i). An electron beam is extremely light (p. 1). It responds quickly and sensitively to voltages. Thus when an alternating voltage is connected to the terminals of the instrument the electron beam moves up and down at the same frequency. It follows the variations of voltage even though its frequency may be extremely high. The speed of the up-and-down movement makes the spot on the screen appear to be a straight line DB, Fig. 7.14 (ii). The length of DB is proportional to twice the amplitude, or peak value, of V because D and B represent the limits of movement of the spot. This is now measured. V is then disconnected from the C.R.O., and a known alternating voltage, V_0, applied. The length, say XY, of the new

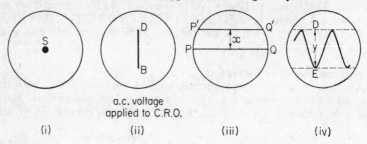

a.c. voltage
applied to C.R.O.

(i) (ii) (iii) (iv)

FIG. 7.14. Cathode-ray oscillograph

line obtained is then measured. The unknown voltage is calculated from the relation $V/V_0 = \mathrm{DB}/\mathrm{XY}$. If V_0 is a r.m.s. value, then V will be a r.m.s. value.

If the time-base of the C.R.O. is used, a line PQ appears on the screen instead of a spot, Fig. 7.14 (iii). When a known d.c. voltage (V_0) is applied to the C.R.O., the line moves through a distance x in a vertical direction to a new position, P′Q′. The d.c. voltage is disconnected and the unknown alternating voltage is connected to C.R.O. A trace of the wave-form can be obtained stationary on the screen, Fig. 7.14 (iv). The distance DE or y represents twice the peak value, V_m, of the alternating voltage, and is measured. Then $2V_m/V_0 = y/x$. Hence V_m can be calculated. The r.m.s. value V can be found, since $V = 0.71 V_m$ (p. 123).

A.C. CIRCUITS—SINGLE COMPONENTS

We now consider circuits to which an a.c. voltage is connected. As r.m.s. values are practical values, we shall be mainly concerned with deducing the r.m.s. value I of the current when the a.c. applied voltage has an r.m.s. value V. Single components are considered here. Circuits containing more than one component are discussed in the next section (p. 144).

A.C. and R

Fig. 7.15 (i) represents the simplest type of a.c. circuit. An alternating voltage of V volts r.m.s. is connected to a resistor of R ohms.

Suppose that the magnitude of the voltage is QB or v at an instant Q (Fig. 7.15 (ii)). The current is then v/R, from Ohm's law, and corresponds to P. At an instant M, the voltage MN is in the opposite direction. The current is MN/R and thus reverses. At the instants O, A, E the applied voltage is zero. Hence the current values are zero. It can now be seen that the variation of i, the resulting current, coincides exactly with the variation of v. Thus i and v are *in phase*. The vectors representing either their peak or their r.m.s. values are as shown in Fig. 7.15 (iii), which is the phasor diagram.

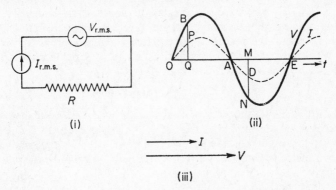

FIG. 7.15.   A.C. and R

When v is a maximum, the current i is a maximum. Thus, using the maximum values V_m and I_m respectively,

$$I_m = \frac{V_m}{R}$$

Multiply both sides by $0.71(1/\sqrt{2})$. Then $0.71 I_m = 0.71 V_m/R$.

$$\therefore I = \frac{V}{R} \tag{1}$$

where I and V are r.m.s. values.

It now follows that $V = IR$, and $R = V/I$, where V is in volts (r.m.s.) and I in amperes (r.m.s.). Hence Ohm's law formulae can be applied to this a.c. circuit.

EXAMPLE

A current of $2mA$ (r.m.s.) flows through a pure resistance of 1,000 ohms. Calculate the alternating voltage across the resistance.

$$V = IR = \frac{2}{1,000} \times 1,000 = 2 \text{ volts.}$$

Note that 2 volts is the r.m.s. value. It is not the peak value, which is 1.41×2 or 2.82 volts.

A.C. and C

Suppose B and G are the plates of a capacitor connected to the terminals A, D of an alternating source of V volts (r.m.s.) Fig. 7.16 (i). Over the positive half-cycle PML shown in Fig. 7.16 (iv), we may imagine that a battery of e.m.f. E is connected to the plates, as shown in Fig. 7.16 (ii). Positive and negative quantities of electricity q of varying amount then reach the plates B and G respectively.

At any instant the charge q on the plates $= Cv$, where v is the voltage at that instant. The *current i* is the change of q per second (p. 6). Since C is a constant it follows that

$$i = C \times \text{change of } v \text{ per second} \qquad (1)$$

Fig. 7.17 (i) shows the variation of v with time t. The change of v per second, or the rate of change of v, is the slope or *gradient* of the graph at the point considered. At the zero value P, the gradient is high; at the peak value M, the gradient is zero. Along ML the gradient is *negative* and at N it becomes zero again. Fig. 7.17 (ii) shows the graph obtained. Note that the zero values of the rate of change of v occur when v is at its peak values.

Now from (1), the current i variation follows the variation in Fig. 7.17 (ii), since C is a constant. This is shown in Fig. 7.17 (iii), where v is also drawn for comparison.

Phase of I

The first deduction we can make is that i leads v by 90°, or v lags on i by 90°. The phasor diagram for this a.c. circuit is therefore as shown in Fig. 7.18, where I, V are r.m.s. (or peak) values.

Magnitude of I

Since

$$i = C \times (\text{change of } v \text{ per sec}), \qquad (1)$$

it follows that the peak value I_m is obtained by mutliplying the peak value of (change of v per sec) by C. It can be seen that the peak value, OH, of the curve in Fig. 7.17 (ii) depends on the *gradient at* P to the voltage curve in Fig. 7.17 (i).

Fig. 7.19 (i) shows two alternating voltages, v_1 and v_2, *of the same frequency*, but v_2 of greater peak value than v_1. At P the gradient, g_2, of the v_2 curve is greater than the gradient, g_1, of the curve for v_1.

It follows from (1) above that, the greater *peak value* of the applied voltage v at a given frequency, the greater is the peak value I_m (2)

Consider now two voltages X and Y of the same peak value, but Y of greater frequency than X (Fig. 7.19 (ii)). If the gradients at P are examined, the gradient (n) for Y can be seen to be greater than the gradient (l) for X.

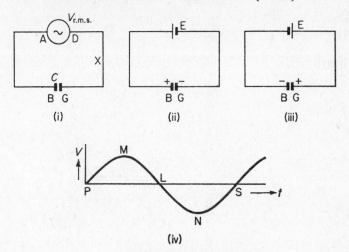

(iv)

Fig. 7.16. A.C. and *C*

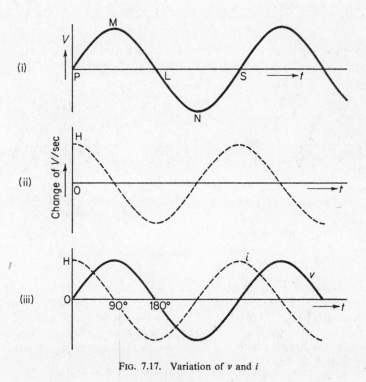

Fig. 7.17. Variation of *v* and *i*

Thus the greater the *frequency* of an applied voltage, v, of given peak value the greater is the peak value I_m (3)

Collecting the information obtained from (1), (2) and (3), it follows that $I_m \propto C \times (V_m \times f)$.

$$\therefore I_m = k \times fC \times V_m$$

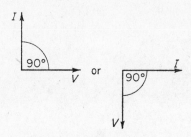

FIG. 7.18. Phasor diagram

where k is a constant. Mathematical investigation (see p. 133) shows that $k = 2\pi$. Thus

$$I_m = 2\pi fC \times V_m$$

Multipling both sides by $0 \cdot 71(1/\sqrt{2})$ to obtain r.m.s. values, I and V.

$$\therefore I = 2\pi fC \times V \qquad (4)$$

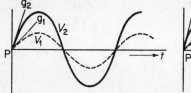

V_2 of greater peak value than V_1

(i)

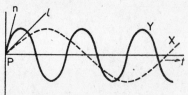

Y of greater frequency than X, but of same peak value

(ii)

FIG. 7.19. Magnitude of I

At this stage it would be wise to discuss the *units* involved in (4). We started with $q = Cv$. When v is in volts and C in farads, then q is in coulombs. We next stated that $i =$ change in q per sec $= C \times$ change in v per sec. If q is in coulombs it follows that i is in amperes. Thus in the above relation I is measured in amperes, C in farads, V in volts, f in Hz.

Calculus proof

Using calculus, $i = dq/dt = Cdv/dt$. But $v = V_m \sin 2\pi ft$.

$$\therefore \frac{dv}{dt} = 2\pi f V_m \cos 2\pi ft$$

$$\therefore i = 2\pi f C V_m \cos 2\pi ft = 2\pi f C V_m \sin (90° + 2\pi ft)$$

$\therefore i$ leads on v by $90°$, and has a peak value $I_m = 2\pi f C V_m$

Reactance of Capacitor

Using the r.m.s. values I and V, from (4) we have

$$I = 2\pi f C \times V$$

$$\therefore \frac{V}{I} = \frac{1}{2\pi f C}$$

Now V/I in d.c. theory represents the magnitude of resistance. By analogy, V/I in a.c. theory represents the magnitude of the 'effective opposition' of a capacitor to alternating current. The term *reactance* is used for 'effective opposition', and given the symbol X_C. Thus, from above,

$$X_C = \frac{1}{2\pi f C}$$

When C is in farads and f in Hz, then X_C is in *ohms*. The corresponding Ohm's law formulae for the a.c. circuit discussed now becomes

$$\frac{V}{I} = X_C, \quad V = I \times X_C, \quad I = \frac{V}{X_C}$$

They are easy to remember as X_C takes the place of R in the d.c. formulae.

Values of X_C for typical capacitors

(a) For a $1\,\mu F$ capacitor, $C = 1\,\mu F = 1/10^6$ F. Since

$$X_C = \frac{1}{2\pi f C},$$

then at the r.f. of 10^6 Hz,

$$X_C = \frac{1}{2 \times 3 \cdot 14 \times 10^6 \times \dfrac{1}{10^6}} = 0 \cdot 16\ \Omega$$

At the a.f. of 1,000 Hz,

$$X_C = \frac{1}{2\pi f C} = \frac{1}{2 \times 3 \cdot 14 \times 1,000 \times \dfrac{1}{10^6}} = 160\ \Omega$$

At the frequency of commercial power, $f = 50$ Hz,

$$X_C = \frac{1}{2 \times 3\cdot14 \times 50 \times \frac{1}{10^6}} = 3{,}180 \ \Omega$$

Note. 1μF must be converted to farads.

From the numerical results, it can be seen that X_C increases as f decreases. In fact, from $X_C = 1/2\pi fC$, it follows that $X_C \propto 1/f$. Thus if X_C is 200 Ω at $f = 100$ Hz, then at $f = 1{,}000$ Hz, which is 10 times

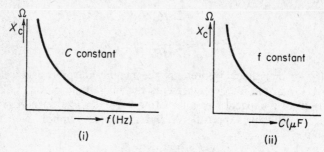

FIG. 7.20. Variation of reactance

higher frequency, X_C is ten times *lower* or 20 Ω. Further, from $X_C = 1/2\pi fC$, it follows that, for the same frequency, $X_C \propto 1/C$. Thus if X_C at 10^6 Hz is $0\cdot16 \ \Omega$ for $C = 1 \mu$F, then for $C = 0\cdot001 \mu$F at the same frequency, X_C is 1,000 times *as great*, or $1{,}000 \times 0\cdot16$ or 160 Ω. Fig. 7.20 illustrates how X_C varies with f and with C.

Separation of A.F. and D.C.

Suppose that a d.c. battery and an a.f. ($f = 1{,}000$ Hz) alternating voltage generator are in a circuit containing phones, Fig. 7.21. The

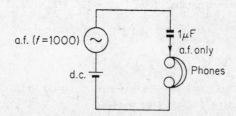

FIG. 7.21. Separation of a.f. and d.c.

d.c. can be eliminated from the phones by placing in series with it a 1μF capacitor. This has a reactance of 160 Ω to $f = 1{,}000$ Hz and an infinite resistance to direct current. The current flowing through the phones is then only a.c. of frequency $f = 1,000$ Hz, and the phones then produce a better response to the sound frequency.

Capacitance Measurement

A simple method of measuring a capacitance of the order of a micro-farad is to connect a suitable voltage from the a.c. mains, and then to measure the current flowing with a suitable a.c. instrument (p. 125).

As an illustration, suppose that an a.c. voltage of 4 V (r.m.s.) is applied to an unknown capacitance C from the mains, $f = 50$ Hz, and the current measured is $1 \cdot 2$ mA (r.m.s.), Fig. 7.22 (i). Then

$$X_C = \frac{V}{I} = \frac{4}{0 \cdot 0012} \; \Omega$$

But
$$X_C = \frac{1}{2\pi f C} = \frac{1}{2\pi \times 50 \times C}$$

where C is in farads.

$$\therefore \frac{1}{2\pi \times 50 \times C} = \frac{4}{0 \cdot 0012}$$

$$\therefore C = \frac{0 \cdot 0012}{2 \times 3 \cdot 14 \times 50 \times 4} \; F$$

$$= \frac{0 \cdot 0012 \times 10^6}{2 \times 3 \cdot 14 \times 50 \times 4} \; \mu F$$

$$= 0 \cdot 96 \; \mu F$$

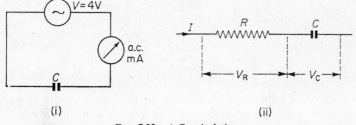

FIG. 7.22.   A.C. calculations

EXAMPLES

1. A p.d. of 220 V (r.m.s.) is established across a capacitor of $0 \cdot 05$ μF If the frequency is 500 Hz, calculate the current flowing:

$$X_C = \frac{1}{2\pi f C} = \frac{1}{2 \times 3 \cdot 14 \times 500 \times \dfrac{0 \cdot 05}{10^6}} = 6{,}370 \; \Omega \text{ (approx.)}$$

$$\therefore I = \frac{V}{X_C} = \frac{220}{6{,}370} = 0 \cdot 0345 \text{ A (r.m.s.)}$$

2. A resistor of 250 ohms and a capacitor of 1 μF are connected in series, and an a.c. of 4 mA and $f = 50$ Hz is flowing in the circuit. Find the voltage across the resistor and across the capacitor (Fig. 7.22 (ii)).

The a.c. value is always understood to be an r.m.s. value unless the peak value is specified. Then, see diagram,

$$V_R = IR = \frac{4}{1,000} \times 250 = 1 \text{ V (r.m.s.)}$$

Also

$$X_C = \frac{1}{2\pi fC} = \frac{1}{2 \times 3\cdot14 \times 50 \times \dfrac{1}{10^6}} = 3,180 \ \Omega$$

$$\therefore V_C = I \times X_C = \frac{4}{1,000} \times 3,180 = 12\cdot7 \text{ V (r.m.s.)}$$

Alternating Voltage Applied to Pure Inductance L

In practice no coil is a *pure* inductance, it has also some resistance, R. In the present case the latter is neglected, and we consider only the inductance L of a coil, as shown in Fig. 7.23 (i). The object is to find the magnitude of the a.c. flowing in the circuit and its phase angle relative to the applied voltage.

It is obvious that an a.c. is able to flow through the turns of the wire

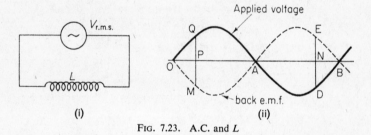

(i)   (ii)

FIG. 7.23.   A.C. and L

which make up the coil. As it does so the current adjusts itself, if there is no resistance, so that a back e.m.f. is set up which is equal and opposite at every instant to the forward e.m.f., following Lenz' law (see Fig. 7.23 (ii)). At the instant corresponding to P, for example, the magnitude PQ of the applied voltage is equal and opposite to the back e.m.f., PM.

Now the induced e.m.f. $= L \times$ (ampere change per second) numerically at any instant, where the induced e.m.f. is in volts if L is in henrys (p. 106). Hence, at any instant the applied voltage, v, is given by

$$v = L \times \text{(ampere change per second)} \qquad (1)$$

To obtain the variation of v with time t, from (1) we need to study the current i-time t graph in Fig. 7.24 (i). As before, the gradients at the different points on the curve give the corresponding values of the ampere change per second. Their variation is shown in Fig. 7.24 (ii). From equation (1) the voltage variation, v, is simply a constant, L,

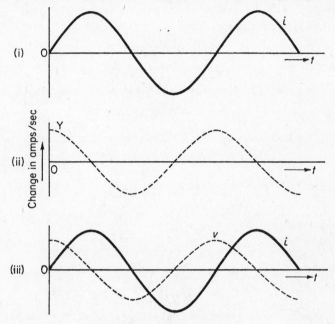

Fig. 7.24.   Variation of v and i

times the values in Fig. 7.24 (ii).   Fig. 7.24 (iii) shows v and i plotted on the same time-axis for comparison.

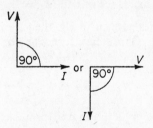

Fig. 7.25.   Phasor diagram

It can now be seen that v leads i by 90°, or i lags on v by 90°. The phasor diagrams are therefore as shown in Fig. 7.25, where V, I are r.m.s. (or peak) values.

Magnitude of V_m

From (1), it follows that the peak value of voltage, $V_m = L \times$ peak value of (ampere change per second). It occurs at O in Fig. 7.24 (ii). The gradient at O depends on the peak value of the a.c. flowing in the circuit and on the frequency, in the same way as was proved in Fig. 7.17 (i), (ii) for a capacitor. Thus

$$V_m \propto L \times (f \times I_m)$$
$$\therefore \ V_m = k \times fL \times I_m$$

where k is a constant. It is proved shortly by mathematics that $k = 2\pi$.

$$\therefore \ V_m = 2\pi fL \times I_m$$

Multiplying both sides by $0.71(1/\sqrt{2})$ to obtain r.m.s. values, V and I.

$$\therefore \ V = 2\pi fL \times I$$
$$\therefore \ \frac{V}{I} = 2\pi fL$$

Calculus Proof

Using calculus, $v = L \, di/dt$. But if $i = I_m \sin 2\pi ft$,

$$\frac{di}{dt} = 2\pi fI_m \cos 2\pi ft$$

$$\therefore \ v = 2\pi fLI_m \cos 2\pi ft = 2\pi fLI_m \sin (90° + 2\pi ft)$$

$\therefore \ v$ leads i by $90°$ and its peak value $V_m = 2\pi fLI_m$, Fig. 7.24 (iii).

Reactance of Coil

By analogy with d.c. theory, V/I represents the 'effective opposition' of a coil to a.c. The term 'reactance' is used, and the symbol is X_L.

$$\therefore \ \text{reactance of coil, } X_L = 2\pi fL$$

When L is in henries and f is in Hz, then X_L is in ohms.
The corresponding Ohm's law formulae for this a.c. circuit now becomes

$$\frac{V}{I} = X_L, \ V = I \times X_L, \ I = \frac{V}{X_L}$$

i.e. X_L takes the place of R in the d.c. formulae.

Values of X_L for typical coils
(a) Soft-iron core, $L = 10$ H.

At r.f. of 10^6 Hz, theoretically

$$X_L = 2\pi fL = 2 \times 3.14 \times 10^6 \times 10 = 63 \times 10^6 = 63 \ \text{M}\Omega$$

At a.f. of 1,000 Hz,

$$X_L = 2\pi fL = 2 \times 3{\cdot}14 \times 1{,}000 \times 10 = 63{,}000\ \Omega$$

At $f = 50$ Hz,

$$X_L = 2 \times 3{\cdot}14 \times 50 \times 10 = 3{,}140\ \Omega$$

(b) Air core, $L = 10$ millihenries $= 0{\cdot}01$ H

At r.f. of 10^6 Hz, $X_L = 2 \times 3{\cdot}14 \times 10^6 \times 0{\cdot}01 = 63{,}000\ \Omega$

At a.f. of 1,000 Hz, $X_L = 63\ \Omega$; at $f = 50$ Hz, $X_L = 3{\cdot}1\ \Omega$

Thus coils vary considerably in reactance because the magnitude of X_L depends on the frequency, f, and the inductance L. In general the soft-iron-cored coil of 10 H has a high reactance (63,000 Ω) to a.f., but the air-cored coil of 10 mH has a low reactance (63 Ω) to the same frequency of 1,000 Hz. The latter coil, however, has a high reactance (63,000 Ω) to r.f. The 10 H coil is therefore known as an a.f. 'choke', i.e. a.c. of this frequency finds it difficult to flow through it. The 10 mH coil is an r.f. choke.

In *theory* the a.f. choke would appear to have an even bigger reactance (63 MΩ) to r.f. than a.f. Due to its self-capacitance (see p. 63), which acts as a shunt to very high frequencies, the total reactance of the coil is very low in practice. It is thus useless as a choke to r.f.

Variation of X_L

$$X_L = 2\pi fL$$

(a) For a given coil, i.e. L constant, $X_L \propto f$. The graph of X_L v. f for a pure inductance is therefore a straight line passing through the origin (Fig. 7.26 (i)).

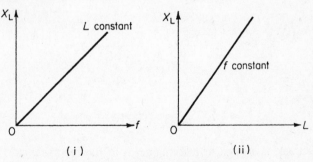

FIG. 7.26. Variation of reactance

If a coil has a reactance of 3,140 Ω for $f = 50$ Hz, then its reactance at $f = 1{,}000$Hz will be 20 times as great, i.e. 62,800 Ω. (See values for X_L calculated previously.)

(*b*) At a given frequency, i.e. f constant, $X_L \propto L$. The graph of X_L v. L is therefore a straight line passing through the origin for pure inductances (Fig. 7.26 (ii)). A 10 H coil has 1,000 times the reactance of a 10 mH coil at the same frequency. (See values for X_L calculated previously.)

Note. In practice, straight-line graphs are not obtained on account of the self-capacitance of the coil.

EXAMPLE

A coil has a reactance of 20 ohms at a frequency of 50 Hz. If it is connected to an alternating voltage of 12 volts (r.m.s.) at $f = 2{,}000$ Hz, calculate the current flowing.

$$X_L \propto f \text{ for the same inductance}$$

$\therefore$ reactance X_L at $f = 2{,}000$ Hz, is

$$\frac{2{,}000}{50} \times 20 \ \Omega = 800 \ \Omega$$

$$\therefore I = \frac{V}{X_L} = \frac{12}{800} \text{ A} = 15 \text{ mA}$$

Comparison between X_L and X_C

At this stage it would be well to compare and contrast the action of a capacitor of capacitance C in an a.c. circuit with that of a coil of inductance L and negligible resistance in series in the same circuit. Both components have a certain reactance. With the capacitor, however,

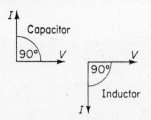

FIG. 7.27. Comparison between phases

the reactance *decreases* with frequency, but the reactance of the coil *increases* with frequency. Further, and this is important, the a.c., i, leads by 90° on the voltage v across the capacitor, while i lags 90° on the voltage v across the coil. Noting the directions of I in the phasor diagrams (Fig. 7.27), it appears that, so far as the phases are concerned, a capacitor and a coil have contrary effects.

EXAMPLE

Write down the frequency, the r.m.s. and the peak values of a voltage wave expressed as $v = 14 \cdot 1 \sin 1{,}000\pi t$. Write down expressions for the current flowing when this voltage is applied across: (a) a 5-Ω resistor, (b) a 1-mH inductor of negligible resistance, (c) a 150-μF capacitor. Sketch the waveforms of these currents, showing clearly: (a) the phase relationship of each current to the applied voltage, (b) the peak value of each current.

(C. & G.)

$$V_{\text{peak}} = V_{\text{m}} = 14 \cdot 1 \text{ V}, \qquad V_{\text{r.m.s.}} = V = 10 \text{ V}, \qquad f = 500 \text{ Hz}$$

(a) $I_{\text{m}} = \dfrac{V_{\text{m}}}{R} = \dfrac{14 \cdot 1}{5} = 2 \cdot 8$

Since current and voltage are in phase.

$$\therefore \quad i = 2 \cdot 8 \sin 1{,}000\pi t$$

(b) $I_{\text{m}} = \dfrac{V_{\text{m}}}{2\pi f L} = \dfrac{14 \cdot 1}{1{,}000\pi \times 10^{-3}} = 4 \cdot 5$

Since current lags on voltage by 90° or $\pi/2$ radians,

$$\therefore \quad i = 4 \cdot 5 \sin \left(1{,}000\pi t - \frac{\pi}{2} \right)$$

(c) $I_{\text{m}} = \dfrac{V_{\text{m}}}{1/2\pi f C} = V_{\text{m}} \cdot 2\pi f C = 14 \cdot 1 \times 1{,}000\pi \times 150 \times 10^{-6} = 6 \cdot 7$

Since current leads on voltage by 90° or $\pi/2$ radians,

$$\therefore \quad i = 6 \cdot 7 \sin \left(1{,}000\pi t + \frac{\pi}{2} \right)$$

For sketches of waveforms, see pp. 129–137.

Filter Circuits

Capacitors and large inductors, which are iron-cored coils or chokes, provide a convenient way of separating voltages of different frequencies. In such a case the arrangement is known as a 'filter circuit'.

Power supply. In power-supply circuits, the d.c. voltage alone is usually required from a mixture with an a.f. voltage. The voltage wave-form of the mixture between X and Y in Fig. 7.28 (i) may be similar to that shown below, if the d.c. voltage is greater than the peak of the a.f. voltage. Though it represents voltage variations in one direction, a much more steady voltage is needed (see p. 190).

In Fig. 7.28 (i), the 30 H choke has a reactance of about 19,000 Ω to $f = 100$ Hz, and the 16 μF capacitor has a reactance of

$$\frac{1}{2\pi f C} = \frac{1}{2 \times 3 \cdot 14 \times 100 \times \dfrac{16}{10^6}} = 100 \text{ Ω}$$

to the same frequency. Most of the a.f. voltage is therefore developed across the choke. Only a very small fraction of it is developed across the capacitor between M and N. The d.c. voltage, however, is unaffected

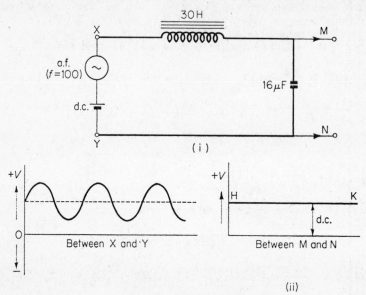

FIG. 7.28. Filter circuit

by the turns of copper wire which make up the coil. The whole of it appears across the capacitor. Thus the voltage applied to a circuit across M and N is a d.c. voltage with a very small 'ripple', Fig. 7.28 (ii).

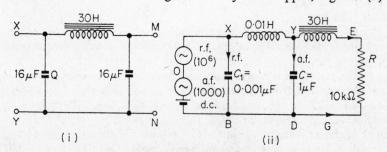

FIG. 7.29. Capacitor-input filter circuit

This arrangement of a coil and capacitor is known as a *choke-input filter*. It is used with rectifiers to obtain d.c. voltage from the a.c. mains (see p. 190). Another arrangement, shown in Fig. 7.29 (i), is known as a *capacitor-input filter* (p. 190).

Detector filter circuit. (See p. 318.) The circuit in Fig. 7.29 (ii) consists of an arrangement of coils and capacitors, used to separate a.f. current from a mixture of r.f. ($f = 10^6$ Hz), a.f. ($f = 1,000$ Hz), and direct currents.

The table below shows the reactances of the various components to the frequencies concerned.

$L = 0.01H$

f Hz	10^6	1,000
$X_L\,\Omega$	62,800	63

$L = 30H$

f Hz	10^6	1,000
$X_L\,\Omega$	188×10^6	188,000

$C_1 = 0.001\,\mu F$

f Hz	10^6	1,000
$X_C\,\Omega$	159	159,000

$C = 1\,\mu F$

f Hz	10^6	1,000
$X_C\,\Omega$	0.16	159

The r.f., a.f., and direct currents will flow in those parts of the circuit which offer the least opposition. The paths open to them are OXBO, OXYDBO, and OYEGBO.

(i) Consider first the r.f. of $f = 10^6$ Hz.

The opposition met in the path OXBO = 159 Ω (0.001 μF)

The opposition met in the path OYDO

$$= 62,800\ \Omega\,(0.01\text{ H})\quad\text{and}\quad 0.16\ \Omega\,(1\ \mu\text{F})$$

The opposition met in the path OEGO

$$= 62,800\ \Omega\,(0.01\text{ H}),\quad 188\text{ M}\Omega\,(30\text{ H}),\quad R = 10,000\ \Omega$$

Thus the r.f. current will flow through the 0.001 μF capacitor.

(ii) Consider the a.f. of $f = 1,000$ Hz

The opposition met in the path OXBO = 159,000 Ω (0.01 μF)

The opposition met in the path OYDO

$$= 63\ \Omega\,(0.01\text{ H})\quad\text{and}\quad 159\ \Omega\,(1\ \mu\text{F})$$

The opposition met in the path OEGO

$$= 63\ \Omega\,(0.01\text{ H}),\quad 188,000\ \Omega\,(30\text{ H}),\quad\text{and}\quad R = 10,000\ \Omega$$

Thus the a.f. current will flow through the 1 μF capacitor, see Fig. 7.29 (ii).

(iii) D.c. cannot flow through capacitors, but it can flow through the turns of the 0·01 H and 30 H coils. It is thus obtained along EG.

Summing up, the r.f. current is diverted through XB, the a.f. current through YD, the d.c. through EG.

A.C. CIRCUITS—SERIES COMPONENTS

L and R in Series

So far we have discussed the effect of applying alternating voltage to a single component. Consider the circuit shown in Fig. 7.30 with a coil of inductance, L, connected in series with a resistance, R. Two facts must be true for this series circuit:

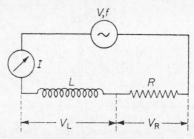

FIG. 7.30. L and R in series

1. The magnitude, I, of the alternating current is the same in L as in R.

2. The voltages V_L and V_R across the individual components together add up to V, the applied voltage. Now we have seen that I

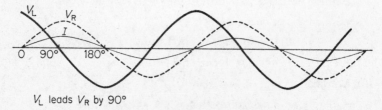

V_L leads V_R by 90°

FIG. 7.31. Phase between voltages

is in phase with the voltage, V_R, across a pure resistance, but lags 90° behind the voltage, V_L, across a pure inductance (p. 137). Thus V_L and V_R are 90° out of phase with each other (Fig. 7.31).

The method of adding two vector quantities out of phase with each other has already been described (see p. 121). Employing r.m.s. values, let OA represent V_R in phase with I, and OB represent V_L, 90°

ahead of I (Fig. 7.32). Complete the parallelogram OBCA. Then OC represents the vector sum of V_L and V_R, and is equal to the applied voltage V.

From Pythagoras' theorem for triangle OAC, $OC^2 = OA^2 + AC^2$,

$$\therefore \ V^2 = V_R{}^2 + V_L{}^2 \tag{1}$$

Now $V_R = IR$, and $V_L = IX_L$, dealing with the single components,

$$\therefore \ V^2 = I^2R^2 + I^2X_L{}^2, \text{ from (1)}$$
$$= I^2(R^2 + X_L{}^2)$$

$$\therefore \ I = \frac{V}{\sqrt{R^2 + X_L{}^2}} = \frac{V}{\sqrt{R^2 + (2\pi fL)^2}} \tag{2}$$

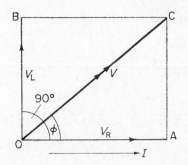

FIG. 7.32.   Phase and magnitude of I and V

It can be seen from Fig. 7.32 that I lags on the applied voltage V by an angle $\phi = $ angle AOC. To calculate θ we have

$$\tan \phi = \frac{AC}{OA} = \frac{V_L}{V_R} = \frac{IX_L}{IR} = \frac{X_L}{R}$$

$$\therefore \ \tan \phi = \frac{X_L}{R} = \frac{2\pi fL}{R} \tag{3}$$

Equation (1) is the relation between the applied voltage, V, and that across the separate components in the circuit.

Equation (2) shows that $I = V/Z$, where

$$Z = \sqrt{R^2 + X_L{}^2} \tag{4}$$

By analogy with d.c. theory it can be seen that $Z \ (= V/I)$ represents the 'effective opposition' of L and R combined in series. Z is in ohms when R and X_L are both in ohms. The term 'reactance' is reserved for a single component, the coil or capacitor, where the phase angle is 90°. With two unlike components, Z is known as the *impedance* of the circuit. Using it, we obtain the following Ohm's law formulae for the above a.c. circuit:

$$I = \frac{V}{Z}, \quad V = I \times Z, \quad Z = \frac{V}{I}$$

EXAMPLE

An alternating voltage of 20 V, $f = 100$ Hz, is applied to a pure inductance coil of 5 H in series with a resistance R of 1,000 ohms. Find the magnitude of the current and its phase angle relative to the applied voltage, and the voltage across the coil, Fig. 7.33 (i).

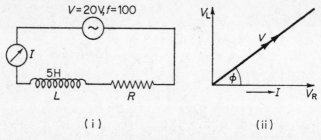

FIG. 7.33. Calculation

(*a*) The reactance of the coil,

$$X_L = 2\pi fL = 2\pi \times 100 \times 5 = 3,140 \ \Omega$$

$$\therefore Z = \sqrt{R^2 + X_L^2} = \sqrt{1,000^2 + 3,140^2}$$

$$= 1,000\sqrt{1^2 + 3 \cdot 14^2} = 3,300 \ \Omega \ \text{(approx.)}$$

$$\therefore I = \frac{V}{Z} = \frac{20}{3,310} = 0 \cdot 006 \ \text{A} = 6 \ \text{mA (approx.)}$$

(*b*) Also, $\tan \phi = \dfrac{X_L}{R} = \dfrac{3,140}{1,000} = 3 \cdot 14$, Fig. 7.33 (ii)

$$\therefore \phi = 72°$$

i.e. I lags on V by 72°.

(*c*) The voltage across the coil,

$$V_L = I \times X_L = \frac{6}{1,000} \times 3,140$$

$$\therefore V_L = 19 \ \text{V (approx.)}$$

(This voltage is 90° out of phase with the current.)

C and R in Series

As with L and R in series,

1. the magnitude, I, of the current is the same in R as in C (Fig. 7.34 (i)).

2. V is the vector sum of V_R and V_C, assuming the r.m.s. values are concerned here.

Now V_R is in phase with I (pure resistance), but V_C lags behind I by 90° (pure capacitance). Thus if I and V_R are drawn horizontally (Fig. 7.34 (ii)), V_C must be drawn vertically downwards.

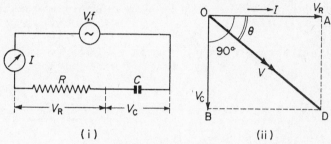

(i)   (ii)

FIG. 7.34. *C, R in series*

From triangle OAD,

$$OD^2 = OA^2 + AD^2$$
$$\therefore V^2 = V_R^2 + V_C^2 \tag{1}$$

Now $V_R = IR$ and $V_C = IX_C$, dealing with the single components.

$$\therefore V^2 = I^2R^2 + I^2X_C^2, \text{ from (1)}$$
$$= I^2(R^2 + X_C^2)$$

$$\therefore I = \frac{V}{\sqrt{R^2 + X_C^2}} = \frac{V}{\sqrt{R^2 + \left(\dfrac{1}{2\pi fC}\right)^2}} \tag{2}$$

From the vector diagram I leads on V by θ = angle DOA, where

$$\tan\theta = \frac{AD}{OA} = \frac{V_C}{V_R} = \frac{IX_C}{IR} = \frac{X_C}{R} \tag{3}$$

Equation (1) is the relation between the applied voltage V and that across the single components.

Equation (2) shows that $I = V/Z$, where

$$Z = \sqrt{R^2 + X_C^2} \tag{4}$$

$$\therefore Z = \frac{V}{I} = \text{the } impedance \text{ of the } C, R \text{ series circuit}$$

Z is in ohms when R and X_C are in ohms.

The Ohm's law formulae are:

$$I = \frac{V}{Z}, \quad Z = \frac{V}{I}, \quad V = I \times Z$$

EXAMPLE

A 100 V, $f = 50$ Hz alternating voltage is applied to a 0·1 μF capacitor in series with a resistor of 20,000 ohms. Calculate (a) the magnitude and phase angle of the current in the circuit, (b) the voltage across the resistor and across the capacitor, Fig. 7.35.

(a) $\quad X_C = \dfrac{1}{2\pi fC} = \dfrac{1}{2 \times 3 \cdot 14 \times 50 \times \dfrac{0 \cdot 1}{10^6}} = 32,000 \; \Omega$ (approx.)

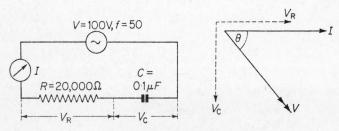

FIG. 7.35. Calculation

Also, $\qquad \tan \theta = \dfrac{X_C}{R} = \dfrac{32,000}{20,000} = 1 \cdot 6$

$$\therefore \quad \theta = 58°$$

and I leads on V by this phase angle, Fig. 7.35.

$$Z = \sqrt{R^2 + X_C^2} = \sqrt{20,000^2 + 32,000^2}$$
$$= 38,000 \; \Omega \text{ (approx.)}$$
$$\therefore \; I = \frac{V}{Z} = \frac{100}{38,000} = 0 \cdot 0027 \text{ A} = 2 \cdot 7 \text{ mA (approx.)}$$

(b) The voltage across R is given by

$$V_R = IR = \frac{2 \cdot 7}{1,000} \times 20,000 = 54 \text{ V}$$

The voltage across C is given by

$$V_C = IX_C = \frac{2 \cdot 7}{1,000} \times 32,000 = 86 \text{ V}$$

(or $V_C = \sqrt{V^2 - V_R^2}$, since $V^2 = V_R^2 + V_C^2$.)

Potential Divider for A.C. Voltage

Consider an alternating voltage of V volts across C and R in series (Fig. 7.36). Then V_R is given by IR, where I is the current in the circuit. But

$$I = \frac{V}{Z} = \frac{V}{\sqrt{R^2 + X_C^2}}$$

$$\therefore V_R = \left(\frac{V}{\sqrt{R^2 + X_C^2}}\right) \times R,$$

i.e.
$$\frac{V_R}{V} = \frac{R}{\sqrt{R^2 + X_C^2}} \tag{1}$$

This is the fraction of the applied alternating voltage V which appears across R.

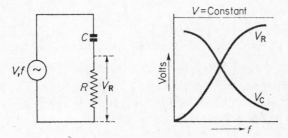

Fig. 7.36. Potential divider

Suppose that f, the frequency, is varied, V, C, and R remaining constant. Then $X_C = 1/2\pi fC$ varies, and becomes smaller the greater the value of f.

Hence the fraction $R/\sqrt{(R^2 + X_C^2)}$ becomes greater as f increases. In such a case most of the applied voltage V appears across the component R, and very little across C. The graphs showing the variation of V_C and V_R as f varies are illustrated in Fig. 7.36. It can be seen from the above that the same effect is obtained if f is kept constant and C varied. A.c. potential dividers, as illustrated here, are used in 'resistance-capacitance coupling' between transistors and radio valves (p. 231).

Impedance Transformation

An important property of a transformer, widely utilized in telecommunications and radio circuitry (p. 268), is the impedance transformation 'reflected' from the secondary to the primary circuit, which we now explain.

Consider an impedance Z_L in the secondary, Fig. 7.37. Then, with the usual notation,

$$\frac{V_s}{I_s} = Z_L$$

The primary circuit can be considered to have an impedance Z'_L given by

$$\frac{V_p}{I_p} = Z'_L$$

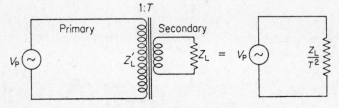

FIG. 7.37.   Impedance transformation

Now in the iron-cored transformer, $V_p = V_s/T$, where T is the turns-ratio, secondary turns/primary turns (see p. 101). Further, the primary current $I_p = TI_s$. Substituting for V_p and I_p,

$$\therefore Z'_L = \frac{1}{T^2} \cdot \frac{V_s}{I_s} = \frac{Z_L}{T^2}$$

The secondary impedance is thus 'transformed' or 'reflected' to the primary circuit by the square of the turns-ratio.

For a resistive load R_L in the secondary, $Z_L = R_L$. Thus with a coil of 10 Ω in the secondary and a step-*down* transformer of turns-ratio 1/12, the reflected resistance R'_L in the primary circuit = = $10/(1/12)^2 = 1,440 \; \Omega$, see p. 269. For an inductance secondary load, $Z_L = \omega L$, and hence $Z'_L = \omega L/T^2 = \omega L'$, where L' is the reflected inductance. Thus $L' = L/T^2$. Similarly, for a capacitance secondary load, $Z_L = 1/\omega C$ and the reflected capacitance $C' = CT^2$.

SUMMARY

1. The peak of an a.c., I_m, is the maximum of the instantaneous value i. The r.m.s., I, is the square-root of the mean of i^2 taken over one complete cycle.

2. For a *sinusoidal* current or voltage, r.m.s. value = peak value/$\sqrt{2}$.

3. A.c. may be measured by a bridge rectifier circuit, a thermocouple meter, a hot-wire meter or the c.r.o.

4. For single components in a.c. circuits, (i) $I = V/R$, (ii) $I = V/X_C$, (iii) $I = V/X_L$. $X_C = 1/2\pi fC$ where f in Hz, C in F and X_C in Ω. $X_L = 2\pi fL$, where L is in H.

5. V leads I by 90° for an inductor L. V lags on I by 90° for a capacitor C.

6. For a L, R series circuit, impedance $Z = \sqrt{R^2 + X_L{}^2}$; $\tan \phi = X_L/R$. For a C, R series circuit, $Z = \sqrt{R^2 + X_C{}^2}$; $\tan \phi = X_C/R$.

7. The impedance reflected from the secondary to the primary of a closed commercial transformer is Z/T^2, where Z is the secondary impedance and T is the turns ratio.

EXERCISE 7

1. How does an alternating current differ from a direct current? Define frequency, peak voltage, and r.m.s. voltage. *(C. & G.)*

2. An alternating voltage is 80 V (r.m.s.). Calculate the peak voltage. What does a thermal meter measure? Explain your answer.

3. What is the r.m.s. value of an alternating current of peak value 8 mA? Describe a *thermocouple meter* and state its advantages in a.c. measurement.

4. Compare the effects arising from the application of (*a*) a low alternating voltage, (*b*) a low direct voltage across (i) a coil of wire on an iron core, (ii) two metal plates immersed in a solution of copper sulphate. *(C. & G.)*

5. Describe how the cathode ray oscillograph and a rectifier bridge circuit can each be used to measure the r.m.s. value of an alternating voltage.

6. Explain the principles of (i) a hot-wire ammeter, and (ii) a moving-iron instrument, and state whether they can be used to measure both d.c. and a.c.

7. Draw sketches on the same time-axis of (i) an a.c., I, (ii) the variation of I^2. Explain with reference to your sketches why the r.m.s. value of the a.c. is about $0.7I_{\text{peak}}$ for a sinusoidal waveform.

8. Describe the principle of operation of a meter suitable for measuring current of a few milliamperes at audio frequencies.

State the factors: (*a*) that limit the sensitivity of the instrument, and (*b*) that reduce its accuracy as the frequency increases. *(C. & G.)*

Single Components

9. Calculate the reactance of the following capacitors at the frequency specified: (*a*) 2 μF at $f = 1,000$, (*b*) 2 μF at $f = 10^6$, (*c*) 0·01 μF at $f = 50$, (*d*) 0·002 μF at $f = 1,000$, (*e*) 300 ρF at $f = 10^6$ (f in Hz).

10. Compare the behaviour of a capacitor, connected in a d.c. circuit, with one of a similar capacitance connected in an a.c. circuit. What effect has frequency upon the result when considering the a.c. case? *(C. & G.)*

11. Calculate the reactance of (i) a 20 H coil at $f = 1,000$, (ii) 100 mH coil at $f = 10^6$ Hz. What other factors of a coil must be taken into account in practice in deducing its effect in an a.c. circuit?

12. (*a*) Draw sketches illustrating the variation of reactance of a capacitor and a coil with frequency. (*b*) Draw the sketch of a filter circuit suitable for separating a.c. from r.f. and d.c. currents, and state the approximate values of your components.

13. A current of 4 mA (r.m.s.) is flowing in a resistor of 5,000 Ω and a capacitor of 1 μF. If the frequency is 100 Hz, find the p.d. across the resistor and across the capacitor, drawing a vector sketch in each case to illustrate the phase difference between the p.d. and the current.

14. A voltage of 100 V r.m.s., $f = 1,000$ Hz, is applied to a 5 H coil of negligible self-capacitance and resistance. Calculate the current flowing, and draw a vector diagram of the voltage and current.

15. A single component X has a reactance of 200 Ω at $f = 1,000$ Hz and a reactance of 400 Ω at $f = 500$ Hz. Another component Y has a reactance of 800 Ω at $f = 1,000$ Hz and a reactance of 400 Ω at $f = 500$ Hz. Write down with reasons all the information you can obtain about X and Y from the above data.

16. With the aid of a sketch representing a sinusoidal waveform explain the meaning of the following terms.

Periodic time, frequency, peak value, root mean square value. Give the values of these terms for a current represented by $i = 2 \cdot 828 \sin 400 \pi t$.

This current is passing through a capacitor of 10 μF. Find the expression representing the voltage across the capacitor. What is the r.m.s. value of this voltage? (C. & G.)

17. The voltage across a reactance carrying an alternating current $i = 10 \sin 200 \pi t$ is given by: $v = 20 \sin (200 \pi t + \pi/2)$.

State (a) the peak values of current and voltage, (b) the frequency, (c) the sign and magnitude of the phase angle of the voltage relative to the current.

Determine from the given expressions the magnitude of the reactance. Is it capacitive or inductive?

Sketch the waveforms of the current and voltage on one pair of axes, showing the scale values. (C. & G.)

18. Explain how a sinusoidal waveform can be derived from a rotating radius vector. Using this method, or otherwise, construct a curve representing one cycle of a sinusoidal alternating voltage having a periodic time of 1/200 second and ampltitude of 10 volts.

On the same axes construct a sinusoidal current waveform of the same frequency leading the voltage by a phase difference of 90° and having an amplitude of 1 ampere. Without calculating any component value, sketch a simple circuit that will produce this phase difference between current and voltage. (C. & G.)

19. With reference to a sinusoidal waveform, explain the meanings of the terms *frequency* and *periodic time*.

What do you understand by the *phase difference* between an alternating current and the voltage it produces across a circuit?

Give waveform sketches to show the phase relations between the current and voltage when a.c. is flowing in (a) a resistance, (b) a capacitance. Why does a capacitance produce the result that you have shown? (C. & G.)

Series Circuits

20. An a.c. generator is connected to a resistance, R, and capacitor, C, in series. Calculate the voltage, X, of the generator if the voltages across the two components are 2 V, 4 V respectively. Draw a vector diagram and sine curves illustrating roughly the variations of X and the voltages across R and C.

21. A 1 H coil of d.c. resistance 100 Ω is connected to a 10 V, $f = 50$ Hz generator. Calculate the impedance of the coil and the current flowing in it, and the phase angle of the latter relative to the applied voltage.

22. An a.c. voltage supply, $f = 50$ Hz, is connected to a 1 μF capacitor in series with a resistance of 2,000 Ω. If the p.d. across the resistor is 25 V, calculate the p.d. across the capacitor. Draw an accurate vector diagram of the current and applied voltage.

23. A current of 1 ampere, frequency 100,000 Hz, is passed through a coil of resistance 20 ohms and inductance 400 microhenries. What is the voltage across the coil? (C. & G.)

24. The impedance of a series circuit consisting of resistance and inductance is 200 ohms when the frequency is 500 kHz. If the value of the resistance is 100 ohms, what is the value of the inductance? (C. & G.)

25. A resistance of 10,000 ohms and a capacitor of 0·01 microfarad are connected in series. If 100 volts at a frequency of 1 kHz are applied across the circuit, what is the potential across (a) the resistance, (b) the capacitor? Find the value of the tangent of the angle between the applied voltage and the voltage across the resistance. (C. & G.)

8: A.C. Resonance. Parallel Circuits. Power

A.C. RESONANCE

A.C. Voltage Applied to L and C in Series

A coil and capacitor in series is an important case in a.c. circuit theory. This arrangement is widely used in radio practice. As an introduction to the practical case, suppose we first consider the theoretical

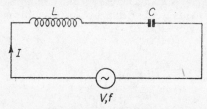

FIG. 8.1. L, C in series

case of a coil of inductance L and negligible resistance in series with a capacitor C, and suppose the applied voltage is V (r.m.s.), Fig. 8.1.

The current I in L and C is then the same. The applied p.d. V is the vector sum of V_L and V_C, the respective voltages across the components.

Now V_L leads by $90°$ on I, but V_C lags by $90°$ on I. The vector diagram is therefore as shown, Fig. 8.2. V_L and V_C are in the same

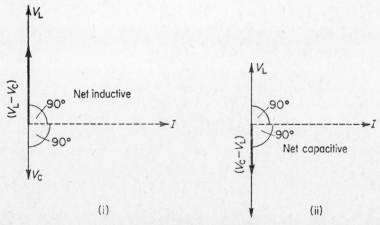

FIG. 8.2. Phasor diagram

154

straight line but in opposite directions. In this special case, therefore, we subtract V_L and V_C to obtain their vector sum.

$$\therefore \ V = V_L \sim V_C \tag{1}$$

When V_L is greater than V_C, V is drawn upward as in Fig. 8.2 (i), and leads by 90° on I. The a.c. circuit is now considered to be 'net inductive'. When V_C is greater than V_L, V is drawn vertically downward as in Fig. 8.2 (ii), and lags by 90° on I. The circuit is now considered to be 'net capacitive'. A curled minus sign is used in (1) instead of an ordinary straight minus to indicate that the smaller voltage must be taken from the larger.

To find I, we have $V_L = IX_L$, $V_C = IX_C$,

$$\therefore \ V = V_L \sim V_C = IX_L \sim IX_C = I(X_L \sim X_C)$$

$$\therefore \ I = \frac{V}{X_L \sim X_C} = \frac{V}{2\pi fL \sim \dfrac{1}{2\pi fC}} \tag{2}$$

Thus the impedance $Z = X_L \sim X_C$ in this case.

Suppose that the frequency, f, of the applied voltage is varied, V, L and C remaining constant. Then, since the impedance Z varies, the current I varies in phase and magnitude according to the values of $2\pi fL$ and $1/2\pi fC$.

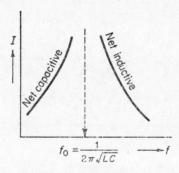

Fig. 8.3. Current variation

A special case is obtained when $2\pi fL = 1/2\pi fC$. Then $I = V/0 = \infty$. It occurs when f is given by

$$2\pi fL = \frac{1}{2\pi fC}$$

i.e.

$$f^2 = \frac{1}{4\pi^2 LC}$$

$$\therefore f = \frac{1}{2\pi\sqrt{LC}}$$

This frequency, $1/2\pi\sqrt{LC}$ or f_0, say, gives an infinite current in this theoretical circuit. It is known as the *resonant frequency* of the circuit. When L is in henries and C in farads, then f_0 is in Hz. A graph showing the variation of I with f when V, L, C are constant is illustrated in Fig. 8.3.

A.C. Voltage Applied to L, C, R in Series

We now consider the case of voltage V applied to an actual coil of inductance L and resistance R in series with a capacitor C, Fig. 8.4 (i). The theory and results should be carefully studied in view of their practical importance.

The current is the same in each of the components (Fig. 8.4 (i)). Also, V is the vector sum of V_L, V_C and V_R.

The phasor diagram is therefore as shown (Fig. 8.4 (ii)) and we shall assume V_L greater than V_C. As V_L and V_C are oppositely drawn their vector sum is represented by $OB = V_L - V_C$, and angle $AOB = 90°$. If V_L is less than V_C their vector sum is drawn in a downward direction.

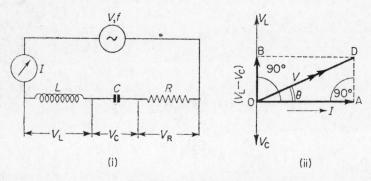

Fig. 8.4. *L, C, R in series*

The applied voltage, V, is the vector sum of V_L, V_C, V_R.

$$\therefore V^2 = (V_L - V_C)^2 + V_R^2$$

from triangle OAD. But

$$V_L = IX_L , \quad V_C = IX_C , \quad V_R = IR$$

$$\therefore V^2 = (IX_L - IX_C)^2 + I^2R^2 = I^2[R^2 + (X_L - X_C)^2]$$

$$\therefore I = \frac{V}{\sqrt{R^2 + (X_L - X_C)^2}} \tag{1}$$

The phase angle θ is given by

$$\tan \theta = \frac{V_L - V_C}{V_R} = \frac{X_L - X_C}{R} = \frac{2\pi fL - \dfrac{1}{2\pi fC}}{R}$$

From (1), it follows that the impedance

$$Z = \sqrt{R^2 + (X_L - X_C)^2} \qquad (2)$$

Series Resonance Curve

Suppose that a constant voltage, V, is applied to a given L, C, R series circuit and the frequency of V is varied. As $Z = \sqrt{R^2 + (X_L - X_C)^2}$ and $I = V/Z$, it will be instructive to plot the variations of X_L, X_C and R separately to obtain the variation of I.

Since $X_L \propto f$, $X_C \propto 1/f$, and R is independent of frequency, the

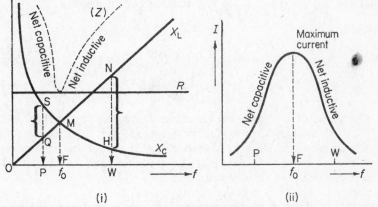

Fig. 8.5. Resonance curve

graphs are as shown in Fig. 8.5 (i). At a frequency corresponding to P, $X_C = PS$, $X_L = PQ$, and $X_L - X_C = SQ$ numerically. Since X_C is greater than X_L the circuit may be considered as 'net capacitive'. At W, $X_L - X_C = NH$ numerically and the circuit is 'net inductive'. At F, $X_L = X_C$ and $X_L - X_C = 0$.

It can therefore be seen that $Z = \sqrt{R^2 + (X_L - X_C)^2}$ decreases from O to F, and increases from F to W and beyond. F corresponds to the frequency f_0 at which Z is a minimum. At this frequency $Z = R$, as shown in Fig. 8.5 (i). The circuit is now 'resistive'.

The current $I = V/Z$. It therefore increases to a *maximum* and then falls off, Fig. 8.5 (ii). The I-f curve is known as a *series resonance* curve.

L, C, R Series Circuit at Resonance

When I is a maximum, *resonance* is said to be obtained in the series circuit. The frequency, f_0, at which this occurs is known as the *resonant frequency*. The idea of 'resonance' occurs in Mechanics. A wooden bridge has a certain natural frequency depending on the properties of the materials used to construct it. If it is subjected to vibrations of this frequency the big response obtained may be sufficient to break the bridge. Soldiers have thus to break step when crossing.

In the same way, an electrical circuit comprising inductance, capacitance, and resistance have a natural resonant frequency, f_0, depending on the electrical constants. If equal voltages at different frequencies are applied to the circuit, the maximum current occurs for that voltage which has the same frequency as the resonant frequency of the circuit, i.e. that frequency is 'accepted' most readily. On this account the a.c. series circuit is sometimes called an 'acceptor' circuit. Now:

(i) $I = \dfrac{V}{\sqrt{R^2 + (X_L - X_C)^2}}$ is a maximum when $X_L = X_C$.

$$\therefore 2\pi f_0 L = \frac{1}{2\pi f_0 C}$$

$$\therefore f_0 = \frac{1}{2\pi\sqrt{LC}} \tag{1}$$

The resonant frequency is therefore determined by the *product* of L and C. It is in Hz when L is in henrys and C is in farads.

(ii) At resonance, $Z = R$. The reactance of the coil has now completely annulled the reactance of the capacitor, and so the circuit impedance reduces to a pure resistance.

The maximum current is therefore given by

$$I = \frac{V}{R} \tag{2}$$

(iii) At resonance, the voltage, V_L, across $L = IX_L = (V/R)X_L$,

$$\therefore \frac{V_L}{V} = \frac{X_L}{R} \tag{3}$$

The voltage, V_C, across the capacitor $= IX_C$.

$$\therefore \frac{V_C}{V} = \frac{X_C}{R} \tag{4}$$

The fundamental relations at resonance are given by equations (1) to (4). Note that $V_L = V_C$, since $X_L = X_C$.

To illustrate the series resonance case, suppose that the applied voltage, $V = 0.1\ V_{\text{R.M.S.}}$, $L = 100\,\mu\text{H}$, $C = 0.0001\,\mu\text{F}$, $R = 10\,\Omega$, Fig. 8.6. Then

$$f_0 = \frac{1}{2\pi\sqrt{LC}} = \frac{1}{2\pi\sqrt{\dfrac{100}{10^6} \times \dfrac{0.0001}{10^6}}} = \frac{10^6}{2\pi\sqrt{100 \times 0.0001}}$$

$= 1.6 \times 10^6$ Hz (approx.) $= 1.6$ MHz
This is the resonant frequency of the circuit.

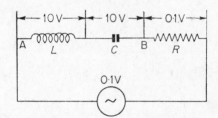

Fig. 8.6.   Calculation on Resonance

The maximum current obtained,

$$I = \frac{V}{R} = \frac{0.1}{10} = 0.01\ \text{A}$$

∴ the voltage across the coil at resonance,

$$V_{\text{L}} = IX_{\text{L}} = 0.01 \times \left(2\pi \times 1.6 \times 10^6 \times \frac{100}{10^6}\right) = 10\ \text{V (approx.)}$$

Also, since $X_{\text{C}} = X_{\text{L}}$ at resonance, the voltage V_{C} across $C = 10$ V. Thus V_{L} and V_{C} are each 100 times as big as the applied voltage. This seems at first to be impossible. However, the p.d. V_{AB} between A and B (across the coil and capacitor) = the vector sum of V_{L} and $V_{\text{C}} = V_{\text{L}} - V_{\text{C}}$.

$$\therefore\ V_{\text{AB}} = 10\ \text{V} - 10\ \text{V} = 0$$

The voltage across $R = IR = 0.01 \times 10 = 0.1$ V = the applied voltage.

Aerial Tuning

An aerial system contains inductance, capacitance and resistance. Thus, as shown in Fig. 8.7, it may be considered as an L, C, R circuit. When a radio wave, which is an electromagnetic wave, reaches the aerial, it induces a small alternating voltage V of the same frequency. As in Fig. 8.7, this can be represented as applied to a series L, C, R circuit. With a given setting of a variable capacitor included in the circuit, the resonant frequency, given by $1/2\pi\sqrt{LC}$, may not be equal to the frequency of the radio waves received, say 10^6 Hz. The capacitor is then varied until $1/2\pi\sqrt{LC} = 10^6$. A maximum current, or maximum 'response', is now obtained. The aerial is then said to be *tuned* to the incoming waves.

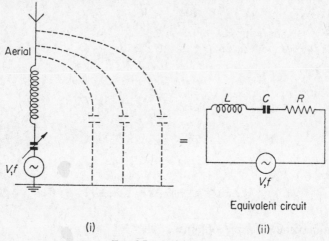

(i)   (ii)

FIG. 8.7.   Aerial tuning

Q-Factor of Tuned Circuit

As already seen, when a series circuit is at resonance, the voltage V_C across its capacitor may be many times the applied voltage V. The same is true for the voltage V_L across the inductance. A resonant

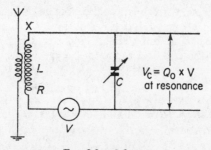

FIG. 8.8.   *Q*-factor

circuit is thus capable of magnifying an induced voltage. As shown in Fig. 8.8, the magnified voltage can be passed to a component in a radio receiver, for example.

The ratio V_C/V or V_L/V, where V_C and V_L are the respective voltages across the capacitor and coil at resonance, is called the *magnification* or Q_0-*factor* of the circuit. Thus, since $V_C = IX_C$ and $V_L = IX_L$, and $V = IR$ at resonance, then, using $\omega_0 = 2\pi f_0$,

$$Q_0 = \frac{IX_C}{IR} = \frac{X_C}{R} = \frac{X_L}{R} \tag{1}$$

or

$$Q_0 = \frac{1}{\omega_0 CR} = \frac{\omega_0 L}{R} \tag{2}$$

Also,

$$Q_0 = \frac{\omega_0 L}{R} = \frac{1}{\sqrt{LC}} \times \frac{L}{R} = \frac{1}{R}\sqrt{\frac{L}{C}} \tag{3}$$

Thus the higher the L/C ratio, the higher is the Q_0-factor. However, increasing L also increases R.

In r.f. tuned circuits, the capacitors used have very low power losses.

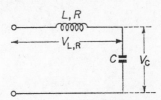

FIG. 8.9. *Q-factor at resonance*

The bulk of the circuit resistance, which also produces power losses, is in the inductor coil. The ratio $\omega_0 L/R$ is known as the 'goodness' of the coil, since a high value of $\omega_0 L$ compared to R is needed to reduce power losses (see p. 179).

Fig. 8.9 shows a r.f. circuit at resonance, containing a coil (L, R) and capacitor (C). If I is the current flowing at resonance, then $V_C = Q_0 V$ as before. But since R cannot be separated from L, the voltage $V_{L,R}$ across the coil is given by $V_{L,R} = IZ = I\sqrt{R^2 + \omega_0^2 L^2}$.

$$\therefore \frac{V_{L,R}}{V} = \frac{\sqrt{R^2 + \omega_0^2 L^2}}{R} = \sqrt{1 + \frac{\omega_0^2 L^2}{R^2}} = \sqrt{1 + Q_0^2}$$

If $Q_0 > 10$, then $V_{L,R} = Q_0 V$ with less than $\frac{1}{2}\%$ error.

Bandwidth

As we saw on p. 41, to which the reader should refer, a reduction of power to one half is equal to a drop of 3 decibels. In terms of current I, this is equivalent to a reduction of $1/\sqrt{2}$ (0·707), since the power in a given resistor is proportional to I^2.

The *bandwidth*, B, of a tuned circuit is defined as the frequency range between the points on either side of the peak of the resonance curve where the current is reduced to $1/\sqrt{2}$ of its resonance value. Thus in

Fig. 8.10, the frequency range between X and Y is the bandwidth B. This value of B is called the 3 *dB bandwidth*, since a reduction to $1/\sqrt{2}$ corresponds to a decrease in response of 3 *dB*.

To find the bandwidth, we use the current formula off-resonance:

$$I = \frac{V}{Z} = \frac{V}{\sqrt{R^2 + (X_L \sim X_C)^2}}$$

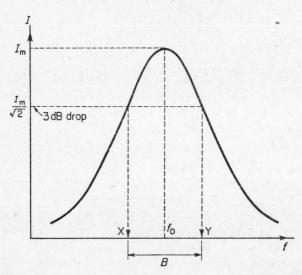

FIG. 8.10. Bandwidth

When $X_L \sim X_C = R$, then

$$I = V/\sqrt{2R^2} = I_m/\sqrt{2}$$

since $I_m = V/R$

Thus, using $\omega = 2\pi f$, where f is the frequency, it follows that at X and Y in Fig. 8.10

$$\omega L - \frac{1}{\omega C} = R$$

$$\therefore \ \omega^2 LC - 1 = \omega CR$$

Now $\omega_0^2 = 1/LC$ (p. 158).

$$\therefore \ \frac{\omega^2}{\omega_0^2} - 1 = \omega CR = \frac{1}{Q}$$

since $Q = 1/\omega CR$ (p. 161) if ω and ω_0 are close (see below).

$$\therefore\ \omega^2 - \omega_0^2 = \frac{\omega_0^2}{Q}$$

$$\therefore\ (\omega - \omega_0)(\omega + \omega_0) = \frac{\omega_0^2}{Q}$$

$$\therefore\ \omega - \omega_0 = \frac{\omega_0^2}{Q(\omega_0 + \omega)} = \frac{\omega_0}{2Q} \qquad (1)$$

since, in practical tuned circuits, the half-power bandwidth is such that $f - f_0$ is small compared to f_0. In this case, to a good approximation, $f = f_0$, or $\omega = \omega_0$, since $\omega = 2\pi f$ and $\omega_0 = 2\pi f_0$. Hence, from (1),

$$f - f_0 = \frac{f_0}{2Q}$$

$$\therefore\ 2(f - f_0) = \frac{f_0}{Q} \qquad (2)$$

For circuits having $Q_0 > 10$, the response curve is reasonably symmetrical about the resonance point. Thus $2(f - f_0)$ is the bandwidth, B (see Fig. 8.10). Hence, from (2)

$$B = \frac{f_0}{Q_0}$$

Selectivity

The *selectivity* of a tuned circuit is a measure of its ability to reject adjacent frequencies in favour of the required frequency to which it is tuned. Obviously a direct measure of 'selectivity' is provided by the

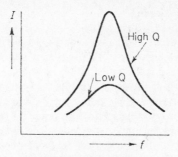

FIG. 8.11.   Selectivity

3 dB bandwidth. The greater the 3 dB bandwidth, the greater is the response to adjacent frequencies. Consequently the *poorer* is the selective performance. Hence, for good selectivity the tuned circuit must provide a relatively low value of bandwidth, that is, it must have an adequately high Q-factor, Fig. 8.11.

Radio frequency transmissions require a certain bandwidth for information to be reproduced accurately. A channel of frequencies in the frequency spectrum is therefore allocated to each transmitter. Fig. 8.12 shows a required channel 2 and adjacent channels 1 and 3. The ideal response curve is rectangular but in practice the curve has a

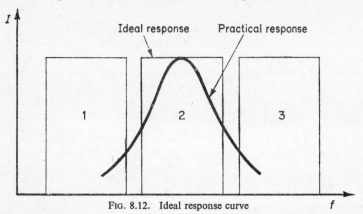

FIG. 8.12.　Ideal response curve

peak and then falls away, as shown. It should be noted that an unwanted frequency of 10 kHz is 10% off resonance at 100 kHz, but at 10 MHz it is only 0·1% off resonance and thus more difficult to reject. The bandwidth chosen to reproduce information sent out by a transmitter must hence be a compromise between adequate adjacent channel selectivity and a fairly reasonable high response to all the frequencies sent out.

Coupled Resonance Circuits

In superhet receivers *coupled tuned circuits* are employed. When the amount of mutual inductance between the circuits is suitably adjusted, a response curve is obtained which has a flattened top, and a sharp fall-off in response immediately beyond the top. This is called *optimum coupling* and is illustrated in Fig. 8.13 by curve 1. If the coupling is increased beyond this value, an increased 'double-humping' occurs in the response curve, as shown by curve 2. At the other extreme, if the coupling is reduced, only a single peak is obtained, as in curve 3.

With optimum coupling, a group or *band* of frequencies, centred about the middle frequency, produces a uniform response. This is needed in the superhet receiver for satisfactory reception from broadcasting stations. The optimum value of coupling factor k which produces curve 1 is related to the Q-factors, Q_1, Q_2, of the two tuned circuits at resonance by $k = 1/\sqrt{Q_1 Q_2}$. The frequency width of the flat top is kf_0 centred on f_0, where f_0 is the common resonant frequency of the two tuned circuits.

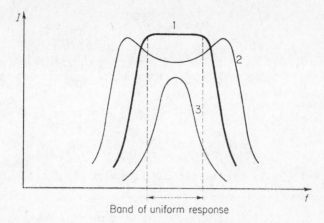

FIG. 8.13. Coupled resonance

EXAMPLE

A series circuit A has $C = 0.0001 \ \mu F$, $L = 400 \ \mu H$, and total resistance $R = 8 \ \Omega$; another series circuit, B, has $C = 0.0002 \ \mu F$, $L = 200 \ \mu H$, and total resistance $R = 10 \ \Omega$.

Calculate (i) the resonant frequency of each circuit; (ii) the voltage across the capacitor when an alternating voltage of 0.1 V (r.m.s.) is applied to each at their resonant frequency, and draw rough sketches to illustrate the frequency-response curves.

(i) The product of L and C is the same for A and B. The resonant frequency, f_0, is therefore the same.

$$f_0 = \frac{1}{2\pi\sqrt{LC}} = \frac{1}{2\pi\sqrt{\dfrac{0.0001}{10^6} \times \dfrac{400}{10^6}}} = \frac{10^3 \times 10^3}{2\pi\sqrt{0.0001 \times 400}}$$

$$= 0.8 \times 10^6 \ \text{Hz (approx.)} = 0.8 \ \text{MHz}$$

(ii) At the resonant frequency the current in the circuit is a maximum and is given by

$$I = \frac{V}{R}$$

$\therefore$ for A,

$$I = \frac{0.1}{8} \ \text{A}$$

$$\therefore \ V_C = IX_C = \frac{0.1}{8} \times \frac{1}{2\pi \times 0.8 \times 10^6 \times \dfrac{0.0001}{10^6}} = 25 \ \text{V}$$

For *B*, $\qquad$ maximum $I = \dfrac{0.1}{10}$ A

$$\therefore\ V_C = IX_C = \frac{0.1}{10} \times \frac{1}{2\pi \times 0.8 \times 10^6 \times \dfrac{0.0002}{10^6}} = 10\ \text{V}$$

Alternative solution

For circuit A,

$$Q_0 = \frac{1}{R}\sqrt{\frac{L}{C}} = \frac{1,000}{8}\sqrt{\frac{400}{100}} = 250$$

$$\therefore\ V_C = Q_0 \cdot V = 250 \times 0.1 = 25\ \text{V}$$

For circuit B,

$$Q_0 = \frac{1}{R}\sqrt{\frac{L}{C}} = \frac{1,000}{10}\sqrt{\frac{1,000}{100}} = 100$$

$$\therefore\ V_C = Q_0 \cdot V = 100 \times 0.1 = 10\ \text{V}$$

To draw a rough sketch of the frequency curves we require the Q of the circuits. For *A*, $Q_0 = V_C/V = 250$ while $Q_0 = 100$ for B. Thus A is more

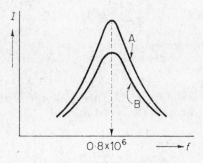

FIG. 8.14. Calculation in resonance

selective, and has a sharper peak in its frequency-response curve. The curves are therefore represented as shown in Fig. 8.14. They have the same resonant frequency, but the maximum current ($0.1/8$ A) for A is greater than that ($0.1/10$ A) for B.

PARALLEL A.C. CIRCUITS

We now consider briefly the principles of parallel a.c. circuits. As in the series a.c. circuits, it is important to know the phase difference between current and voltage.

(1) *L* and *R* in parallel. The special features of this circuit (Fig. 8.15(i)) are (*a*) the voltage across $R =$ the voltage across $L =$ the applied

voltage V, (b) the current I in the main (outside) circuit is the vector sum of the currents I_R, I_L in the two branches.

Consider the two current components separately. I_R is in phase with V but I_L lags 90° behind V (see p. 137). The phasor diagram is therefore as shown in Fig. 8.15 (ii).

$$\therefore I^2 = I_R{}^2 + I_L{}^2$$

But $I_R = V/R$ and $I_L = V/X_L$ from the circuit in Fig. 8.15 (i).

$$\therefore I^2 = \frac{V^2}{R^2} + \frac{V^2}{X_L{}^2} = V^2 \left(\frac{1}{R^2} + \frac{1}{X_L{}^2} \right)$$

$$\therefore I = V \sqrt{\frac{1}{R^2} + \frac{1}{X_L{}^2}}$$

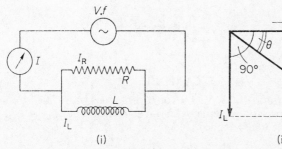

(i)   (ii)

FIG. 8.15. L, R in parallel

It *lags* behind the applied voltage V by a phase angle θ given by

$$\tan \theta = \frac{I_L}{I_R} = \frac{\dfrac{V}{X_L}}{\dfrac{V}{R}} = \frac{R}{X_L}$$

(2) C and R in parallel (Fig. 8.16(i)). As in the above, I is the vector sum of I_R and I_C. Consider the two components. I_R is in phase with V but I_C leads on V by 90° (see p. 132). The phasor diagram (Fig. 8.16 (ii)) is therefore as shown,

$$I^2 = I_R{}^2 + I_C{}^2$$

But $$I_R = \frac{V}{R}, \quad I_C = \frac{V}{X_C}$$

$$\therefore I^2 = \frac{V^2}{R^2} + \frac{V^2}{X_C{}^2} = V^2 \left(\frac{1}{R^2} + \frac{1}{X_C{}^2} \right)$$

$$\therefore I = V \sqrt{\frac{1}{R^2} + \frac{1}{X_C{}^2}}$$

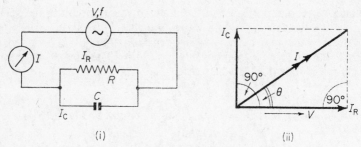

FIG. 8.16 *C, R* in parallel

and *leads* on V by a phase angle θ given by

$$\tan \theta = \frac{I_C}{I_R} = \frac{\dfrac{V}{X_C}}{\dfrac{V}{R}} = \frac{R}{X_C}$$

EXAMPLE

An alternating voltage of 10 V, $f = 50$ Hz, is applied to a 1 μF capacitor and a 1,000-ohm resistor in parallel. Find the main current flowing, and its phase angle relative to the applied voltage (Fig. 8.17).

$$I_R = \frac{V}{R} = \frac{10}{1,000} = 10 \text{ mA}$$

$$I_C = \frac{V}{X_C} \quad \text{and} \quad X_C = 3,180 \ \Omega$$

$$\therefore I_C = \frac{10}{3,180} = 3\cdot15 \text{ mA}$$

$$\therefore I^2 = I_R{}^2 + I_C{}^2 = 10^2 + 3\cdot15^2$$

$$\therefore I = \sqrt{10^2 + 3\cdot15^2} = 10\cdot5 \text{ mA}$$

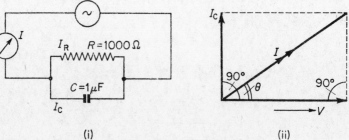

FIG. 8.17. Calculation

The phase angle is given by

$$\tan \theta = \frac{I_C}{I_R} = \frac{3 \cdot 15}{10} \left(= \frac{R}{X_C} \right) = 0 \cdot 315$$

$$\therefore \theta = 17°$$

and I leads on V by this angle.

N.B. As the above example illustrates, no impedance formulae need be memorised for the simple parallel cases just discussed. I, the main current, is also known as the *source*, or *line*, current.

L and C in parallel. Consider the *theoretical* case of a coil of inductance L and negligible resistance in parallel with a capacitor C. If the applied voltage is V, then the main current I is the vector sum I_L and I_C.

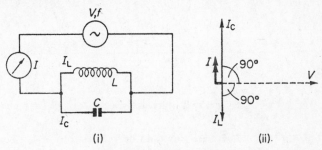

FIG. 8.18. L, C in parallel

When the two currents are drawn in a vector diagram they are in the same straight line but oppositely drawn (Fig. 8.18).

$$\therefore I = I_C \sim I_L$$

When I_C is greater than I_L, as shown, I is 90° ahead of V. When I_C is smaller than I_L, I is 90° behind V. Now

$$I_C = \frac{V}{X_C} \quad \text{and} \quad I_L = \frac{V}{X_L}$$

$$\therefore I = \frac{V}{X_C} \sim \frac{V}{X_L} = V \left(\frac{1}{X_C} \sim \frac{1}{X_L} \right)$$

and lags or leads by 90° on V according to the magnitudes of X_C and X_L.

Suppose that V, L, C are kept constant and the frequency, f, of the source is varied. The phase and magnitude of $I(=I_C \sim I_L)$ then varies according to the relative magnitudes of $1/2\pi fC$ and $2\pi fL$ (see

Fig. 8.19 (i)). A special case occurs when $1/X_C = 1/X_L$, i.e. $X_C = X_L$, in which case $I = 0$. The frequency, f_0, is then given by

$$\frac{1}{2\pi fC} = 2\pi f_0 L$$

i.e.

$$f_0 = \frac{1}{2\pi\sqrt{LC}}$$

The curve showing the variation of current with frequency in L and in C is illustrated in Fig. 8.19 (ii). The parallel LC circuit is known

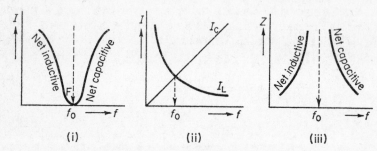

(i)   (ii)   (iii)

FIG. 8.19.   Resonance curve

as a 'rejector' circuit because the main current is zero at f_0. It should be carefully noted, though, that there is a current in C and in L at resonance whose magnitudes are the same, the phase difference being 180°. This is called the 'circulating current'.

The variation of impedance, Z, of the circuit with frequency can be deduced, since $Z = V/I$. At f_0, for example, $Z = \infty$. The Z-f curve, which may be termed a response curve, is illustrated in Fig. 8.19 (iii).

Coil (L, r) in Parallel with Capacitor (C)

A parallel combination of a coil and capacitor is used in many radio circuits. At the outset it would be well to state that we are interested in the *impedance*, Z, of this circuit as the applied frequency varies, unlike the series case.

In practice a coil has resistance, r, as well as inductance, L. V is therefore applied across (i) L and r in series and (ii) C (Fig. 8.20). If the current in the coil is I_1, it lags by an angle ϕ on V where $\tan\phi = X_L/r$ (see p. 145). I_1 is therefore represented as shown in the vector diagram (Fig. 8.21 (i)). The current I_2 in C leads by 90° on V. The vector sum, I, is represented by the diagonal of the completed parallelogram OADB and two cases are shown in Fig. 8.21 (i). In one case I leads on V, and in the other case I lags on V. The variation of impedance, Z, is shown in Fig. 8.21 (ii).

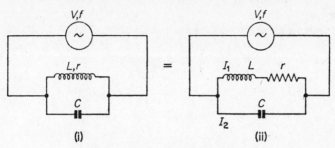

FIG. 8.20. Coil-capacitor in parallel

Resonance Case

At a particular frequency f_0, however, I and V are *in phase*. The circuit impedance Z then reduces to a pure resistance. This case is show in Fig. 8.22 (i). From the diagram, it follows that

$$\text{the external current } I = I_1 \cos \phi$$

and
$$I_1 \sin \phi = I_2$$

$$\therefore I = \frac{I_2}{\sin \phi} . \cos \phi = I_2 . \cot \phi = \frac{V}{X_C} . \cot \phi$$

But $\cot \phi = r/X_L$ (p. 170) $= r/\omega_0 L$ and $X_C = 1/\omega_0 C$.

$$\therefore I = V\omega_0 C \times \frac{r}{\omega_0 L} = \frac{VCr}{L}$$

$$\therefore \frac{V}{I} = \text{impedance at resonance} = \frac{L}{Cr}$$

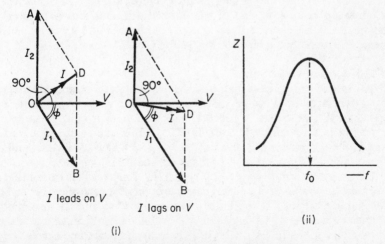

I leads on V

I lags on V

(i)

(ii)

FIG. 8.21. Phasor diagram. Variation of Z

Summary

The results can now be summarized as follows:

(a) The variation of Z with f is a curve with a peak at resonant frequency f_0 (compare the I–f series resonance curve).

(b) The maximum impedance is obtained at $f_0 = 1/2\pi\sqrt{LC}$ (approx.), where C is in farads, L in henries. This is known as the resonant

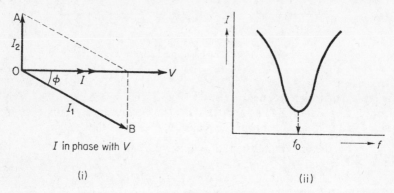

I in phase with V

(i)   (ii)

FIG. 8.22. Parallel resonance

frequency of the parallel circuit. (Compare f_0 in the series resonance case.)

(c) The circuit reduces to a pure resistance equal to L/Cr ohms at resonance, when L is in henries, C in farads, r in ohms. (Compare the series circuit at f_0.) In this case I is in phase with V (Fig. 8.22 (i)).

The I–f curve for the parallel circuit is shown in Fig. 8.22 (ii). I has a minimum value at f_0, and L, r in parallel with C is thus a 'rejector' circuit. At f_0 the circuit reduces to a pure resistance of L/Cr ohms, and hence the minimum value of I is $V \div L/Cr$.

Use of L, r in Parallel with C

A pentode radio valve may be considered in certain circumstances as a generator of constant alternating current, say I in magnitude (p. 288). Suppose that a parallel combination of a coil (L, r) and capacitor (C) is connected to it (Fig. 8.23). Then the voltage obtained across the combination is given by $V = I \times Z$. Since I is a constant, the voltage V is proportional to the magnitude of Z.

Suppose that radio waves of $f = 10^6$ Hz from a given transmitter are received by the valve and that currents of this frequency flow through the parallel circuit. If the latter is tuned by C so that its resonant frequency is 10^6 Hz, its impedance Z will then be a maximum and correspond to M in Fig. 8.24 (i). The maximum voltage across the combination is then obtained.

This parallel arrangement is used for r.f. voltage amplification in valve circuits. Besides the advantage of high Z and high voltage at resonant frequency, the combination may be made very selective.

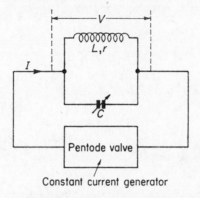

Fig. 8.23.   Pentode as constant current generator

Thus unwanted r.f. of 0.8×10^6 Hz from another transmitter is not amplified as much, since the impedance of the parallel circuit to it

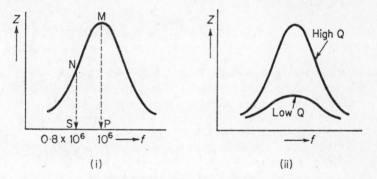

Fig. 8.24.   Selectivity of parallel circuit

drops to the value SN (Fig. 8.24 (i)). The Q of a parallel circuit, a measure of its selectivity, can be shown to be given by $2\pi f_0 L/R$ as for series combination, where R in this case is equal to r (see Fig. 8.24 (ii)).

EXAMPLE

A coil of inductance 800 μH is connected in parallel with a 800-pF loss-free capacitor. This circuit is driven from a constant-current (high-impedance) source at the resonant frequency. If the driving current is 100 μA and the voltage developed across the circuit is 20 V, sketch the vector diagram. Calculate: (i) the frequency, (ii) the current through the capacitor, (iii) the Q-factor of the coil, (iv) the voltage when a resistance of 200 kilohms is connected across the circuit. (C. & G.)

(i) The circuit is at resonance, and $800\ \mu\text{H} = 800 \times 10^{-6}$ H, $800\ \text{pF} = 800 \times 10^{-12}$ F.

$$\therefore f_0 = \frac{1}{2\pi\sqrt{LC}} = \frac{1}{2\pi\sqrt{800 \times 10^{-6} \times 800 \times 10^{-12}}} = \frac{10^7}{16\pi} = 198 \cdot 6\ \text{kHz}$$

(ii) $I_C = \dfrac{V}{X_C} = 2\pi f_0 CV = 2\pi \times \dfrac{10^7}{16\pi} \times 800 \times 10^{-12} \times 20$

$$= 2 \times 10^{-2}\ \text{A} = 20\ \text{mA}$$

(iii) The resistance at resonance $= V/I = 20/100 \times 10^{-6}$
$= 200{,}000\ \Omega = L/CR$, where R is the coil resistance.

$$\therefore R = \frac{L}{200{,}000C} = \frac{800 \times 10^{-6}}{200{,}000 \times 800 \times 10^{-12}} = 5\ \Omega$$

$$\therefore Q_0 = \frac{2\pi f_0 L}{R} = \frac{2\pi \times 10^7 \times 800}{5 \times 16\pi \times 10^6} = 200$$

(iv) When $200\ \text{k}\Omega$ is added in parallel to $200\ \text{k}\Omega$, the effective resistance is reduced to $100\ \text{k}\Omega$.

$$\therefore V = I_0 \times 100{,}000 = \frac{100}{10^6} \times 100{,}000 = 10\ \text{V}$$

Comparison between Series and Parallel Resonance Circuits

We may now compare the series and parallel resonance circuits:

1. The series one is an acceptor circuit; it gives maximum current at the resonant frequency. The parallel one is a rejector circuit; it gives maximum impedance at resonant frequency.

2. In both cases the resonant frequency $f_0 = 1/2\pi\sqrt{LC}$, provided the Q-factor is reasonably high.

3. At resonance, the series circuit reduces to a pure resistance, which is the minimum impedance; the parallel circuit reduces at resonance to a pure resistance L/Cr ohms, which is its maximum impedance.

4. Both circuits are selective, and the Q-factor is given by $2\pi f_0 L/R$.

5. The series combination is used in tuning an aerial, when the greatest current is obtained. The parallel combination is used to obtain maximum impedance, so that the voltage across it is a maximum for a constant current generator.

The above is sufficient to show the correspondence between series and parallel circuits. The I–f curve for the series circuit has a similar shape to the Z–f curve in the parallel circuit.

Power in A.C. Circuits

Power in d.c. is calculated from IV or V^2/R or I^2R. There must be a difference for a.c. because the current i and voltage v are usually out of phase. The power dissipated by components in a.c. circuits is of considerable practical importance. It affects both the performance and the costs.

(1) Perfect capacitor—pure capacitance. The current i and voltage v in this circuit (Fig. 8.25 (i)) are 90° out of phase and are shown in Fig. 8.25 (ii). From A to D, i and v are both positive. But from D to E, v is positive while i is negative. Now the power p at any instant $= iv$. Noting the signs of i and v over the period AB, it can be seen that the power p varies with time according to the graph of Fig. 8.25 (iii).

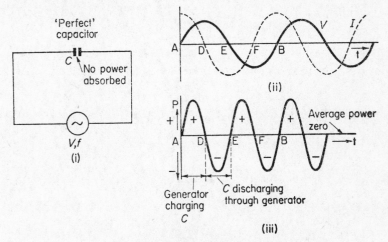

FIG. 8.25. Power variation in pure C

Taken over a lengthy period, the average power absorbed by the capacitor is therefore *zero*.

This result is explained by the fact that the capacitor absorbs an amount of energy in the first quarter of the cycle (A to D) as C charges but returns it to the generator in the next quarter (D to E) as it discharges, and so on. The electric field between the plates of the capacitor, where the energy is stored, disappears at the end of every half-cycle, when the voltage across C has then a zero value.

(2) Perfect coil—pure inductance. In this case (Fig. 8.26) I lags on V by 90° (Fig. 8.26 (ii)). The power $p = iv$ has therefore the same waveform as for the capacitor (Fig. 8.26 (iii)), and the average power absorbed over a long period of time is likewise zero. The energy is stored in the magnetic field surrounding the coil in one quarter of a cycle as the current increases, but returns to the generator during the next

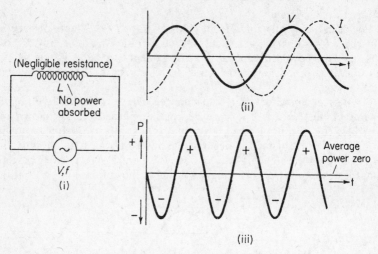

FIG. 8.26. Power variation in pure L

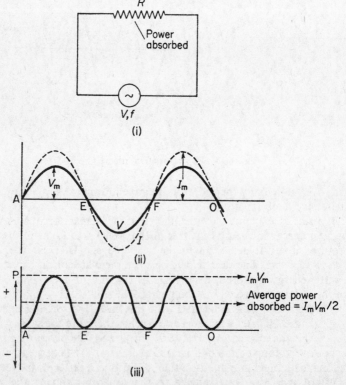

FIG. 8.27. Power variation in R

quarter as the current decreases. The magnetic flux in the coil disappears at the end of every half cycle, when the current is then zero.

(3) **Pure resistance.** Fig. 8.27(i). Unlike the previous two cases the current and voltage are in phase, Fig. 8.27 (ii)). Thus the instantaneous power $p = iv$ is positive during the time AE and the time EF (Fig. 8.27 (iii)). The power curve has obviously a maximum value of $P = I_m V_m$, where I_m, V_m are the amplitudes of i, v, and the curve can be shown to be a sine wave (Fig. 8.27 (iii)). The resistance consequently absorbs power continuously, which reappears in the form of heat.

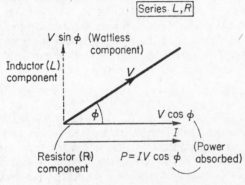

Fig. 8.28. Power absorbed

It can be seen that the average power absorbed is $I_m V_m / 2$. Since the r.m.s. values are $I_m / \sqrt{2}$ and $V_m / \sqrt{2}$, it follows that the power P absorbed by a pure resistance when a.c. flows in it is

$$P = IV \text{ watts}$$

where I, V are the r.m.s. values in amperes and volts.

Since $I = V/R$, it follows also that

$$P = I^2 R \quad \text{or} \quad \frac{V^2}{R}$$

These formulae are similar to those for power in d.c., except that I and V are r.m.s. values here.

(4) **R and L in series.** As shown on p. 145, in this case v leads on i by an angle ϕ given by $\tan \phi = X_L / R$ (Fig. 8.28). Now the r.m.s. voltage V in the vector diagram may be considered to consist of two parts or *components*. One component, $V \cos \phi$, is in phase with I, the r.m.s. current vector. The other, $V \sin \phi$, is 90° out of phase with I, as shown. We can now deal with the two components in place of V. As we have seen, alternating current and voltage in phase (as with

a resistance) is equivalent to an absorption of power equal to the product of their r.m.s. values. But a 90° phase difference (as with a coil or capacitor) is equivalent to no absorption of power. Therefore the total power absorbed in the R, L series circuit is given by

$$P = I \times (V \cos \phi) = IV \cos \phi$$

The component $V \cos \phi$ may be regarded as that part of V required to overcome the resistance, when power is absorbed. The component $V \sin \phi$ may be regarded as that part of V required to overcome the reactance, when no power is absorbed. $V \cos \phi$ is known as the *in-phase* component with I. $V \sin \phi$ is known as the *wattless* component, since it contributes nothing to the power absorbed in the circuit.

The power absorbed may also be expressed in terms of I and R. It is simply $P = I^2R$, as I is the current in that part of the circuit, R, where power is absorbed.

Power Factor

The product of I and V in the L, R series circuit is the power that one would have expected from d.c. theory to be the power expended in the circuit. The product IV is known as the 'apparent' power in a.c. theory for this reason. IV is also the maximum power which could be absorbed in the circuit, if all the components were resistors.

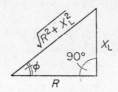

FIG. 8.29. Power factor in L, R circuit

The *true power*, however, is $IV \cos \phi$, and is less than IV.

In general, the ratio $\dfrac{\text{true power absorbed}}{\text{apparent power}}$ is known as the *power factor*. It gives a measure of the power absorbed in an a.c. circuit compared to the maximum which could be absorbed, for the given values of I and V.

$$\therefore \text{Power factor} = \frac{IV \cos \phi}{IV} = \cos \phi$$

In the L, R series circuit, $\cos \phi = R/\sqrt{R^2 + X_{\text{L}}^2}$, Fig. 8.29. Thus the smaller R is compared to X_{L}, the smaller is the power factor.

Q of Coil

On p. 161, the Q-factor of a coil of inductance L and resistance r was defined as $2\pi fL/r$. Suppose an a.c. voltage is applied across the coil, Fig. 8.30. Then

$$\text{power factor} = \frac{r}{\sqrt{r^2 + X_L{}^2}}$$

Assuming r small compared to X_L, the reactance, then power factor $= r/X_L = 1/Q$. Thus the greater Q, the less is the energy dissipated

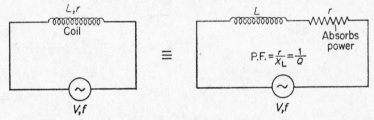

FIG. 8.30.   Power factor of coil

in the coil when it is used in an a.c. circuit. Q is therefore a 'figure of merit' for a coil.   A well-designed coil should have a high Q, in which case its power dissipation is relatively low.

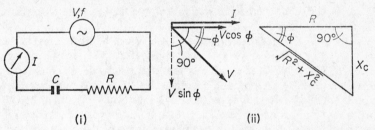

FIG. 8.31.   Power in C, R circuit

C and R in Series. (Fig 8.31(i)). The vector diagrams for the applied voltage V and current I are as shown in Fig. 8.31 (ii), where $\tan \phi = X_C/R$ (see p. 147). The wattless component is $V \sin \phi$.

The power absorbed $= I \times V \cos \phi = I^2 R$. The

$$\text{power factor} = \frac{\text{true power absorbed}}{\text{apparent power}} = \frac{IV \cos \phi}{IV} = \cos \phi$$

$$= \frac{R}{\sqrt{R^2 + X_C{}^2}}$$

When X_C is much greater than R, the power factor $= R/X_C$ (approx.) $= 1/Q$ (p. 161).

Practical Capacitors

Paper, mica, air and electrolytic capacitors absorb a certain amount of power owing to dielectric losses (see p. 62). The presence of these losses may be accounted for by imagining a resistance R in series with a capacitance C (Fig. 8.32). The power factor of the C-R combination is a measure of the dielectric losses. The power factor of air is almost zero, i.e. it has practically no dielectric losses, and this is an advantage of an air capacitor. Mica is also a high-grade dielectric as its power

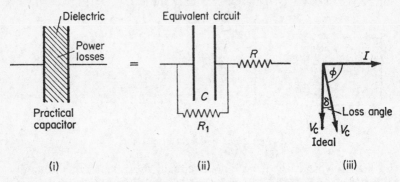

FIG. 8.32. Power absorbed in capacitors. Loss angle

factor is very low. Paper has a high power factor. The losses in an electrolytic capacitor are considerable.

With a loss-free capacitor, the phase angle between current and voltage is 90°. With power losses represented by a series resistor R in Fig. 8.32 (i), which is much less than the reactance X_C, the angle is less than 90° by an amount δ sometimes known as the *loss angle*, Fig. 8.33 (ii). The vector diagram shows that, since δ is small, its value in radians is given by $\delta = R/X_C$, to a good approximation (p. 179). As shown on p. 179, this is also the magnitude of the power factor of the capacitor.

Besides dielectric losses of power, capacitors have leakage currents through the dielectric when they are used. This may be represented electrically by a shunt resistance R_1 across a perfect capacitor C, as in Fig. 8.32 (ii).

EXAMPLES

1. Draw a vector (phasor) diagram to show the phase relationship between the applied voltage and the current in a capacitor and hence explain the meaning of the term *loss angle*. State the main reasons for power loss in a capacitor with a solid dielectric.

An alternating voltage of 1 V r.m.s. at a frequency of 1 kHz is applied to a capacitor whose reactance is 1,000 Ω. Calculate (*a*) the capacitance, (*b*) the current in the circuit. If the loss angle of the capacitor is 10^{-4} radians, calculate (c) the power dissipated, (d) the equivalent series resistance.

(C. & G.)

First part, see p. 180.

(a) $f = 1,000$ Hz, $X_C = 1,000 \, \Omega$. From $X_C = 1/2\pi fC$,

$$\therefore C = \frac{1}{2\pi fX_C} = \frac{1}{2\pi \times 1,000 \times 1,000} \, \text{F}$$

$$= \frac{10^6}{2\pi \times 1,000 \times 1,000} \, \mu\text{F} = 0 \cdot 16 \, \mu\text{F}$$

(b) $I = \dfrac{V}{X_C} = \dfrac{1}{1,000} \, \text{A} = 1 \, \text{mA}$

(c) Power $= IV \times$ power factor. Now for small loss angles, we have power factor = loss angle in radians.

$$\therefore \text{Power} = IV \times \text{loss angle} = 1 \times 10^{-3} \times 10^{-4} = 10^{-7} \text{ watt}$$

(d) Loss angle $\simeq R/X_C$ (p. 180),

$$\therefore R = \text{loss angle} \times X_C = 10^{-4} \times 10^3 = 10^{-1} = 0 \cdot 1 \text{ ohm (approx.)}$$

2. A coil has an inductance of 200 μH and a Q-factor of 100 at a frequency of 400 kHz. It is connected in series with a loss-free capacitor across a constant-voltage source of 10 mV r.m.s. at 400 kHz. Calculate, for this circuit at resonance, (a) the value of the capacitance, (b) the current flowing, (c) the power dissipated, (d) the voltage across the capacitor, (e) the current when a resistance of 5 Ω is connected in series with the circuit.

(C. & G.)

(a) Since $L = 200 \, \mu\text{H} = 200 \times 10^{-6}$ H and $f_0 = 400,000$ Hz, then, from $f_0 = 1/2\pi\sqrt{LC}$,

$$C = \frac{1}{4\pi^2 f_0^2 L} = \frac{10^6}{4\pi^2 \times 400,000^2 \times 200} \, \text{F}$$

$$= 780 \times 10^{-12} \, \text{F} = 780 \, \text{pF}$$

(b) Since $Q_0 = \dfrac{1}{R}\sqrt{\dfrac{L}{C}}$

$$\therefore R = \frac{1}{Q_0}\sqrt{\frac{L}{C}} = \frac{1}{100}\sqrt{\frac{200 \times 10^{-6}}{780 \times 10^{-12}}} = 5 \, \Omega \text{ (approx.)}$$

$$\therefore I = \frac{V}{R} = \frac{10 \, \text{mV}}{5 \, \Omega} = 2 \, \text{mA}$$

(c) Power, $P = I^2 R = (2 \times 10^{-3})^2 \times 5$ watts $= 20 \times 10^{-6}$ watts (see p. 177).

(d) $V_C = Q_0 \times V = 100 \times 10 \, \text{mV} = 1,000 \, \text{mV} = 1 \, \text{V}$.

(e) At resonance, circuit reduces to pure resistance of 5 Ω. With additional 5 Ω, total resistance = 10 Ω.

$$\therefore I = \frac{V}{R} = \frac{10 \, \text{mV}}{10} = 1 \, \text{mA}$$

SUMMARY

1. At resonance, the impedance of L, C, R in series reduces to a pure resistance (R), and the current has its maximum value. The resonant frequency, $f_0 = 1/2\pi\sqrt{LC}$. At this frequency the voltage across the capacitor and across the coil $= Q$ times the applied voltage, where $Q = 2\pi f_0 L/R$. The Q of a coil should be high in order to increase the selectivity of the circuit in which it is used.

2. At resonance the impedance of a coil (L, r) and capacitor (C) in parallel reduces to a pure resistance of magnitude L/Cr ohms. The selectivity is governed by $Q = 2\pi f_0 L/r$.

3. The I–f curves of L, r in series with C are identical with the Z–f curves of L, r in parallel with C when the same coil and a capacitor are used in the two cases. The series (acceptor) circuit gives a high voltage across the capacitor or coil when it is tuned to the incoming frequency, and this is utilised when voltages from the aerial are passed to the first stage in a receiver set. The parallel (rejector) circuit has a maximum impedance at resonance, and for a constant alternating current has therefore maximum voltage developed across it.

4. No power is absorbed by a pure capacitance or pure inductance. In a series L, R or C, R circuit the power absorbed $= I^2 R$ in each case, where I is the current flowing. The power, P, absorbed can also be evaluated from the relation $P = IV\cos\phi$, where V is the applied voltage, ϕ the phase angle between I and V.

5. The power factor = true power absorbed/apparent power $= \cos\phi$

For a coil the power factor is practically equal to $1/Q$. Losses in a coil can therefore be minimised by using one with a high Q.

The power factor of an air capacitor is practically zero. Mica is also a high-grade dielectric.

EXERCISE 8

L, C, R Series Circuits

1. An r.f. voltage is applied across a circuit comprising resistance, capacitance and inductance in series. If the voltage across each of the three components is 100 V, what is the voltage across the whole circuit? Illustrate your answer with a diagram. (*C. & G. R.*1.)

2. A circuit is tuned to a frequency of 1,000 kilocycles per second when its capacitance is 0·05 microfarad. What is its inductance? (*C. & G. R.*1.)

3. A current of 3 A is flowing in an L, C, R series circuit at the resonant frequency. If $L = 2$ H, $R = 50$ Ω, $C = 0·3$ μF, calculate (*a*) the voltage across L, (*b*) the voltage across C, (*c*) the applied voltage.

4. An a.c. voltage of 2 V is applied to a coil of inductance 3·24 mH and d.c. resistance 20 Ω in series with a 0·001 μF capacitor. Find (i) the current, (ii) the voltage across the capacitor, (iii) the Q of the circuit, if the frequency of the applied voltage is that of the resonant frequency of the circuit.

5. What do you understand by the term 'Resonant frequency' of an a.c. circuit? A coil having an inductance of 1 millihenry and a resistance of 5 ohms is connected in series with a capacitor of 10 microfarads. What would be the current flowing through this circuit if an a.c. voltage of 100 volts is applied having a frequency of (i) $5,000/2\pi$ Hz, (ii) $10,000/2\pi$ Hz. (*C. & G. T.E.*2.)

6. Sketch the response curves of current against frequency for an acceptor circuit, showing the effect of extra resistance in the circuit. An acceptor circuit consists of a coil of inductance 20 mH and resistance 50 Ω connected to a 0·0002 μF capacitor. Calculate the voltage across the capacitor at resonance if the applied voltage is 20 mV.

7. Use vectors drawn to scale to find the voltage across a circuit consisting of a coil of self-inductance 0·2 H and resistance 50 Ω connected in series with a capacitor of 10 μF, the circuit carrying a current of 2 A at 100 Hz.

Determine the voltage across the terminals of the inductor.

What is the phase angle between the current flowing and the voltage across the whole circuit? (*C. & G.*)

8. Distinguish between the terms *reactance* and *impedance*. Why is the impedance of an inductor always greater than its reactance, whereas for a good-quality capacitor the reactance and impedance are almost equal?

Sketch on one pair of axes the reactance frequency curves for (*a*) a 0·05-H inductor, and (*b*) a 2-μF capacitor.

Sketch a curve showing how the combined reactance varies with the frequency when the inductor and capacitor are connected in series. Hence explain the condition for resonance.

Calculate the frequency at which resonance occurs. (*C. & G.*)

9. Explain what is meant by *resonance* in a tuned circuit. Briefly discuss the variation of impedance with frequency of a tuned circuit near resonance.

An inductor is tuned to series resonance at 1,500 kHz by a capacitor of 1,600 pF. What is the new frequency of resonance if the capacitance is increased by 4,025 pF? (*C. & G.*)

10. Discuss the main differences in the constructional features of inductors used in the audio and radio frequency stages of a radio receiver.

A tuned circuit comprises an inductor and capacitor in series and is tuned to a resonant frequency 1 MHz.

If the value of the inductance is increased by 21%, what is then the frequency of resonance? (*C. & G.*)

Parallel Circuits

11. A resistance of 1,500 ohms and an inductance of 5 henries are connected in parallel across a 50 Hz alternating current supply of 1,000 volts r.m.s. What will be the total current taken? (*C. & G.*)

12. An inductance of $1/\pi$ mH and a capacitance of $0·1/\pi$ microfarad are connected in parallel across an a.c. supply. If the frequency is 100 kHz and the value of the current in the inductance arm is 1 ampere, find (*a*) the voltage across the parallel circuit, (*b*) the current in the capacitance arm, (*c*) the total current in the common external circuit. (*C. & G.*)

13. A 50 Hz a.c. supply at a pressure of 100 volts is applied across a resistance of 1,000 ohms, an inductance of 0·5 henry and of negligible resistance, and a capacitance of 10 μF, all of which are connected in parallel. What is the total current drawn from the supply and what is the phase angle of this current relative to the applied voltage? Illustrate your answer by a vector diagram. (*C. & G.*)

14. Explain the advantages of using a parallel combination of coil and capacitor as an impedance. A 100 μH coil of resistance 4 Ω is placed in parallel with a 0·0004 μF capacitor. Calculate (a) its resonant frequency, (b) its maximum impedance, (c) the voltage across the combination, when an a.c. of 8 mA and frequency equal to the resonant frequency flows outside in the main circuit.

15. A rejector circuit consists of a coil of inductance 20 μH and resistance 10 Ω and a 0·0005 μF capacitor. Calculate (i) the impedance of the circuit at resonance, (ii) the Q of the circuit, (iii) the current in the capacitor branch at resonance if the applied voltage is 10 V.

16. An inductor has a reactance of 1,300 ohms at 1 MHz and a series resistance of 10 ohms which is independent of frequency. A capacitor has a reactance of 800 ohms at 1 MHz and negligible series resistance. Calculate the resonant frequency if the two components are connected in parallel.

Evaluate the Q-factor at the resonant frequency and the 3 dB bandwidth of the tuned circuit.

Draw a sketch to show how the magnitude of the circuit impedance varies with frequency, and state the value of this impedance at zero and at infinite frequency. (*C. & G.*)

Power

17. Compare the heating effect, when flowing in equal resistances, of a direct current of 2 amperes with that of an a.c. having a maximum value of 2 amperes. What would be the effect on the amount of heat produced, in each case, if a capacitor were inserted in series with each resistance?
(*C. & G.*)

18. An a.c. of 2 mA is flowing in a series circuit containing three components, $L = 0·2$ H, $C = 0·1$ μF, $R = 2,000$ Ω. Calculate the power dissipated.

19. An a.c. of 1 ampere at a frequency of 800 cycles per second flows through a coil the inductance of which is 2·5 millihenries and the resistance of which is 5 ohms. What is the p.d. across the coil, the power absorbed in the coil, and the power factor? (*C. & G.*)

20. What is the meaning of *power-factor*? If a series circuit consisting of capacitance and resistance has a power-factor of 0·0005 and a capacitance of 0·002 microfarad, what is the product of the frequency and resistance?
(*C. & G.*)

21. An alternating voltage of 10 V r.m.s. at a frequency of 159 kHz is applied across a capacitor of 0·01 μF. Calculate the current in the capacitor.

If the power dissipated within the dielectric is 100 μW, calculate (a) the loss-angle, (b) the equivalent series resistance, (c) the equivalent parallel resistance. (*C. & G.*)

22. What is meant by the *self-inductance of a coil*? State the factors on which this depends.

A coil dissipates 150 W when a battery maintains 30 V across its terminals. The coil dissipates the same power when an a.c. supply of 60 V at 50 Hz replaces the battery. Although the power dissipation is the same in each case why are the a.c. and d.c. voltages different?

Neglecting any core losses, calculate: (a) the resistance of the coil, (b) the current taken in each case, (c) the phase angle between the voltage and current in the a.c. case, (d) the inductance. (*C. & G.*)

9. The Diode Valve

Thermionic Emission. Hot Cathodes

When a fine tungsten wire is heated in a vacuum to a high temperature some of the free electrons inside the metal are able to escape from it. These electrons have received sufficient extra energy from the heat supplied to overcome the inward attraction of the metal atoms (ions), which keeps them inside the metal. This method of liberating electrons from metals is called *thermionic emission*. The number of electrons emitted per second from a given wire depends only on its temperature. The metal is called a *hot cathode*, Fig. 9.1 (i).

Indirectly Heated Cathode

The common source of voltage from the mains is usually a.c. If a low a.c. voltage is applied directly to a tungsten wire, which then emits electrons, experiment shows that the output from the valve will also

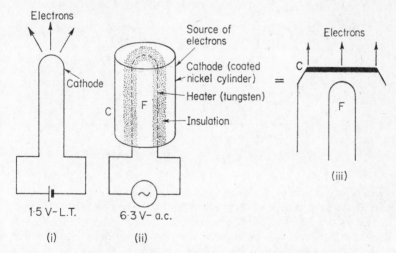

Fig. 9.1. Directly—and indirectly—heated cathodes

contain a mains frequency variation, especially at low frequencies. This is undesirable. An indirect method of obtaining electrons is therefore used.

Fig. 9.1 (ii) represents a fine tungsten wire F, insulated by silica from a nickel cylinder C. The surface of C is coated with a mixture of barium and strontium oxides. These oxides emit large numbers of electrons at relatively low temperatures, about 1,000°C.

The low voltage a.c. supply, 4 or 6·3 V for example, is connected to F. Heat conducted from F through the silica reaches the nickel surface. The oxides then become a source of electrons, as shown. It should be carefully noted that F is connected to the a.c. supply, so that the filament is the *heater* and not the source of electrons. Fig. 9.1 (iii) shows F and the cathode C diagrammatically. Frequently in circuit diagrams only the cathode C is shown. This is because we are interested only in the source of electrons, C, and in the potential of other electrodes relative to C, which influence electron movement.

Diode Valve

The earliest radio valve was the two-electrode or *diode valve*, invented by Fleming in 1902.

This consists essentially of a cathode C, and a nickel metal plate A known as the anode. These two elements constitute the electrodes, and are placed inside an evacuated glass envelope, Fig. 9.2 (i). The

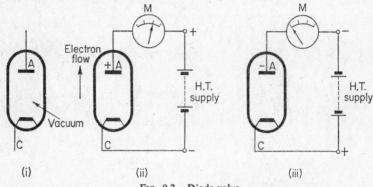

FIG. 9.2. Diode valve

vacuum is essential if the electrons are to travel far from C. To maintain a potential difference between A and C, a source of d.c. voltage, known as the *high-tension (h.t.) supply*, is connected between A and C. Fig. 9.2 (ii). When A is maintained at a positive potential relative to C, as shown, some electrons are attracted towards A and reach A. A current then flows in the anode circuit, and a reading is therefore observed on a milliammeter M. The electrons flow through the battery and return to C, where emission occurs. We thus have a current everywhere in the circuit, through the valve and outside it.

If A is at a negative potential relative to C, as in Fig. 9.2 (iii), electrons are repelled by A and cannot flow through the valve. The valve has therefore an infinite resistance in the direction anode to filament.

It conducts in the reverse direction C to A, and has therefore a 'one-way' action—hence the name valve.

Characteristic of Diode

The characteristic (I–V) curve of a diode valve may be found from a circuit such as that in Fig. 9.3 (i). The anode potential V_a relative

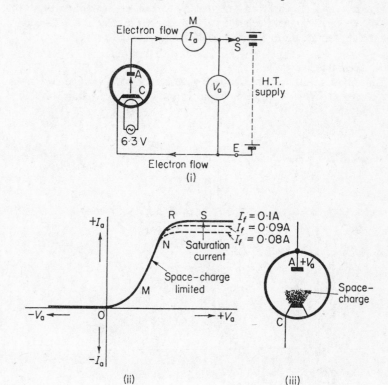

FIG. 9.3.   Diode characteristics

to C can then be varied and the corresponding anode current I_a measured by the milliammeter M.

Fig. 9.2 (ii) shows a typical characteristic curve OMNRS. After an initial small curvature, I_a increases along a straight-inclined line MN and then becomes fairly constant along RS no matter how much V_a is increased.

RS is the *saturation current*. It is a measure of the total number of electrons per second emitted by the cathode at its particular temperature. This temperature varies with the heater current I_f. At lower values of I_f the saturation current is reduced, as shown.

For lower voltages than that corresponding to R, the 'cloud' of electrons between C and A repel electrons back to the cathode since they are negatively charged. The dense electrons round C constitute a *space-charge*, Fig. 9.3 (iii). Thus the current varies along the curve OMN and is said to be 'space-charge limited'. At a positive voltage corresponding to R the repulsive effect of the space-charge is fully overcome. All the electrons emitted by C now reach the anode A.

When V_a is negative relative to C no electrons reach A. Thus part of the characteristic in Fig. 9.3 (i) is the horizontal line left of O.

A.C. Resistance

In radio circuits, we are frequently concerned with voltage variations or changes. When a diode is used, we may therefore require to know

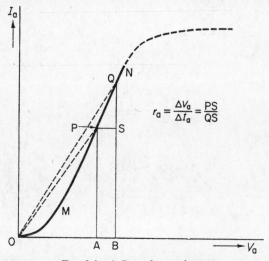

$$r_a = \frac{\Delta V_a}{\Delta I_a} = \frac{PS}{QS}$$

FIG. 9.4. A.C. or slope resistance

its *a.c. resistance or slope resistance*, r_a. This is defined for the straight line MN in Fig. 9.4 as the ratio:

$$\frac{\text{change in } V_a(\Delta V_a)}{\text{change in } I_a(\Delta I_a)} = \frac{PS}{QS}$$

Other names for r_a are 'a.c. impedance' or 'internal resistance'. It is the effective resistance of the valve in the circuit concerned when changes of V_a and I_a are made in the region MN. If a change of 20 V is made in V_a and the change in I_a is 2 mA, then

$$r_a = \frac{\Delta V_a}{\Delta I_a} = \frac{20}{2/1,000} = 10,000 \ \Omega$$

Do not confuse r_a with the *d.c.* resistance of the valve in the region PQ, which is the ratio OA/AP or OB/BQ.

Diode as Rectifier

The diode valve is a perfect rectifier—it does not conduct when its anode A is negative in potential relative to the cathode C. One of its important uses is to convert a.c. voltage from the mains to d.c. voltage, as in power supplies. In what follows we are concerned only with the principles of the rectification action.

Fig. 9.5 (i) shows a simple rectifier circuit. The a.c. input voltage

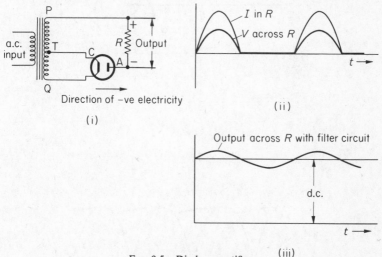

Fig. 9.5.   Diode as rectifier

from the mains is applied to the primary of a transformer and the secondary PQ is connected to the diode and a 'load' resistance R. The filament-heating current may be obtained from a tapping T on the secondary turns, as shown.

The a.c. voltage V applied between anode A and cathode C of the valve is that between P and Q. On one half-cycle, A is positive in potential relative to C and the diode conducts, Fig. 9.5 (ii). On the other half of the same cycle, A is negative relative to C and hence no anode current flows. Pulses, or bursts, of current, I, thus flow through R on alternate half-cycles. The voltage V across R hence varies as shown in Fig. 9.5 (ii). It has an average voltage in one direction or average d.c. voltage. In order to 'smooth' the fluctuating output current and voltage a filter circuit is used (see p. 141). The voltage wave-form across R is then a straight line with a small ripple in it, as shown in Fig. 9.5 (iii), and thus represents a fairly steady d.c. voltage.

This type of rectification is known as *half-wave rectification* because the effect of one-half of a cycle is obtained in the load R.

Full-wave Rectification

A circuit which gives a higher value of the average d.c. voltage than the half-wave rectifier is shown in Fig. 9.6 (i). A secondary XY centre-tapped at T is used, so that equal and *opposite* polarity of voltages are applied simultaneously to two diodes D_1 and D_2. Thus if

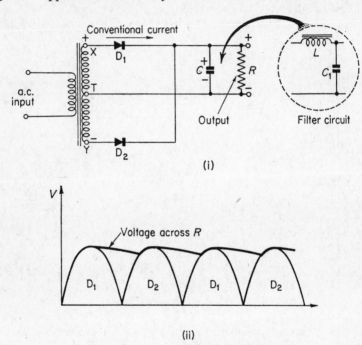

(i)

(ii)

Fig. 9.6. Full-wave rectification

D_1 conducts, D_2 does not. On the other half of the same input cycle, D_2 conducts but D_1 does not. The output voltage variation is hence as shown in Fig. 9.6 (ii) and this is called *full-wave rectification*.

The use of a large capacitor C helps to increase the mean d.c. voltage and to smooth the voltage variation. It becomes charged up to the input maximum, and then discharges through R when the input voltage falls and the rectifier ceases to conduct. The voltage variation across R is then as shown in Fig. 9.6 (ii). The ripple in the voltage is further smoothed by the *filter circuit L*, C_1, Fig. 9.6 (i). If L is 10 H, its reactance at 100 Hz, the ripple frequency, $= 2\pi f L = 6{,}000 \ \Omega$ (approx.). If $C_1 = 16 \mu F$, its reactance at 100 Hz $= 1/2\pi f C = 100 \ \Omega$ (approx.).

Thus only about 1 part in 60 or 1·5% of the fluctuating or a.c. part of the voltage appears across C_1 or R. The d.c. part of the voltage appears fully across R (see also p. 218). Electrolytic capacitors with high capacitance are used for C and C_1.

Diode and Capacitor

Suppose a capacitor C, initially uncharged, is placed in series with a diode and an input V_i of peak voltage 30 V is applied, Fig. 9.7.

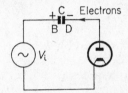

FIG. 9.7. C in series with diode

In Chapter 4, we saw that a capacitor would 'block' direct current but would allow direct *voltage* to reach other capacitors in series with it (p. 54). Now the diode can be considered as a capacitor, with its

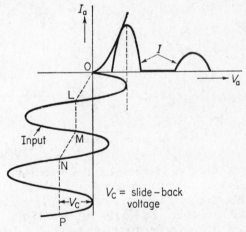

FIG. 9.8.   Slide-back effect

separated anode and cathode as the two plates. The capacitance is only a few pF. Thus if C is uncharged initially, the full voltage of V_i is across the diode.

Consider the first swing of V_i. The anode is then positive relative to the filament, and electrons reach the right-hand plate D of the capacitor (Fig. 9.7). The left-hand plate B automatically obtains an equal and opposite charge, Q say, by induction, and so the capacitor is now charged. The voltage across it is given by $V = Q/C$, where C is the capacitance. With its negative plate D connected to the anode and its positive plate B joined effectively to the cathode through the generator, V opposes the positive voltage swing of the input V_i, so far as the valve is concerned. The effect of V as it increases, due to electron flow, is illustrated in Fig. 9.8. The input swings of V_i 'slide back', producing less current flow. Eventually, when the voltage across C is equal to 30 V, the *peak* value of the input, no electrons flow and the valve ceases to conduct.

Diode Voltmeter

The slide-back action produced by the presence of a capacitor plays an important part in detector action (p. 316), and auto-bias in oscillators (p. 302). It is also utilised in a *diode voltmeter*, widely used for measuring a.c. voltages.

As we have just shown, the final voltage V_C across C in the circuit in Fig. 9.9 (i) is equal to the peak value of the a.c. input V_i. Now V_C

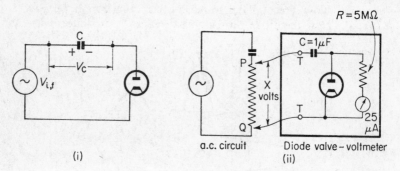

FIG. 9.9. Diode valve voltmeter principle

is a d.c. voltage. Thus if a suitable *d.c. voltmeter* is incorporated, as shown in Fig. 9.9 (ii), an unknown alternating voltage, X volts, across a component PQ, for example, can be measured. Care must be exercised in choosing the d.c. meter. In Fig. 9.9 (ii), a 0–25 μA d.c. meter of 500 Ω resistance has been converted to act as a 0–125 V d.c. voltmeter by adding about 5 MΩ in series. The time constant, CR, is then 5 seconds. If the a.c. voltage is mains frequency, 50 Hz, its period is 1/50 sec. In this case, therefore, the charge across C does not leak away much before it is recharged to the peak value. Thus the voltage across C is fairly constant.

Suppose a deflection of 5 μA is obtained on the meter, corresponding to a d.c. voltage of 25 V. Then the peak a.c. voltage is 25 V.

$$\therefore \text{ r.m.s. voltage} = 0.71 \times 25 = 18 \text{ V (approx.)}$$

In instrument practice the sensitivity of the voltmeter can be increased by using a d.c. amplifier.

Cathode-ray Tube

The cathode-ray tube is widely used in industry and research. It displays electrical waveforms on a screen. These may be obtained from radar equipment or a radio receiver or acoustic apparatus or devices for examining heart beats, for example. The tube contains a beam of electrons, or cathode-rays, as they were formerly known. Electrons are extremely light (p. 1). The beam can thus move up and down in response to a.c. voltages ranging from low to very high frequencies. Here we shall describe only the principle of operation and a simple form of tube—further details must be obtained from specialist books.

Electron Gun

The tube contains an indirectly heated *cathode* C or emitter of electrons, which consists of an enclosed nickel cylinder holding the oxide emitters in an indentation at one end, Fig. 9.10. The electron beam passes through

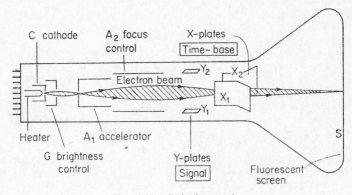

FIG. 9.10.   Cathode-ray tube

a hole in a cylindrical electrode G called the control electrode or *grid*. This limits the beam to a narrow cross-section. Further, by applying a negative voltage to G relative to C, the number of electrons per second per unit area of cross-section, or beam density, can be controlled.

The beam is accelerated to a high velocity by anode cylinders A_1 and A_2, maintained at positive potentials of 1 to 5 kV relative to C. Both cylinders together also act as an 'electron lens'. The electric field between them is varied by altering the potential on A_2, so that the beam can be focused on a screen S at the other end of the tube.

The cathode, grid and anodes together constitute the *electron gun* of a cathode-ray tube. Commercial tubes may have three anodes.

X- and Y-plates

After leaving the anodes, the beam passes through two pairs of plates called X- and Y-plates. The signal or voltage examined is always connected to the Y-plates, so that the beam, and hence the spot of light in the screen, moves up and down vertically. The X-plates are normally used to spread out the signal variations in a horizontal direction and to provide a 'time-axis' or *time-base*. A special varying voltage is therefore connected to the X-plates when the signal waveform is required. It is called a *time-base voltage* and is illustrated in Fig. 9.11. This sweeps the beam across the screen with a speed

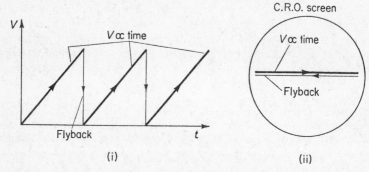

FIG. 9.11. Time-base and fly-back

proportional to the time, and then returns the beam extremely fast to its original position (flyback) so that the movement begins again, Fig. 9.11 (ii). A permanent time-base line is thus kept on the screen and the actual waveform of the signal is then seen. The X-plates are shaped so that the beam will not be cut off when deflected to the outermost edges of the screen. Details of time-base circuits are outside the scope of this book.

The time-base circuit and cathode-ray tube are contained inside the *cathode-ray oscilloscope* or *oscillograph*. This is the name given to the apparatus for examining or making measurements on the waveforms exhibited on the screen. A perspex sheet, with ruled horizontal and vertical lines acting as a graph, can be fitted over the screen in the latter case.

Screen Material

The screen is coated with fluorescent material called a *phosphor* on the inside of the cathode-ray tube. This material glows under impact from an electron beam. The colour of the light depends on the phosphor used—zinc sulphide produces a greenish-blue colour, for example—and the brightness of the light depends on the beam velocity and its density.

All fluorescent materials continue to emit light for some time after the electron bombardment has ceased. A short-persistence phosphor may have an 'afterglow' of the order of 20 milliseconds. A long-persistance phosphor may be visible for several seconds after the electron beam has disappeared.

Magnetic Focusing and Deflection

A current-carrying straight wire, which has electrons drifting along it in one direction (p. 4), is deflected in a perpendicular magnetic field. This was described on p. 82. In the same way, electron beams are deflected by current-carrying coils which produce magnetic fields perpendicular to the

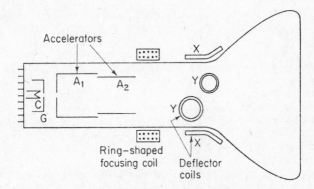

FIG. 9.12.   Magnetic focusing and deflection

direction of the beam. Thus a cathode ray tube can be focused and deflected by magnetic fields. Fig. 9.12 illustrates how this is done. The focusing field may be provided by a short iron-clad current-carrying coil or by a ring magnet surrounding the tube. The deflecting fields are often provided by coils such as X and Y. They may be saddle-shaped, as X, so as to fit snugly on the neck of the tube. Magnetic focusing and deflection are mainly used in television practice.

SUMMARY

1. Electrons are emitted by hot cathodes (thermionic emission).

2. In an indirectly heated cathode, the filament provides the heat and the cathode near it provides the electron emission.

3. The diode valve allows electrons to flow through it only when the anode is positive in potential relative to the cathode. It does not conduct when the anode is negative in potential relative to the cathode.

4. The valve (I–V) characteristic has an initial small curvature, then a straight inclined line (space-charge limited) and finally a horizontal line (saturation current—the repulsion effect of the space-charge is now completely overcome by the anode potential).

5. The slope or a.c. resistance is usually the ratio *change in V_a/change in I_a* for the straight inclined line.

6. With a capacitor C in series with a diode valve, the p.d. across C rises to the peak value. This is utilised in the diode valve voltmeter for measuring a.c. voltage.

EXERCISE 9

What are the missing words in the statements 1–9?

1. The rate of emission of electrons from a cathode depends on its . . .

2. A diode valve conducts when the anode is . . . relative to the cathode.

3. The flat part of the diode characteristic is a measure of the . . . of electrons from the . . .

4. A diode valve does not conduct when its anode is . . . relative to the cathode.

5. The . . . round the cathode in the diode valve form a . . . which repels electrons back to the . . . before the saturation value is reached.

6. With a resistor in series with a diode valve, the output wave shape when an a.c. voltage is applied is . . .

7. When a capacitor C is in series with a diode and an a.c. voltage is applied, C becomes charged to a p.d. which is the . . . value of the a.c.

8. The a.c. resistance of a valve applies to . . . voltages, whereas the d.c. resistance applies to . . . voltages.

9. The output voltage of a half-wave rectifier with a resistance load has a . . . component and a . . . component.

10. Describe briefly the operation of a thermionic diode as a rectifier.

Two diode rectifiers are to be used to provide full-wave rectification to supply a load resistance. Sketch the current waveform in this load:

(*a*) in the absence of any smoothing circuit, (*b*) with a typical smoothing circuit. Sketch, and explain the action of, the smoothing circuit employed for (*b*). (*C. & G.*)

11. In a thermionic diode valve what factors limit the value of the current that can be rectified? Include in your answer an explanation of the importance of space charge.

Give circuit diagrams and explain the operation of units employing thermionic rectifiers connected for (*a*) half wave, (*b*) full-wave-bridge rectification. Discuss the relative advantages of (*a*) and (*b*). (*C. & G.*)

12. Describe a *diode valve-voltmeter* and explain fully how it works.

13. When an a.c. voltage is applied to a capacitor C in series with a diode valve, C charges to a steady final value. Draw diagrams to illustrate the stages by which this happens and explain the variation of electron flow in the circuit.

14. Draw a labelled diagram of the electrodes inside a cathode-ray oscillograph. Indicate the approximate d.c. potential of each electrode.

Why is the screen connected to an anode?

15. Explain how to control the brilliance and focus in a cathode ray tube. (*C. & G.*)

16. Explain fully the purpose of the X- and Y-plates in a cathode-ray oscillograph. With the aid of a sketch, show how X- and Y-shifts are obtained.

10. Semiconductors. The Junction Diode

Semiconductors

As we have previously seen, pure metals are good conductors of electricity. Pure copper, for example, has a low resistivity of $1 \cdot 7 \times 10^{-8}$ ohm m at normal temperatures. Insulators have a very high resistivity, mica, for example, has a resistivity of about 9×10^7 ohm m, which is about 10^{11} times as great as copper.

Semiconductors, such as germanium and silicon, have resistivities between those of good conductors and insulators. At ordinary temperatures, for example, pure germanium has a resistivity of about 6000 ohm m. This class of materials was neglected for many years. About 1943, extensive investigations were begun into the properties of semiconductors by Shockley, Bardeen and Brattain. These led to the invention of the junction transistor about 1950, discussed later, and to important applications in radio, telecommunications and computers, to name some examples of the use of semiconductors.

Semiconductor. Valence Electrons

To understand the electrical behaviour of a semiconductor, we must first consider its atomic structure. An atom of a semiconductor such as germanium (Ge) consists of a central core or nucleus positively charged, with four electrons in its outermost orbit round the nucleus. (Other electrons occupy inner orbits and need not concern us.) The four electrons are called *valence electrons*. They form bonds called 'covalent bonds' with the valence electrons in surrounding atoms, and these bonds maintain the crystal structure of the solid, Fig. 10.1.

At absolute zero, about $-273°C$ or $0°K$, all the outer electrons are held firmly in their valence bonds. No free electrons therefore move when a p.d. is applied, and so the semiconductor is an *insulator*. As the temperature is raised, however, the thermal energy of the atoms, that is, their kinetic energy due to temperature, is increased, thus increasing their vibrational energy. The valence electrons are part of the atoms and some electrons gain sufficient energy to overcome the forces keeping them in covalent bonds. These 'thermally generated' electrons now become free electrons. Since they are available for conduction a small current flows through germanium at ordinary temperatures when a p.d. is applied, that is, the material is a *semiconductor* at ordinary temperatures.

As the temperature of a semiconductor rises further, the increased thermal energy enables more electrons to be liberated from their covalent bonds. Thus more current carriers become available. Hence the resistance of a pure semiconductor *decreases* with temperature

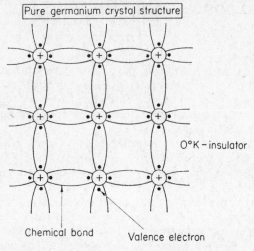

FIG. 10.1.   Crystal structure of semiconductor

rise. Pure metals, however, *increase* in resistance as their temperature rises, Fig. 10.2. This is due to the more frequent 'collisions' of the free

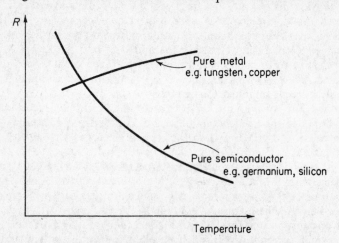

FIG. 10.2.   Effects of temperature rise

electrons with the vibrating atoms of the metal as the temperature rises, since the amplitude of vibration then increases.

Conduction in Semiconductors. Hole Concept

When a valence electron leaves its particular atom at ordinary temperatures owing to its thermal energy, and becomes a free electron, it leaves behind a vacancy or *hole* in the atom concerned, X say, Fig. 10.3. X now has a net *positive* charge, which may be thought of as present in the space vacated by the electron. X thus attracts a valence electron from a neighbouring atom Y. A hole then appears in Y. In turn, Y attracts a valence electron from a neighbouring atom, so that a hole now appears in this atom. Thus a hole, a positive charge,

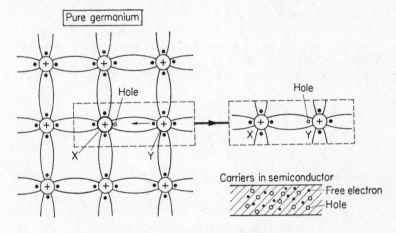

Semiconductor at room temperature

FIG. 10.3.   Electron and Hole

spreads or moves through the crystal. The hole movement, like that of the free electron, is a random one through the crystal structure.

Since an electron carries a charge $-e$, where e is the numerical value of the electronic charge, the hole it leaves behind has a charge $+e$. We therefore think of hole movement as equivalent to the movement of a *positive charge* $+e$. Of course, a pure or intrinsic semiconductor has equal numbers of free electrons and holes. Since each electron gives rise to a hole, they are often called *electron-hole pairs*. It should be remembered that these carriers of current are thermally generated.

When a p.d. is applied to a pure semiconductor, the free electrons are urged in one direction and holes in the opposite direction. The current which flows through the semiconductors is due to both electrons and holes, that is, the carriers are negative and positive charges. In contrast, the carriers of current through a pure metal are only electrons, or negative charges. The speed of an electron is greater than that of a hole when a p.d. is applied to a given semiconductor.

Impurity Semiconductors

By a manufacturing process, a considerable increase can be deliberately made to the number of free current carriers in a semiconductor. This is done by adding to it a minute but controlled amount of a foreign element or impurity. An 'impurity-type semiconductor' is then produced. If the impurity produces a great majority of electrons or *N*egative charges, it is called an *n-type* or *n-semiconductor*. If a great majority of holes or *P*ositive charges are produced, it is called a *p-type* or *p-semiconductor*.

n-Type Semiconductor

An n-type semiconductor can be made by adding a small amount of arsenic, antimony or phosphorus. These elements are characterized by the fact that their atoms have five valence electrons. When an arsenic atom, for example, is introduced into germanium, it replaces

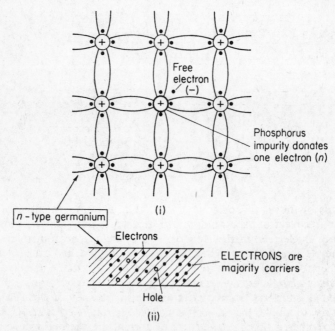

FIG. 10.4. n-type semiconductor

a germanium atom at a site in the crystal structure. Four of its five valence electrons now form covalent bonds with neighbouring germanium atoms. *The fifth electron becomes free*, Fig. 10.4. Thus one free electron per arsenic atom is obtained.

Although a minute amount of impurity, such as 1 part in 100 million by weight, is introduced into the semiconductor, each of the enormous number of impurity atoms contributes one electron or negative charge which is available for conduction. The resulting impure semiconductor is thus *n-type germanium*. The predominantly large number of negative charges available for conduction are called *majority carriers*. The relatively few holes (positive charges), which were thermally generated, are called minority carriers. It should be noted that the whole of the n-semiconductor is electrically neutral since the impurity atoms are electrically neutral. Thus the metal contains ions (charged atoms) equal in number to the total majority and minority carriers. The ions are fixed in the crystal structure of the metal, whereas the carriers are mobile. The impurity atoms are called *donor atoms* since they 'donate' free electrons.

p-Type Semiconductor

Atoms of indium, boron or gallium have only three valence electrons. Thus if an atom of indium is absorbed into the crystal structure of germanium, it takes up a valence electron from a neighbouring germanium atom to form four covalent bonds, Fig. 10.5. A *hole* is then left in the germanium atom. The number of holes produced by the

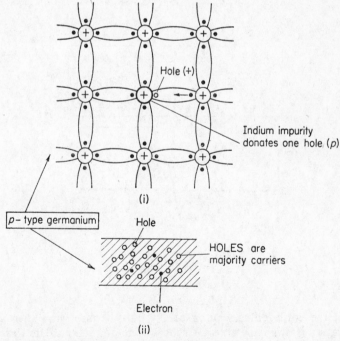

FIG. 10.5. p-type semiconductor

impurity is equal to the number of impurity atoms, and as this is an enormous number, about 10^{16} per cm^3, positive charges are produced for conduction which are the majority carriers. On this account, the impure semiconductor is called a *p-type* or *p-semiconductor*. The minority carriers are negative charges or electrons, which were thermally generated. The impurity atoms are called *acceptor atoms*, because they 'accept' a valence electron from a neighbouring germanium atom.

The great advantage gained in producing p- and n-type semiconductor material lies in the fact that electrical conduction will be mainly due to free positive holes or mainly to free negative electrons in the respective cases. In intrinsic (pure) semiconductors, conduction is due to the thermally generated electron-hole pairs, which are more liable to recombination on their own. The p- and n-semiconductors ensure much more current carriers when a suitable quantity of impurity is injected into the pure semiconductor.

The P–N Junction

When a perfume bottle is opened, one can immediately smell the scent. The high concentration of molecules of perfume in the vapour

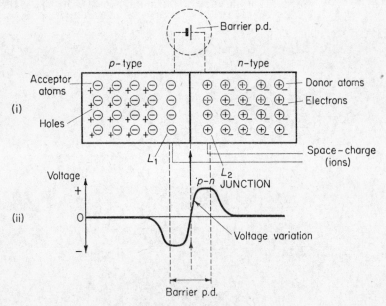

FIG. 10.6. p-n junction

inside the bottle diffuses automatically into the air, where their concentration is originally zero. A similar state of affairs occurs with the high concentration of carriers inside p- and n-type semiconductors.

When they are fused together, the high concentration of holes in the p-semiconductor part causes holes to diffuse into the n-semiconductor part across their junction, where they were in a minority. Likewise, the high concentration of electrons in the n-semiconductor causes electrons to diffuse into the p-semiconductor, where they were in a minority.

The movement of holes, positive charges, across the junction, leaves behind a layer L_1 of 'uncovered' or negative ions in the p-semiconductor, Fig. 10.6 (i). Similarly, the movement of electrons, negative charges, leaves behind a layer L_2 of positive ions in the n-semiconductor. Together, the negative and positive ions form a *space-charge*, which opposes the diffusion of more than a certain number of electrons and holes across the junction. Thus diffusion soon ceases. The effect of the space-charge is equivalent to an opposition or *barrier p.d.*, estimated at a few tenths of a volt, and is represented by a fictitious battery in Fig. 10.6 (i). Fig. 10.6 (ii) shows the voltage variation.

The space or gap between the charges at the junction of the two semiconductors is hence a region depleted of charges or free carriers. This space-charge region is called a *depletion layer*; it is extremely narrow, typically less than 1/1,000 cm. The junction between the two semiconductors is called a *p-n junction*.

Forward-bias. Reverse-bias

When a small p.d. of more than a few-tenths of a volt is applied to the p-n junction, so that the p-semiconductor is positive and the n-semiconductor is negative, the barrier p.d. is overcome. The excess p.d.

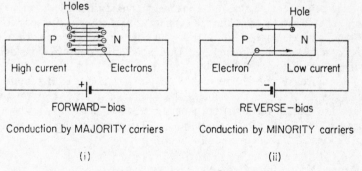

FIG. 10.7. Forward- and reverse-bias

forces holes (positive charges) from p to n, and electrons (negative charges) from n to p, across the junction, Fig. 10.7 (i). A current thus flows in the circuit and the p-n junction is said to be *forward-biased*. It can be seen from Fig. 10.7 (i) that the battery urges holes and electrons in the two semiconductors towards their junction and hence the width of the depletion region diminishes. The current flowing across the p-n junction increases as the applied p.d. increases (p. 205).

Suppose that the battery terminals are now reversed, so that this time the positive pole is joined to the n-semiconductor and the negative pole to the p-semiconductor, Fig. 10.7 (ii). It can be seen that the barrier p.d. is then increased. The p-n junction is now said to be *reverse-biased*. The majority carriers in the two semiconductors do not flow across the junction, but the minority carriers (the holes or positive charges in the n-semiconductor and the electrons or negative charges in the p-semiconductor) are attracted across the junction by the reverse p.d. Thus a very small current flows. The current reaches a saturation value at only a small p.d., as the number of minority carriers is relatively small. It will be recalled that the minority carriers in the semiconductors were thermally generated and so an increase in temperature will increase this reverse saturation current (see p. 205). Since the battery in reverse-bias urges the majority electrons and holes away from the junction, the width of the depletion region increases.

Junction Diode Capacitance

As we have just seen, when the junction is reverse-biased there is a particular width of depletion region and no mobile charge carriers. Uncovered ions or charges exist in the p- and n-semiconductors on either side of the region. The depletion region thus acts as a capacitor and its capacitance is known as the *junction capacitance*.

Unlike an ordinary capacitor, the junction diode capacitance is voltage dependent. Thus, if the reverse voltage is increased, the depletion width is increased. Since the capacitance is inversely proportional to the distance between the 'plates', the junction capacitance decreases when the reverse-bias increases. The capacitance may be considered to be in parallel with the diode.

At low frequencies the reactance of the capacitance is high and can be ignored. At high frequencies the reactance is low. Current may then flow partly through the capacitance at reverse-bias, instead of through the high diode resistance. The junction diode thus has limitations at high frequencies.

Junction Diode Characteristic

A circuit for obtaining the current, I, v. voltage, V characteristic of a p-n junction, D, is shown in Fig. 10.8. The forward p.d. can be applied by means of a low-resistance potentiometer P capable of carrying the relatively large forward currents, with a switch, SW, for the forward-bias at F or the reverse-bias at R *via* Q. The voltmeter V should have a very high resistance, preferably a valve voltmeter, so that no appreciable error occurs especially in reverse-bias. The current-measuring instrument should be capable of reading currents which may vary from microamps to milliamps.

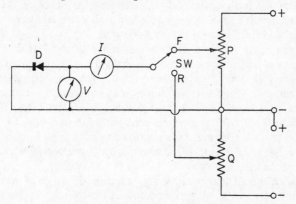

Fig. 10.8. Junction diode circuit

Fig. 10.9 shows a typical germanium p-n junction diode *I–V* character-istic. As the minority carriers increase at higher temperatures, the reverse saturation current at 60°C is higher than at 25°C. It can now

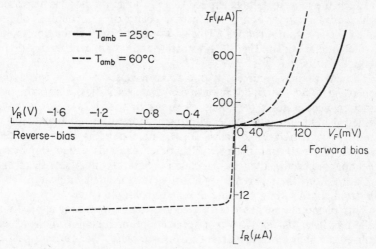

Fig. 10.9. Junction diode characteristic

be seen that, like the diode radio valve, the p-n junction acts as a *rectifier*. It conducts well when forward-biased and only slightly when reverse-biased. Unlike the diode valve, however, the carriers in a junction diode are both positive and negative charges and the junction diode conducts slightly in the reverse direction. It may also be noted that the diffusion of the charge carriers through the semiconductor material is a much slower process than the passage of electrons across the vacuum of a radio valve. At high frequencies, therefore, the charges in the junction diode may not be able to follow completely the variation of voltage and its efficiency is hence reduced.

The germanium junction diode is particularly useful as a rectifier in low-voltage supply units but it has a limited range of operating temperature, about 100°C maximum, due to the temperature-sensitive reverse current. Silicon-type diodes can operate to much higher temperatures, up to 200°C, but have a much greater internal voltage drop, about 0·8 to 1·0 V as compared with 0·2 to 0·5 V, for a given forward current. However, silicon diodes can be made to withstand a much higher reverse voltage. Large silicon power rectifiers can handle currents of many amperes.

In forward-bias, a low-frequency junction diode may have a d.c. resistance of the order of tens or hundreds of ohms. In reverse-bias, the d.c. resistance of a germanium diode is of the order of hundreds of kilohms and that of the silicon diode is of the order of tens of megohms.

Avalanche and Zener Effect

When the reverse voltage applied to a p-n junction diode is increased sufficiently, a sudden sharp current rise occurs at a particular voltage called the *breakdown voltage*. This is shown at Z in the junction diode *I–V* characteristic in Fig. 10.10, corresponding to a reverse p.d. of about 50 volts.

The sharp rise in current is due to two causes. One is called the *avalanche effect*. The high intensity of the electric field across the p-n junction accelerates the valence electrons to speeds when they have sufficient high energy to knock out many more electrons from neutral atoms. An '*avalanche*' of new electron-hole pairs is then produced and the current rises sharply. The other cause is called the *Zener effect* or *breakdown*, after the original discoverer of this effect. Electrons are torn from their parent atoms owing to the high intensity of the electric field, resulting in many more electron-hole pairs.

This phenomenon has led to a very useful commercial application called a *Zener diode*. This is a special type of junction diode which utilises the sharp rise in current in reverse-bias. The current passed may then be tens of milliamps or more. The breakdown voltage in a particular silicon Zener diode used for voltage stabilization is practically a constant value. After breakdown the voltage across the diode increases slightly and this voltage is called the *reference voltage* of the diode.

Fig. 10.11 (i) shows the basic features of a stabilizer circuit. The

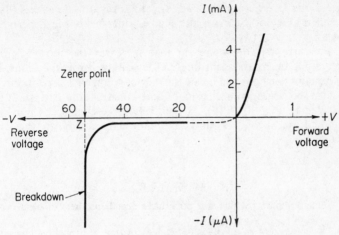

FIG. 10.10. Zener effect

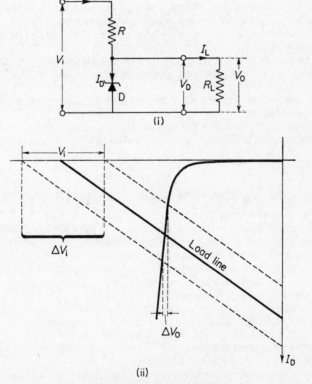

(i)

(ii)

FIG. 10.11. Zener diode stabilizer circuit

Zener diode D is across the load R_L, and a resistor R ensures that the current in D is not excessive although D operates in the Zener voltage range.

If the current I_L drawn by the load increases, the current I_D in the Zener diode decreases accordingly. The voltage across the diode, however remains constant and hence the output voltage V_0, is constant. This can also be seen from the load line construction (see p. 221), as illustrated in Fig. 10.11 (ii). A relatively large change ΔV_i in V_i, the input voltage, produces only a small change ΔV_0 in the output voltage, V_0.

SUMMARY

1. Semiconductors which are pure have equal numbers of electrons and holes.

2. The movement of a hole is equivalent to that of a positive charge $+e$; $-e$ is the charge on an electron. The current through a semiconductor is carried by both electrons and holes.

3. In a p-semiconductor, the majority carriers are holes (positive charges) and the minority carriers are electrons (negative charges).

4. In a n-semiconductor, the majority carriers are electrons and the minority carriers are holes.

5. The p–n junction diode conducts well in forward-bias (p positive and n negative in potential) but very slightly in reverse-bias. It thus acts as a rectifier.

6. In reverse-bias, the depletion region has a 'junction capacitance' which is voltage dependent.

7. The Zener diode utilises the breakdown at a particular reverse voltage, when the diode suddenly conducts well. This is used for voltage stabilization.

EXERCISE 10

What are the missing words in the following statements 1–17?

1. Two common semiconductor elements are . . . and . . .

2. As the temperature rises, the resistance of a pure semiconductor . . .

3. The resistance of the semiconductor element . . . is less sensitive to temperature rise than the semiconductor element . . .

4. The carriers of current through a pure semiconductor are . . . and . . .

5. Of the two carriers in a semiconductor, the . . . have usually the greater velocity when a battery is applied.

6. Since phosphorus has five valence (outermost) electrons, phosphorus impurity changes pure silicon to a . . . -type semiconductor.

7. Those phosphorus atoms which provide carriers are called . . .

8. Indium has three valence electrons and hence indium impurity changes pure silicon to a . . . -type semiconductor.

9. In a n-type semiconductor, the majority carriers are . . . and the minority carriers are . . .

10. In a p-type semiconductor, the majority carriers are . . . and the minority carriers are . . .

11. The p.d. across a p–n junction is called a 'junction barrier' because it sets up a p.d. which . . . the movement of carriers.

12. In forward-bias the p–n junction diode . . ., and the diode has then a . . . resistance.

13. In reverse-bias the current flowing is . . . than in forward-bias.

14. In reverse-bias the current flowing is due to . . . carriers in the p- and n-semiconductors.

15. In the junction diode, temperature rise has an appreciable effect on the . . . current.

16. When reverse-bias is increased, breakdown occurs at the . . . voltage and a . . . current then flows.

17. A diode which utilises the breakdown is called a . . . diode. It is used to . . . the voltage in a circuit.

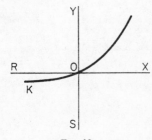

Fig. 10A

18. Fig. 10A represents a typical junction diode characteristic. (i) Label the two axes RX, YS after copying the diagram. (ii) Draw a circuit diagram showing how the characteristic would be obtaining, marking the polarity of the battery terminals clearly. (iii) Which part of the curve is due to majority carrier flow and which to minority carrier flow? (iv) Show on your diagram what happens beyond K. (v) Why is the reverse current a 'saturation' current?

19. What do you understand by the following terms: *semiconductor, impurity semiconductor, hole movement, donor, majority carrier*?

20. In p-type silicon, which carriers are (i) minority carriers, (ii) majority carriers, (iii) increased by thermal or temperature rise?

21. (i) What affect has temperature rise on a pure semiconductor? Explain what happens. (ii) Describe and explain briefly how a n-type semiconductor may be made.

22. The p–n junction has a 'capacitance' property. Explain, with diagrams, what happens under conditions of reverse bias to the magnitude of the capacitance.

23. What is meant by the following terms: (*a*) thermally generated electron-hole pairs, (*b*) a covalent bond, (*c*) p-type germanium, (*d*) depletion region in a junction diode.

24. Draw a circuit diagram of a p–n junction diode (i) in forward-bias,

(ii) in reverse-bias, marking the polarity of the battery in both cases. Explain what happens in each case.

What are the advantages and disadvantages of the junction diode compared with a diode valve?

25. From the OA10 characteristic in Fig. 10.9, p. 205, estimate the reverse d.c. resistance at −1 V and the forward d.c. resistance at 120 mV.

26. Fig. 10.9, p. 205, shows the OA10 characteristics at 25°C and 60°C. Explain why the characteristics are different.

27. A junction diode requires a forward bias of 0·5 V to pass 10 mA. Calculate the series resistance required with a 9 V battery so that the diode will pass 10 mA. Draw the circuit diagram.

28. By reference to the formation of a potential barrier and to a current/voltage characteristic, explain the rectifying action of a p-n junction.

29. What is *Zener diode*? Explain how Zener diodes can be used for voltage stabilization, drawing a circuit and characteristic curves in your answer.

11. Triode Valve and Circuit Principles

The diode or two-electrode valve can only rectify an alternating voltage. As seen later, the *triode valve* can *amplify* audio-frequency, a.f., voltages. Although it has been superseded today by the transistor as an a.f. amplifier (p. 235), the principles concerned in the valve action, and its operation when used in circuits, can also be applied to the case of the transistor.

Effect of Grid

The triode is a three-electrode valve. It contains a nickel grid G between the anode A and cathode C. This consists of a wire helix surrounding C and shown diagrammatically in Fig. 11.1. (i) We shall not be concerned with any constructional details. Owing to the fact that it is nearer to the cathode, changes in the voltage on the grid G

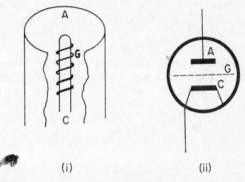

(i)   (ii)

Fig. 11.1. Three-electrode valve

are able to affect the intensity of the electrostatic field round C to a very much greater degree than corresponding changes in the anode voltage. As G is an open wire, most of the electrons pass through it and are collected by A when G is at a small positive potential relative to C. We also see later that anode current flows even when G is negative in potential relative to C. In this case no electrons are collected by G; they all move to A.

The introduction of the grid between the cathode and anode thus provides an easy and delicate control over the current which flows in the main (anode) circuit or *output* circuit. An important advantage is that the grid absorbs no electrons under certain conditions, in which case no power is absorbed from the circuit supplying the grid or *input* circuit. See Fig. 11.2.

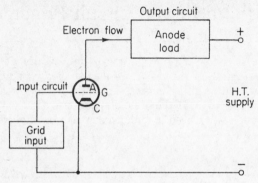

Fig. 11.2. Input and output circuits

Triode Static Characteristics

There are four electrical variables when the triode is used, compared o two in the diode. They are the anode current, I_a, the grid voltage, V_g, the anode voltage, V_a, and the grid current, I_g. We shall be mostly concerned with the first three.

The *anode characteristics* are the I_a–V_a curves when V_g is kept constant. The *mutual characteristics* are the I_a–V_g curves when V_a is kept constant. Either characteristic may be obtained from the circuit shown in Fig. 11.3.

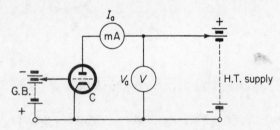

Fig. 11.3. Circuit for characteristics

The results are shown in Fig. 11.4 (i), (ii). The anode characteristics are initially curved at O, A or D, and then approximately straight along the major parts M, N or H. When the grid voltage V_g is more negative, anode current does not begin to flow until the anode voltage V_a is made higher, as at A and D. If V_a is sufficiently increased, saturation may be obtained as at L (p. 187). The mutual characteristics are also initially curved, as at A, D or H, and then approximately parallel long straight lines, BC, EF and LM. When the grid voltage V_g is sufficiently negative, as at D or A, no anode current flows.

When V_g is maintained negative relative to the cathode C, the

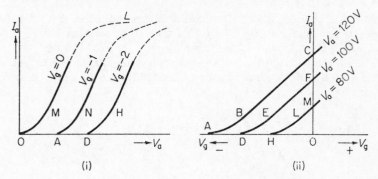

FIG. 11.4. Anode and mutual characteristics

electrons are collected by the anode only. On some occasions in valve circuits V_g may be slightly positive relative to C. In this case some of the electrons are collected by the grid wires and a small current then flows in the grid circuit.

Valve Parameters

Three important properties or parameters of the triode, needed in circuit analysis, are as follows:

(i) *A.c. or slope resistance or impedance, r_a.* This is defined by

$$r_a = \frac{\text{change in } V_a (\Delta V_a)}{\text{change in } I_a (\Delta I_a)}$$

when V_g is constant.

For the *straight part* DC of the anode characteristic for $V_g = 0$ in Fig. 11.5 (i), a change of V_a from 60 to 70 V produces a change of I_a from 2·0 to 4·0 mA. Thus $r_a = 10$ V/2 mA = 5,000 Ω.

(ii) *Mutual conductance, g_m.* This is defined by

$$g_m = \frac{\text{change in } I_a (\Delta I_a)}{\text{change in } V_g (\Delta V_g)}$$

when V_a is constant.

For the *straight part* DC of the mutual characteristic for $V_a = 120$ V in Fig. 11.5 (ii), a change of V_g from −3 to −1 V produces a change of I_a from 4·0 to 8·0 mA. Thus $g_m = 4$ mA/2 V = 2 mA per volt, where 'volt' refers to grid voltage. The mutual conductance is thus a measure of the anode current change when the grid voltage changes.

(iii) *Amplification factor, μ.* This is defined by

$$\mu = \frac{\text{change in } V_a(\Delta V_a)}{\text{change in } V_g(\Delta V_g)}$$

where the changes in $V_a(V_g = \text{constant})$ produces the *same change in I_a* as the change in $V_g(V_a = \text{constant})$. To understand how μ may be found, consider the mutual characteristics in Fig. 11.5 (ii). When V_a is constant at 120 V, a change of grid voltage from -3 to -1 V or 2 V along DC produces a current change from 4 to 8 mA, E to F.

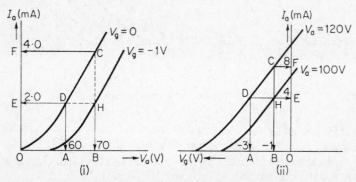

Fig. 11.5. Parameters (constants) of valve

We may keep V_g constant at -1 V by moving along the vertical line BHC from H to C. Then a change of anode voltage from H (100 V) to C (120 V) produces the *same* current change, from E (4 mA) to F (8 mA). Hence $\mu = \Delta V_a / \Delta V_g = 20 \text{ V}/2 \text{ V} = 10$. From the anode characteristics in Fig. 11.5 (i), it can be seen by following changes of V_a from A to B, and changes of V_g from H to C, that

$$\mu = \text{AB volts}/1 \text{ volt} = 10/1 = 10.$$

We shall see later that μ is concerned in the amplification produced by the valve. Here it may be noted that if $\mu = 10$, and a change of 0·1 V is made in the grid voltage, then this is equivalent to a change of *anode* voltage of $10 \times 0\cdot1$ V or 1 V, because it produces the same anode current change.

The three parameters μ, r_a, g_m are related to each other. This may be seen from Fig. 11.5 (i), for example. Here $r_a = \Delta V_a / \Delta I_a = \text{AB}$ volts/EF mA from DC. From the vertical line BHC,

$$g_m = \Delta I_a / \Delta V_g = \text{EF mA}/1 \text{ volt}$$

Thus

$$r_a \times g_m = \frac{\text{AB volts}}{\text{EF mA}} \times \frac{\text{EF mA}}{1 \text{ volt}} = \frac{\text{AB volts}}{1 \text{ volt}}$$

But $\mu = AB$ volts/1 volt. Hence

$$\mu = r_a \times g_m$$

A valve with $r_a = 20,000\ \Omega$ and $g_m = 3$ mA/V thus has an amplification factor $\mu = 20,000 \times 3/1,000 = 60$, expressing g_m in *amperes* per volt.

A.F. Amplification

Previously, valves were used considerably in receivers as a.f. amplifiers. Nowadays they have been superseded for this purpose by transistors (p. 244). The principles concerned in amplification, however, have general application and are now considered.

When a valve is used as an a.f. amplifier, the *signal* or *input voltage*

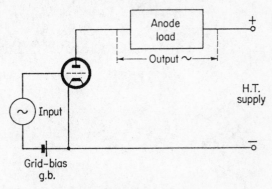

Fig. 11.6. Triode amplifier

V_i is always applied to the grid-cathode circuit, Fig. 11.6. The *output current* and *voltage* are developed in the anode circuit. The nature of the output, both in magnitude and waveform, depends considerably on the *grid-bias*. This is the name given to the average or constant voltage present in the grid circuit while the grid voltage varies. In Fig. 11.6, the grid-bias is represented by the steady voltage of the battery shown. Usually the grid-bias is negative.

Class A Amplification

The nature of the output can be deduced by drawing the line MP produced corresponding to the negative grid-bias, and then showing the variation of the input voltage V_i *with this line as axis*, Fig. 11.7. This gives the actual grid voltage changes or swing while V_i varies. Since the anode current varies along the straight part HL of the characteristic, the output current has a waveform exactly the same as the input voltage V_i. This is called *class A amplification*. Provided the grid swings take place on the straight part AL of the characteristic, other grid-bias voltages may be used to provide class A amplification.

Note that a distorted output is produced if the grid swings move into the lower curved part of the characteristic, or if V_g becomes positive at any part of the cycle. In the latter case, some electrons are collected by the grid (p. 213).

Although an undistorted output is essential in amplifiers, a serious

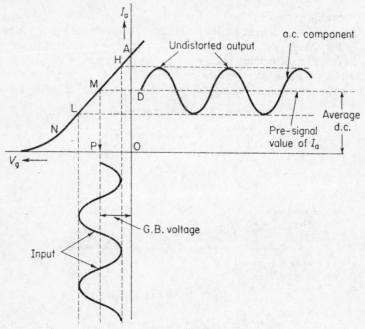

FIG. 11.7.   Class A amplification

disadvantage of class A amplification is the drain produced on the h.t. supply. This can be seen from Fig. 11.7. The pre-signal anode current corresponds to the height OD. While the amplifier is operating, the average direct current (d.c.) from the h.t. supply is the same as before, which is high. The maximum a.c. output power obtained in the anode circuit can be shown to be theoretically only 50% of the input power from the h.t. supply, but in practice class A amplifiers are much less efficient than this value (see p. 270).

Class B Amplification.   Push-pull Amplification

If the valve is biased *near to the cut-off*, as at D, *class B amplification* is obtained (Fig. 11.8). The main features of class B amplification are:

(i) The output is distorted, since no anode current flows during the negative half cycle (see PQ in the output variation).

(ii) The pre-signal anode current is practically zero, but the average I_a increases when the input signal V_i is received, Fig. 11.8. Compared with class A, class B amplification is much more efficient because it uses much less power from the supply.

A *class B push-pull* arrangement is a device using two valves which retains the efficiency but overcomes the distortion obtained with a single valve, i.e. it supplies the other half-cycle. The circuit is shown in Fig. 11.9 (i). With the input in the primary L_1 of the transformer,

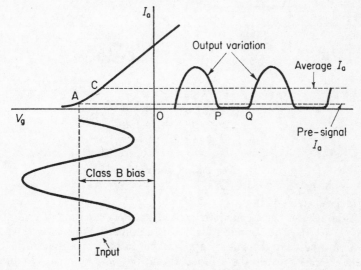

FIG. 11.8. Class B amplification

the centre-tapped secondary L_2 applies equal and opposite alternating voltages to the grids. Thus when valve (1) is conducting (positive half-cycle), valve (2) is cut-off (negative half-cycle), and vice versa (see graphs P and Q in Fig. 11.9 (i)).

The anode currents I_a flow on alternate half-cycles through the centre-tapped primary L_3. Since they are in opposite directions through it (see graphs R and S) the effect is the same as a normal sine wave a.c., Fig. 11.9 (ii), if the valves have identical characteristics. This induces a sine wave voltage in the secondary L_4, which is the output circuit.

From Fig. 11.9 (i), it can be seen that the d.c. component of the anode current due to valve 1 in L_3 is neutralised by that due to valve 2, since this flows in the opposite direction. Thus d.c. magnetisation of the core does not occur, which would otherwise produce a distorted output.

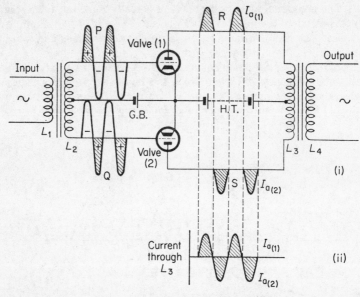

FIG. 11.9.   Class B push-pull amplifier

Grid-bias. Cathode Bias

Although it is not used in practice, a dry battery can provide grid-bias, Fig. 11.10 (i). The common method is automatic *cathode bias*, which needs no battery. In this case a suitable resistor R is placed in the cathode lead between the cathode E and the h.t.$^-$ terminal D, with a large capacitor C, such as $50\,\mu F$ electrolytic capacitor, in parallel.

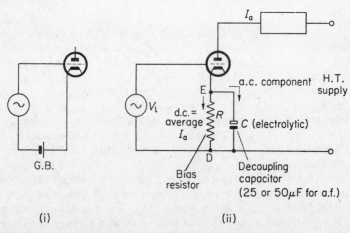

FIG. 11.10.   Bias. Cathode bias

C is called a *decoupling* or *bypass capacitor* because it decouples the a.c. component from R, explained shortly.

We can see how cathode bias works from our results for class A amplification. Here the output anode current, which also flows between E and D to complete the circuit flow, consists of a d.c. component and an a.c. component. See Fig. 11.10 (ii). The large value of C produces a very low reactance, and so the a.c. component is filtered through C and away from R. Further, owing to the low reactance, the a.c. voltage across R is extremely small. The d.c. component I flows only through R. If it is 3 mA, for example, and $R = 1 \text{ k}\Omega = 1,000 \Omega$, the d.c. voltage across $R = IR = 3$ V. The electrons, negative charges, flow from D back to the cathode E. Hence the potential of D is 3 V *lower* than that of E or -3 V. The grid bias is hence -3 V.

Since C is electrolytic, care must be taken to join its positive terminal to the point E (see p. 62). If C were absent, the a.c. component would flow through R, and the alternating voltage applied between grid and cathode would no longer be simply that due to V_i. 'Feed-back' to the grid circuit would occur, giving rise to a reduction in the output in this case (see p. 277).

Automatic Grid-current Bias

A negative bias may also be applied between grid and cathode by means of a capacitor, C, and resistance, R, placed in the grid circuit, as shown in Fig. 11.11. When V_i is applied, G becomes positive relative

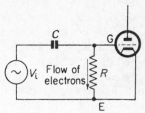

Fig. 11.11. Grid bias

to E for the input positive half-cycles (see p. 54), and electrons reach the right-hand plate of C. On the negative half-cycles no further electrons are collected by G, and some of those already on the capacitor leak away through R at a rate depending on the time-constant, CR, of the combination (see slide-back voltage, p. 301). The current, I_g, through R settles down to a steady average value, say, 50 μA. Thus if $R = 40,000 \Omega$, the p.d. between G and E $= I_g R = 2$ V. The electrons flow from G to E, and G is therefore at a potential lower than zero, in this case -2 V.

This method of bias, called *automatic* grid-current bias, is used when class C amplification is required in oscillators, discussed later (p. 301).

Resistance Load. Dynamic Characteristics

As we saw on p. 216, an undistorted anode current variation is obtained with class A amplification. If a signal output *voltage* is required, a high resistance load R of many kilohms is required for the anode current to flow through. This develops an appropriate voltage drop, Fig. 11.12. It should be carefully noted that the output voltage V_0 is derived from the *alternating* component I_0 of the output current and not the direct current (see Fig. 11.7). Thus $V_m = I_m R$, where V_m and I_m are the peak values of the alternating component.

Suppose that, in the circuit in Fig. 11.12, $R = 20,000$ ohms and that the e.m.f. E of the h.t. supply is 150 V. Then, as there is a steady anode

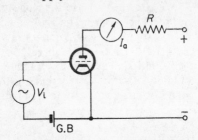

Fig. 11.12.   Dynamic characteristics

current, the steady anode voltage V_a is less than 150 V by the voltage drop in R. When an input, V_1, is applied to the valve operating under class A conditions, the varying anode current, I_a, in R causes a varying potential drop across R. The *actual* anode voltage, V_a, is therefore fluctuating. The relation between I_a and V_g for a given load R is now known as the *dynamic* characteristic. It is a characteristic of the circuit while it is operating and depends on the magnitude of R, whereas static characteristics (p. 212) are characteristic of the valve alone.

Dynamic characteristics may be obtained by experiment. Thus if V_1 is omitted from the circuit shown in Fig. 11.12, and the g.b. (grid-bias) varied, the resulting I_a enables an I_a–V_g curve to be obtained for the particular resistance load R used. The experiment may be repeated with other resistance loads.

Dynamic characteristics may also be derived from the static characteristics of the valve. Suppose that the latter are known for $V_a = 120$, 110, 100, 90, 80 V (Fig. 11.13), and that $E = 150$ V and $R = 20,000 \, \Omega$.

(a) When $V_a = 120$ V, the p.d. across $R = 150 - 120 = 30$ V.

∴ the anode current, I_a

$$= \frac{30}{20,000} = 1 \cdot 5 \text{ mA}$$

and corresponds to A on the static $V_a = 120$ V curve.

(b) When $V_a = 110$ V, the p.d. across $R = 150 - 110 = 40$ V.

$$\therefore I_a = \frac{40}{20,000} = 2 \text{ mA}$$

and corresponds to B on the static $V_a = 110$ V curve.

(c) When $V_a = 100$ V, $I_a = 50/20,000 = 2 \cdot 5$ mA and corresponds to C.

When $V_a = 90$ V, $I_a = 3$ mA and corresponds to D, and when $V_a = 80$ V, $I_a = 150$ mA and corresponds to E. Generally,

$$V_a = 150 - I_a R$$

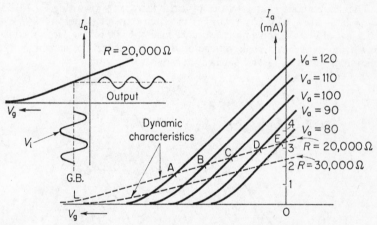

FIG. 11.13. Dynamic characteristics by calculation

Thus when $V_a = 150$ V, $I_a = 0$. This corresponds to the bottom point L on the static characteristic for $V_a = 150$ V, which is not drawn in the diagram.

The dynamic characteristic for a load resistance of $R = 30,000$ Ω is also shown. Dynamic characteristics for a pure resistance load are straight except for a curved portion as they tail off towards L. When the output current with a given load is required, the input voltage variations must actually be taken about the dynamic and not the static characteristic (Fig. 11.13). The slope of the latter is greater in a triode than that of the dynamic characteristic, as can be seen from Fig. 11.13. The dynamic characteristic is used to provide information about the output current or voltage while the valve is operating in a circuit.

Load Line

As we have just seen, when a valve is operating under class A conditions with a resistor load R, the input voltage V_i causes variations of anode current I_a. If the h.t. supply voltage is E, the anode voltage V_a fluctuates with the current I_a, since $V_a = E - I_a R$. This is the equation of a straight line for V_a and I_a. The variation of V_a with I_a is called the *load line* for the particular value of R. We shall see later that it is used for estimating a number of factors, such as the power supplied to the valve.

The load line is thus drawn across the static anode characteristics, whereas the dynamic characteristic is drawn across the static mutual characteristics. The following example illustrates how the load line is obtained:

The static anode characteristics of a triode are as shown (Fig. 11.14) for $V_g = 0$, -10, -20 V. The valve is used with an h.t. supply of 240 V, a grid-bias of -10 V, and a pure resistance load of 5,000 ohms. Draw the load line if the input has a peak voltage of 10 V, and obtain the maximum and minimum values of V_a and I_a when the valve is operating.

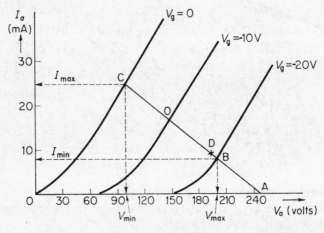

FIG. 11.14. Load line

From the load line equation, $V_a = E - I_a R$, when $I_a = 0$, $V_a = 240$ V. This corresponds to the point A.

When $I_a = 10$ mA, $V_a = 240 - I_a R = 190$ V. This corresponds to point D. In general $V_a = 240 - I_a R = 240 - 5,000 I_a$ represents a straight-line relation between I_a and V_a, and thus the two points A and D are all we require to draw the load line. Suppose it intersects $V_g = 0$, -10, -20 V curves at C, O, B respectively. Then O is the quiescent (no signal) point. When V_i is applied, the grid swings with a peak value of 10 V about this point, and I_a and V_a swing from values corresponding to C and B.

From the sketch shown,

$$I_{max} = 25 \text{ mA}, \quad I_{min} = 8 \text{ mA; swing} = 17\text{mA}$$
$$V_{max} = 200 \text{ V}, \quad V_{min} = 100 \text{ V; swing} = 100\text{V}$$

The Phase Relations between V_g, V_a, I_a.

So far we have considered only the magnitude of the output current and voltage in a.f. amplifiers. The *phase*, or sign, of the output compared with the input plays an important part in oscillators and in negative feedback, discussed later.

When a valve is operating with a resistance load in the anode circuit (Fig. 11.15 (i)) the actual voltage variation, V_g, on the grid is in phase with the variation of I_a in the load (Fig. 11.15 (ii), (iii)). As V_g increases so does I_a, and as V_g decreases I_a decreases.

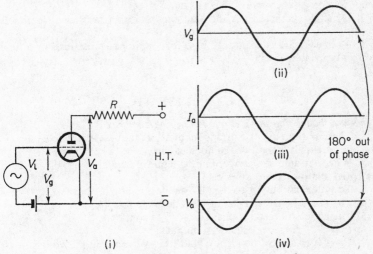

FIG. 11.15. Phase relations

Now $V_a = E - I_a R$ with a pure resistance load from above. As I_a increases, therefore, V_a decreases. As I_a decreases, V_a increases. Thus I_a and V_a are 180° *out of phase* with each other, which makes V_g and V_a 180° out of phase (Fig. 11.15 (ii), (iv)). We have already seen that voltage variations on the grid of a triode are equivalent to voltage variations of μ times that amount in the anode circuit. In addition to this we now know that the valve action changes the phase of the input voltage by 180° in the case of the pure resistance.

The phase difference between input and output voltage is also 180° when a tuned parallel combination of coil and capacitor is used in the anode circuit, as the impedance of the load then reduces to a pure resistance (L/Cr ohms). (See p. 172).

SUMMARY

1. The grid potential of a triode has a much greater control over the anode current than the anode potential.

2. $r_a = \dfrac{\text{change in } V_a}{\text{change in } I_a}$ (V_g constant). $g_m = \dfrac{\text{change in } I_a}{\text{change in } V_g}$ (V_a constant)

$\mu = \dfrac{\text{change in } V_a}{\text{change in } V_g}$ (to produce the same change in I_a),

the changes taking place on the straight portion of the characteristics in each case. $\mu = r_a \times g_m$.

3. Classes of amplifiers are distinguished by the operating point. (i) Class A amplification gives no distortion; but is inefficient. (ii) The distortion in class B amplification is eliminated by a 'push-pull' arrangement, and class B amplification is much more efficient than class A.

4. Dynamic characteristics and load lines are characteristics for particular anode loads.

5. V_a and V_g are 180° out of phase for a pure resistance load or a tuned coil and capacitor load.

EXERCISE 11

What are the missing words in the following statements 1–12?

1. The input circuit of a triode amplifier is the . . . -cathode circuit and the output circuit is the . . . -cathode circuit.

2. When an amplifier is working, the grid potential is usually at a . . . potential relative to the cathode.

3. To obtain an output voltage the anode circuit must have a . . .

4. The mutual characteristic of a triode is the I_a- . . . variation.

5. The anode characteristic is the I_a- . . . variation.

6. Class A bias provides an . . . output.

7. Class B bias corresponds to about the . . . value of grid voltage.

8. A . . . push-pull amplifier provides low power consumption.

9. The amplification factor of a valve concerns the ratio of a small change in . . . to a small change in . . .

10. The mutual conductance of a valve is the change in . . . divided by the change in . . . when the anode voltage is constant.

11. When a class A amplifier is driven by a grid signal of 1·4 V (r.m.s.), the grid bias should not be less than . . . V.

12. If the grid bias in a class A amplifier is 1·4 V, the grid signal must not be greater than . . . V (r.m.s.).

13. The resistance load of a class A amplifier is 10 kΩ, the battery supply is 150 V and the quiescent (no signal) current is 5 mA. What is the mean anode voltage when the amplifier is working?

14. In Qn. 13, the amplifier requires a grid-bias of 5 V. Calculate the cathode resistance needed for self-bias. What is the least bypass-capacitance required if the reactance at 100 Hz is to be 2% of the cathode resistance?

15. A valve with a 10 kΩ resistor as a load has a battery supply of 120 V. (i) At what anode current does the anode voltage become theoretically zero? (ii) At what anode voltage is the anode current theoretically zero? (iii) Draw a sketch of the load line, labelling the axes and the points used to draw the line.

16. A three-electrode valve has the following static characteristics:

Grid voltage	+2·5	0	−2·5	−5	−7·5	−10
Anode current in mA with 120 V h.t.	7·00	6·35	5·40	4·45	3·5	2·55
Anode current in mA with 80 V h.t.	4·75	3·80	2·85	1·90	1·0	0·50

Plot the characteristic grid voltage-anode current curves, and determine the internal impedance at zero grid voltage, the amplification factor and mutual conductance. (*C. & G.*)

17. What is the meaning and significance of the mutual conductance of a three-electrode thermionic valve? If the valve has an amplification factor of 30 and an impedance of 20,000 ohms, what is its mutual conductance?
(*C. & G.*)

18. Outline the functions of the electrodes in a triode valve when used as an amplifier and explain the process of amplification. Define the terms *mutual conductance* and *anode a.c. resistance*.

Derive an expression for the amplification of a single-stage triode valve amplifier with resistance as anode load. (See also p. 216.) (*C. & G.*)

19. The following readings were taken on a three-electrode valve. Plot the characteristic grid voltage-anode current curves, and determine the internal impedance at zero grid voltage, the amplification factor, and mutual conductance.

Grid voltage	0	−2	−4	−6	−8	−12	−14	−16	−17
Anode current in mA									
(a) with 130 V h.t.	15	13	11	9	7	3	1·5	0·7	0·2
(b) with 100 V h.t.	10	8	6	4	2	0·4	0·1	—	—

(*C. & G.*)

20. The following values of anode current were obtained with a triode:

Anode voltage	25	50	75	100
Anode current in mA with grid voltage = 0 V	0·4	2·8	6·0	8·5
Anode current in mA with grid voltage = −4 V	0	0·6	3·0	5·7
Anode current in mA with grid voltage = −8 V	0	0	1·0	2·9

Plot the anode current-anode voltage characteristic curves. If a battery of 150 volts and a resistance of 15,000 ohms are connected in series with the anode and cathode, what will be the anode current at the above three values of grid voltage? (*C. & G.*)

21. Describe two methods of obtaining a grid-bias voltage, and explain how the grid-bias value is found in each case.

22. 'In class A amplification the anode current variation consists of an a.c. and a d.c. component.' Explain this statement, drawing sketches to illustrate your answer. What is the advantage and disadvantage of class B amplification?

23. What do you understand by class A and class B amplification? Draw sketches to illustrate each operation, and state their main features.

24. Draw a sketch of a class B 'push-pull' arrangement for obtaining an undistorted output, and explain its action. What is the advantage of such an arrangement over class A amplification?

25. Plot the characteristics in Qn. 20 and draw the load line when a battery supply of 120 V and a load resistor of 10 kΩ is used. From it obtain (i) the quiescent (no signal current), (ii) the maximum and minimum currents if the grid swing is 4 V.

26. Plot the characteristics in Qn. 19 and draw on them part of the dynamic resistance when a battery supply of 150 V and resistor 10 kΩ load are used.

12. A.F. Amplifiers. Couplings

In general, any complete electronic circuit consists of an active electronic device, such as a transistor or triode valve, together with suitable components such as resistors, capacitors and inductors. Electronic devices such as transistors or valves can be usefully represented as an *a.c. generator* with an internal a.c. resistance.

Valve as A.C. Generator

Consider an alternating or signal voltage of r.m.s. value V_i applied between grid and cathode of a valve operating under class A conditions (Fig. 12.1 (i)). If the μ of the valve is 30 and the grid potential changes by 0·1 volt, the change of anode current would be the same as if a change of $30 \times 0·1$ V were made in the *anode* circuit. This follows

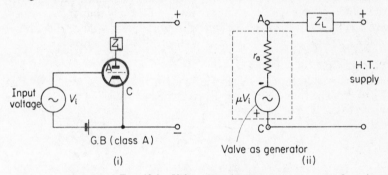

FIG. 12.1. Valve as a.c. generator

from the definition of μ. If we now consider the alternating voltage V_i applied to the grid, then this causes the same changes of anode current that an alternating voltage $\mu \times V_i$ would make operating in the anode circuit. Under these class A conditions we regard the valve as a generator of alternating voltage μV_i operating in the anode circuit, with an internal resistance equal to r_a, the a.c. or slope resistance (Fig. 12.1 (ii)). The phase of V_i is changed by 180° when its effect in the anode circuit is considered and the sign of μV_i should thus be minus (see Fig. 11.15). As we shall only need numerical results here, this will be ignored.

Equivalent Valve Circuit

When a valve is used as a 'voltage amplifier', the voltage concerned is only the *alternating* component across the load in the output or anode circuit (p. 216). Suppose a load Z_L is used, as shown. Since Z_L is usually of the order of thousands of ohms, the small internal resistance of the h.t.-supply can be ignored. Thus one end of Z_L is joined to the

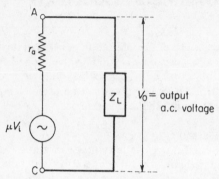

FIG. 12.2. Valve equivalent circuit

cathode C from an a.c. point of view. The other end is joined to A, the anode. From an a.c. point of view, Fig. 12.2 is thus the *equivalent valve circuit*. It is an a.c. circuit with an applied voltage μV_i and r_a and Z_L in series. The output a.c. voltage V_0 is that across Z_L.

Voltage Gain

Consider a *resistance R* as the load in the anode circuit, so that $Z_L = R$. The total circuit resistance is then $(R + r_a)$. The a.c. voltage V_0 across R is thus given by

$$V_0 = \frac{R}{R + r_a} \times \mu V_i = \frac{\mu R}{R + r_a} \cdot V_i$$

$$\therefore \frac{V_0}{V_i} = \frac{\mu R}{R + r_a}$$

The ratio V_0/V_i is the ratio of the output to the input a.c. voltage. It is thus the *voltage gain*, A_V. Thus

$$A_V = \frac{\mu R}{R + r_a} \tag{1}$$

As an example, suppose $V_i = 0\cdot1$ V (r.m.s.), $\mu = 30$, $r_a = 20{,}000\ \Omega$, and the load $R = 40{,}000\ \Omega$. Then

$$A_V = \frac{30 \times 40{,}000}{60{,}000} = 20 \quad \text{and} \quad V_0 = 20 \times 0\cdot1 = 2\ \text{V (r.m.s.)}$$

If the resistance load is increased to $80{,}000\ \Omega$, then

$$A_V = \frac{30 \times 80{,}000}{100{,}000} = 24$$

Theoretically, therefore, it appears that increasing R will increase the magnitude of the A_V. This can be seen from (1), since A_V is practically equal to μ when R becomes very large compared to r_a. In practice, however, R cannot be increased beyond a certain value owing to the potential drop existing across it. Thus if the h.t. supply is 120 V and the average anode current (the d.c. component) is 2 mA when the valve operates, the average anode potential, V_a, for $R = 40,000 \, \Omega$ is $120 - 80 = 40$ volts. Owing to the variation of V_a during the input cycle, the curved part of the dynamic characteristic may be reached, with consequent distortion of the output. Hence the valve cannot operate properly with a very large load.

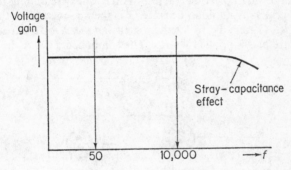

FIG. 12.3. Voltage gain and frequency

The voltage gain-frequency curve is obtained for a given load when the frequency, f, of the given input is varied. The gain is independent of f from equation (1), i.e. it is constant for different frequencies, and the graph should therefore be a straight line parallel to the frequency-axis. Theoretically, then, audio-frequencies between $f = 0$ and $f = 10,000$ Hz are amplified to the same degree by a pure resistance load, and no distortion occurs. This is the great advantage of a resistance load, which is therefore in the anode circuits of high-fidelity a.f. amplifiers. At frequencies above 10 kHz, however, the stray capacitance of the circuit will shunt some of the a.c. in the anode current, and the gain will diminish (Fig. 12.3).

Valve Couplings

A valve is not a single component on its own in a radio circuit. When the circuit is operating the valve must hand on its output to another, which in turn hands on its output to the next valve, and so on until the end of the circuit is reached. In the case of a radio receiver, for example, the aerial is the beginning and the loudspeaker the end of the circuit inside it, and between them are valves 'coupled' one to the other. There are various standard methods of valve coupling. The common feature is that the output of one valve must be handed to the grid-cathode of the next in order to utilise the amplification property of the valve.

Resistance-capacitance (R-C) Coupling

Valve 1 in Fig. 12.4 represents an a.f. amplifier valve operating under class A conditions, with a pure resistance load R in its anode circuit and an input V_i applied to its grid. In order to hand on the alternating voltage developed across R, a connection must be made from R to the grid of the succeeding valve 2. A piece of wire joining the anode A to the grid G is no good because G is then connected to the h.t. $+$ through R. G must be isolated from the anode A by a capacitor C_g; the negative bias is applied via R_g. The components C_g, R_g in Fig. 12.4

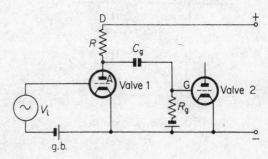

FIG. 12.4.   *R-C* coupling

are known as the *coupling capacitor* and *coupling resistance*, and the voltage across R_g is handed on to valve 2.

At this point it is important to realise that we are concerned with passing on *alternating* voltages developed across R to the grid-cathode circuit of the next valve. In order to see the matter in its true perspective, an equivalent valve circuit for a.c. voltages is essential. Fig. 12.5 is the whole equivalent circuit, and that for valve 1 is enclosed by the dotted lines. The h.t. and g.b. do not concern us here. So far as a.c. is concerned, one plate of C_g is connected to A (see Fig. 12.5) and one end of R_g is connected to D via the small internal resistance of the g.b. and h.t. batteries shown. Thus, as represented in Fig. 12.5, C_g and R_g *are in series across* R *from an a.c. viewpoint.*

Suppose that R_g is much greater than R, so that C_g and R_g have negligible shunting effect on R. Then, as already deduced, the a.c. voltage V_R, across $R = \mu R/(R + r_a) \times V_i =$ the a.c. voltage across AD in Fig. 12.5.

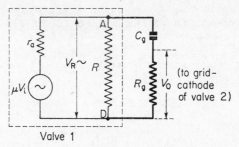

FIG. 12.5.   Effect of C_g-R_g

But C_g and R_g are in series across R.

$$\therefore \text{ the voltage, } V_0, \text{ across } R_g = \frac{R_g}{Z} \text{ of } V_R,$$

where $Z = \sqrt{R_g^2 + X_C^2}$, X_C being the reactance of the coupling capacitor C_g (Fig. 12.5).

$$\therefore V_0 = \frac{R_g}{\sqrt{R_g^2 + X_C^2}} \times V_R$$

$$\therefore \frac{V_0}{V_i} = \frac{R_g}{\sqrt{R_g^2 + X_C^2}} \times A_V \text{ for load of valve 1.}$$

The ratio $\dfrac{\text{output voltage to valve 2}}{\text{input voltage to valve 1}}$ is known as the *stage-gain* of the circuit arrangement of Fig. 12.4. Thus

$$\text{stage-gain} = \frac{V_0}{V_i} = \frac{R_g}{\sqrt{R_g^2 + X_C^2}} \times A_V \qquad (1)$$

Stage-gain

The stage-gain is a more practical ratio for voltage amplification than voltage gain, A_V. The voltage gain A_V by itself is never concerned in the output available for the next value, because coupling components are always required.

Equation (1) shows that the stage-gain depends on the magnitudes of C_g and R_g, the coupling components. From Fig. 12.5, R_g and C_g may be regarded as an a.c. potential divider for V_R. Thus V_0 will be large if R_g is large compared to the reactance X_C of C_g. Further, since $X_C = 1/2\pi fC$, the stage-gain will vary with the frequency amplified. From (1), it follows that the stage-gain is low if X_C is large. Thus low frequencies are not amplified as much as high frequencies and this may lead to frequency distortion of the a.f. voltage input of valve 1.

As a numerical illustration, suppose the minimum stage-gain permissible is 70% of the voltage gain when the frequency falls to 100 Hz.

Now it can be seen that

$$\frac{R_g}{\sqrt{R_g{}^2 + X_C{}^2}} = \frac{1}{\sqrt{2}} = 70\% \quad \text{when} \quad X_C = R_g$$

$$\therefore \frac{1}{2\pi f C_g} = R_g \text{ when } f = 100 \text{ Hz}$$

$C_g = 0{\cdot}05 \ \mu\text{F}$, $R_g = 0{\cdot}25 \ \text{M}\Omega$ are suitable values for a.f. amplifiers. In this case, when $f = 1{,}000$ Hz,

$$X_C = \frac{1}{2\pi \times 1{,}000 \times \dfrac{0{\cdot}05}{10^6}} = 3{,}200 \ \Omega$$

$$\therefore \text{ stage-gain} = \frac{R_g}{\sqrt{R_g{}^2 + X_C{}^2}} \times A_V \frac{250{,}000}{\sqrt{250{,}000^2 + 3{,}200^2}} \times A_V$$

$$= 99\% \text{ of } A_V.$$

Frequency-response

The frequency-response curve of an R–C coupled a.f. amplifier is shown in Fig. 12.6 (i). It represents stage-gain plotted against the various frequencies. Even response is obtained for practically the whole

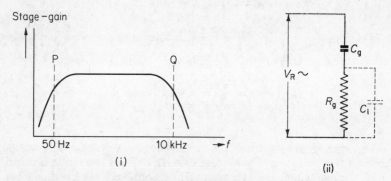

FIG. 12.6.   Frequency response

of the a.f. range, and this is therefore the type of coupling used for high-fidelity a.f. amplification.

The curve falls off at P for the lower frequencies because X_C is large at these frequencies. It also falls off at Q for the higher frequencies for the following reason: Although it was omitted previously from the equivalent valve circuits, the grid circuit of valve 2 reflects a capacitance, C_i, of the order of 50 to 250 pF across R (Fig. 12.6

(ii)). C_i is known as the 'input-capacitance' of valve 2, and is in parallel with R_g as shown.

At low frequencies C_i has a very large reactance and its effect may be neglected. At the high audio frequencies, however, its reactance is considerably decreased, and this reduces the effective load impedance of the preceding valve and its gain. The voltage V_0 obtained across R_g is thus diminished, and the stage-gain is lower at Q on the frequency-response curve.

Transformer Coupling

Transformer coupling between two valves 1 and 2 is illustrated in Fig. 12.7. It should be noted that no actual contact is made to the anode circuit of valve 1 as was done with R–C coupling. The alternating voltages are transferred to the secondary by the process of electro-magnetic induction, and no coupling capacitor or resistance is required

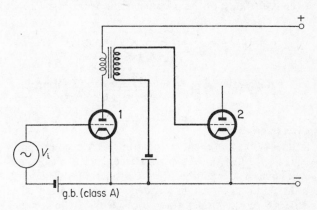

FIG. 12.7.   Transformer coupling

to hand them on to the grid-cathode circuit of valve 2. The advantage of transformer coupling is that the resistance of the primary coil is relatively small, so that the d.c. potential drop across it is low. This means that practically the full d.c. potential of the h.t. supply is available for the anode of valve 1. With R–C coupling, however, which employs a resistance load of the order of thousands of ohms, the d.c. potential drop is relatively high.

If the impedance in the secondary circuit is infinite, the output voltage, V_0, obtained across its windings = T × voltage across load in primary, where T is the turns ratio of the transformer. In practice this is only an approximate relation, as the input-capacitance of valve 2 is across the secondary.

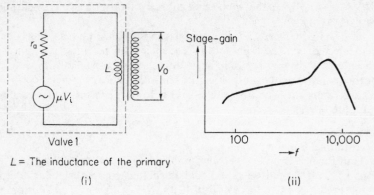

L = The inductance of the primary

(i)   (ii)

FIG. 12.8. Equivalent circuit

If L is the inductance of the primary, then, from Fig. 12.8 (i),

$$V_0 = \frac{\mu X_L V_i}{\sqrt{R_a^2 + X_L^2}} \times T \text{ (approx)}$$

$$\therefore \text{ stage-gain} = \frac{V_0}{V_i} = \frac{\mu X_L}{\sqrt{R_a^2 + X_L^2}} \times T \text{ (approx)}$$

Frequency-response

The frequency-response curve for transformer coupling is shown roughly in Fig. 12.8 (ii). At higher frequencies, resonance in the secondary increases the amplification considerably. The curve shows low-note loss, and at very high frequencies the shunting effect of the self-capacitance of the transformer turns tends to lower the voltage amplification. On account of the self-capacitance, the turns-ratio, T, is usually never more than about 4:1. An R–C-coupled amplifier has a much more even response to all the frequencies in the audible range (p. 232).

SUMMARY

1. The voltage gain obtained with a resistance load R is $\mu R/(r_a + R)$, because the valve acts as a generator of e.m.f. μV_i and internal resistance r_a.

2. The resistance load is used for high-fidelity a.f. amplification; the anode d.c. potential is less than the h.t. value by the potential drop.

3. R–C and transformer couplings may be used for a.f. amplifiers. In R–C coupling, the coupling capacitor C_g must have a low reactance compared to R_g, so that most of the output a.c. voltage is developed across R_g.

EXERCISE 12

What are the missing words in the statements 1–8?

1. Under class A conditions, a valve with an applied signal 0·01 V (r.m.s.) and an amplification factor 20 acts as an equivalent a.c. generator of e.m.f . . .

2. In Qn. 1, the internal impedance of the generator may be considered to be the . . . of the valve.

3. If the a.c. impedance of a valve is 20 kΩ and the amplification factor is 12, the voltage amplification or gain with a load of 10 kΩ is . . .

4. A coupling capacitor between two amplifier stages isolates the high-tension voltage from the . . . of the next valve.

5. In *R–C* coupling, a coupling resistor provides the . . . for the next valve.

6. With transformer coupling, practically the full . . . is applied to the anode.

7. With transformer coupling, the . . . of the primary shunts the very high frequencies and so the stage-gain is . . . than at the middle frequencies.

8. With *R–C* coupling, the low-frequency drop in amplification is due to the . . .

9. A valve has an amplification factor of 30 and a mutual conductance of 2 mA/V. Calculate the voltage amplification with a resistance load of 10,000 Ω.

10. The amplification factor of a valve is 40 and the a.c. resistance is 20 kΩ. Find the voltage gain with a resistor load of 12 kΩ.

11. Explain fully why the voltage gain with a resistance load *R* in a valve of amplification μ and a.c. resistance r_a is $\mu R/(r_a + R)$ under certain conditions.

12. The slope of the I_a–V_g curve of a triode is 1·2 mA/V, and that of the

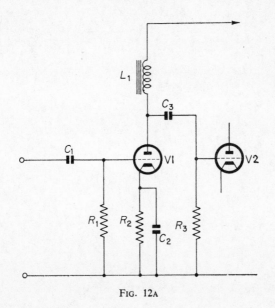

FIG. 12A

I_a–V_a curve is 0·20 mA/V. Calculate the voltage gain obtained with this valve when the load resistance is 10,000 ohms.

13. A triode amplifier has an a.c. resistance of 20,000 ohms and an amplification factor of 20. Calculate the voltage obtained across the anode load if it is (a) a resistance of 30,000 ohms, (b) an inductor of 5 H, the frequency of the input voltage, 0·1 V, being 2 kHz.

14. An R–C coupled amplifier has $\mu = 30$, an a.c. impedance of 20 kΩ, and a resistance load of 30 kΩ. The coupling capacitor is 0·02 μF and the grid resistor of the second stage is 0·2 megohm. Calculate (i) the voltage gain at a frequency of 1,000 Hz, (ii) the low frequency when the stage-gain drops to half that at middle frequencies.

15. What is the function of a coupling capacitor? Explain how the values of C_g, R_g affect the voltage delivered to the next valve in R–C coupling.

16. Draw an equivalent circuit diagram for the inductor-capacitor coupled audio-frequency amplifier shown in Fig. 12A at low, middle and high frequencies.

By reference to gain-frequency response curves, briefly discuss the relative advantages and disadvantages of (a) resistor-capacitor, (b) transformer-coupled audio-frequency valve amplifiers. (C. & G.)

17. Describe, with circuit diagrams, the principles of action of transformer-coupled, and resistance-coupled audio-frequency amplifiers. How do the characteristics of each type vary with frequency? (C. & G.)

13: Transistors and Amplifiers

Transistor

In the chapter on *semiconductors*, p. 201, it was explained that an impurity semiconductor of the p-type contained majority carriers which were *holes* or positive charges. An impurity semiconductor of the n-type contained majority carriers which were *electrons* or negative charges. Bardeen and Brattain in America found in 1948 that p- and n-type semiconductors, suitably arranged, could produce current gain, or act as a *current amplifier*. They called the arrangement a *transistor*.

In 1950 Shockley invented the *junction transistor*, which is the type widely used today. Basically, it consists of two similar semiconductor regions such as p-type with a very thin region of the opposite or n-type between them, Fig. 13.1 (i). This is called a 'p-n-p transistor'. A 'n-p-n'

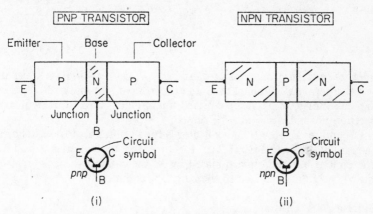

FIG. 13.1.   Transistors

transistor consists of two n-type semiconductor regions with a very thin p-type region between them, Fig. 13.1 (ii). The circuit symbols for both types of transistors are shown. The arrow represents the direction of the holes (positive charges) when the transistors are used, as explained shortly.

Forward-bias and Reverse-bias

A p-n-p transistor has two p-n junctions back-to-back. If a battery V_{EB} is joined with its positive terminal to the p-semiconductor E and its negative terminal to the n-semiconductor B, the p-n junction concerned is then *forward-biased* by the battery, Fig. 13.2 (i). This p-semiconductor is called the *emitter*, E, of the transistor because it then 'emits' holes towards the n-semiconductor, which is called the *base*, B, of the transistor. The p-semiconductor on the right, the third semiconductor of the transistor, is called the *collector*, C, since it collects most of the holes emitted by E, as explained shortly. *The*

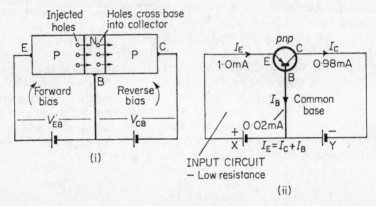

FIG. 13.2. Transistor circuit

collector and base are reverse-biased by the battery V_{CB}, that is, its negative terminal is joined to C and its positive terminal to B. Unless the collector-base is reverse-biased in circuits, transistors will not function normally and may be ruined.

The emitter E, base B and collector C for a p-n-p transistor are shown diagrammatically in Fig. 13.2 (ii) together with the batteries X and Y. The emitter-base is forward-biased by X, the collector-base is reverse-biased by Y, and the lead to the base B is common.

Currents in Transistor

Since the emitter-base p-n junction is forward-biased, the majority carriers or holes (+ve charges) flow, or are injected, into the base from the emitter, Fig. 13.2 (i). Some of the holes recombine with the majority electrons in the base. Others are diverted towards the base terminal, where they combine with electrons flowing along the wire. The base is deliberately made extremely thin in manufacture, and the collector area is made large, so practically all the holes come under the attractive influence of the p.d. V_{CB} applied to the collector-base, since this is reverse-biased. The great majority of holes then flow into the collector. Thus a collector current, I_C, is obtained which is nearly equal to the emitter current, I_E. In a particular transistor with suitable p.d.s, for example, I_E is 1·00 mA and I_C is 0·98 mA, Fig. 13.2 (ii).

The difference between the emitter and collector currents, 0.02 mA, is the base current, I_B, from Kirchhoff's first law (p. 26). It is small compared with the emitter or collector currents. Generally,

$$I_E = I_C + I_B$$

Input and Output Circuits. Slope (A.C.) Resistance

In the transistor arrangement shown in Fig. 13.2 (ii), which is not the only arrangement, the emitter-base is the *input circuit*, that is, a signal or varying current is applied here. The collector-base is the *output circuit*, that is, the output varying current is obtained here.

As in the case of the radio valve, it is important to distinguish between the circuit and transistor under steady or d.c. conditions, when no signal is received, and the circuit and transistor under varying or a.c. conditions, when a signal is applied or received. The d.c. resistance of the emitter-base circuit is V_{EB}/I_E. Under a.c. conditions, the *input resistance* or *slope resistance*, r_i, is $\Delta V_{EB}/\Delta I_E$, where ΔV_{EB} and ΔI_E are the small changes in p.d. and current under the signal conditions ('Δ' means 'a small increase in'). Likewise, the d.c. resistance of the collector-base circuit is V_{CB}/I_C but in estimating the output signal, the slope or a.c. *output resistance* r_o, $\Delta V_{CB}/\Delta I_C$, is used.

It may be noted that as the emitter-base circuit in Fig. 13.2 is forward-biased it has a low resistance. The collector-base circuit is reverse-biased and has a high resistance. A current is thus transferred from a low- to a high-resistance circuit, which is the origin of the name 'transistor'.

Characteristics

The suitability of a transistor for a particular circuit can be judged from its characteristic curves. Fig 13.3 shows apparatus for determining

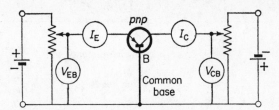

FIG. 13.3   Circuit for characteristic

experimentally the characteristics of a p-n-p transistor used in a *common-base* (CB) arrangement, that is, the base is common to the input and output circuits. The most important are (1) *the output characteristics*, I_C v. V_{CB} (collector-base voltage) for different constant emitter currents, I_E, (2) the *input characteristics*, I_E v. V_{EB} (emitter-base voltage) for different constant collector voltages, V_C.

Output Characteristics

The experimental results for typical output characteristics are shown in Fig. 13.4 (i). The curves show that at first, in the region OA, the collector current increases rapidly, but after a fraction of one volt

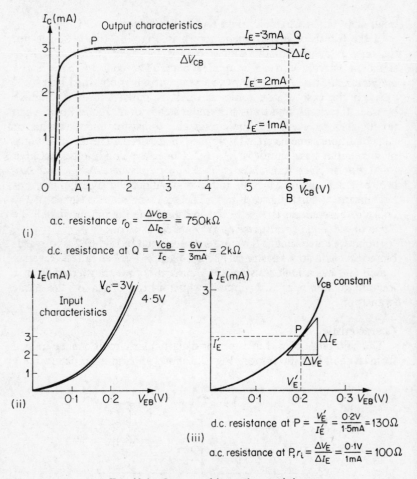

a.c. resistance $r_0 = \dfrac{\Delta V_{CB}}{\Delta I_C} = 750\,\text{k}\Omega$

(i)

d.c. resistance at Q $= \dfrac{V_{CB}}{I_c} = \dfrac{6V}{3mA} = 2\,\text{k}\Omega$

(ii)

d.c. resistance at P $= \dfrac{V'_E}{I'_E} = \dfrac{0.2V}{1.5mA} = 130\,\Omega$

(iii)

a.c. resistance at P, $r_i = \dfrac{\Delta V_E}{\Delta I_E} = \dfrac{0.1V}{1mA} = 100\,\Omega$

Fig. 13.4. Output and input characteristics

the current rises very slowly and uniformly in the region AB. Along AB a fairly constant collector current is thus produced as the p.d. changes. This is due to the fact that the collector current depends mainly on the emitter current and not on the collector p.d., as explained on p. 238.

The flat part of the characteristic such as PQ represents a slope or a.c. resistance, $\Delta V_{CB}/\Delta I_C$, of about 1 megohm for low-power transistors. The transistor generally has a high output resistance, r_0, when functioning as an amplifier under signal conditions. Thus with a given r.m.s. input signal value, V_i, the r.m.s. value of the output (collector) current is independent of the resistor load used in the collector circuit. Hence, with particular d.c. conditions the *transistor can be treated as an alternating current generator when a signal is applied.*

Input Characteristics

A typical input characteristic or I_E v. V_{EB} curve is shown in Fig. 13.4 (ii). The curve is practically independent of V_C, the collector voltage, as illustrated. The d.c. resistance, V'_{EB}/I'_E, is of the same order of magnitude as the incremental or a.c. resistance r_i, $\Delta V_{EB}/\Delta I_E$, when the transistor is operating under signal conditions, Fig. 13.4 (iii). This is not the case, however, in the output or collector-base circuit. Here the collector-base path may have a d.c. resistance of 2 kilohms but an a.c. resistance r_0 of 750 kilohms, for example. As the input characteristic curve in Fig. 13.4 (iii) is non-linear, the magnitude of the a.c. resistance depends on the d.c. operating point such as P, for example. It becomes larger as I_E is reduced.

The transistor a.c. parameters above, r_i and r_0, are often known as the *small signal parameters* because they operate only over a small part of the characteristics. Large signals may be dealt with by graphical methods.

Current Relations. Transfer Ratio

We have already seen (p. 239) that the emitter, collector and base currents are related, from Kirchhoff's first law by

$$I_E = I_C + I_B.$$

Fig. 13.5 shows the I_C v. I_E or *current transfer characteristic* for a given collector voltage. From a signal or a.c. point of view, an important ratio is the *current transfer ratio*, α. This is defined as the ratio $\Delta I_C/\Delta I_E$, where 'Δ' represents 'small change in'. Since the collector voltage V_C is maintained constant, this can be written.

$$\alpha = \frac{\Delta I_C}{\Delta I_E} (V_C \text{ constant})$$

The symbol h_{fb} is also used in place of α and is called a *hybrid parameter* (see p. 260).

For all transistors, α is typically about 0·98. The fairly straight line characteristic in Fig. 13.5 shows that, for most practical d.c. calculations, $\alpha = I_C/I_E$ or $I_C = \alpha I_E$. Thus the base current,

$$I_B = I_E - I_C = (1 - \alpha)I_E$$

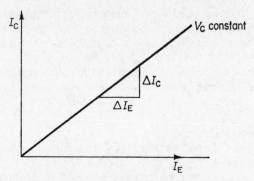

FIG. 13.5. Current transfer ratio

For the transistor above, where $\alpha = 0.98$, then $I_B = 0.02 I_E$. Hence if $I_E = 2$ mA, $I_B = 0.02 \times 2 = 0.04$ mA $= 40\,\mu$A.

Common-base (CB) Amplifier

We now consider the a.f. small signal amplification produced by a transistor. Fig. 13.6 shows a simple 'common-base (CB) amplifier', so called because the base is common to the input (emitter-base) circuit

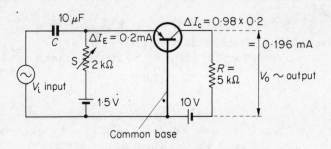

FIG. 13.6. Common-base (CB) amplifier

and the output (collector-base) circuit. The emitter-base is forward-biased by a 1·5 V battery and a potentiometer S, used as a variable resistor, is adjusted to provide a suitable emitter current. The collector circuit is reverse-biased by a 10 V supply, for example, and has a load resistor R of 5 kilohms.

A small alternating voltage V_i is applied as the input or signal voltage, as shown, *via* a large capacitor C such as $10\,\mu$F. The reactance of C at 1,000 Hz is only about 16 ohms and offers an easy path to a.c. but blocks any d.c.

Voltage Amplification

In Fig. 13.6, suppose that S is adjusted so that the steady collector current, I_C, is 1·0 mA, the emitter current I_E is 1·02 mA and the base current I_B is 0·02 mA. The voltage drop in R is then 5 kΩ × 1 mA or 5 V. Thus (10 V − 5 V) or 5 V of reverse-bias is applied between collector and base. Now consider the effect of the a.c. signal.

From the slope of the input characteristic, suppose the input resistance $\Delta V_{EB}/\Delta I_E$ is 50 ohms. If the peak voltage of V_i is 10 mV, then the peak value of the input current = 10 mV/50 Ω = 0·2 mA. The peak value of the consequent changes in collector current = α × peak value of input current = 0·98 × 0·2 mA = 0·196 mA, Fig. 13.6. This produces a peak voltage change across the load R. Thus

output voltage peak = 0·196 mA × 5,000 Ω = 980 millivolts

∴ voltage amplification A_V of circuit

$$= \frac{\text{output voltage peak}}{\text{input voltage peak}}$$

$$= \frac{980 \text{ mV}}{10 \text{ mV}} = 98$$

Generally, if r_i is the input resistance, and V_o and V_i are the peak or r.m.s. output and input voltages respectively, then

$$A_V = \frac{V_o}{V_i} = \frac{\Delta I_C \cdot R}{\Delta I_E \cdot r_i} = \frac{\alpha R}{r_i}$$

Variation of α with Frequency

If the frequency of an applied signal is very high, the reversals of emitter current in a transistor may have a period of the same order as the transit time for charges to cross from emitter to collector. In this case the diffusion current through the transistor cannot keep pace with the input current variation. Consequently, the full effect of a change in input current is not reproduced in the output current and the current gain α is now less than its low frequency value. This effect is equivalent to a capacitance at the input called the *diffusion capacitance*, C_D. It should not be confused with the 'depletion capacitance', described on p. 204, which is much less than the diffusion capacitance. Transistors for a.f. amplifiers may have relatively high values of C_D such as 2,000 pF; some r.f. transistors may have values as low as 50 pF.

It is thus important to appreciate that α *decreases appreciably at high frequencies*. The frequency at which it falls to $1/\sqrt{2}$ (0·71) of its low frequency value is called the 'alpha cut-off frequency' and denoted by $f_{\alpha co}$. A small base width produces a smaller transit time and hence a higher value of $f_{\alpha co}$, which is an advantage. The higher mobility of free electrons also reduces the transit time. Thus n-p-n transistors usually have higher values of $f_{\alpha co}$ than p-n-p types. In judging the suitability of a transistor for a particular circuit, its frequency cut-off value should always be noted from the manufacturer's details.

Common-emitter Amplifier

On p. 238 we saw that the base current, I_B, is small when a transistor is functioning, for example $I_B = 0.02 \text{ mA}$, and that the collector current, I_C, is relatively large, for example $I_C = 0.98 \text{ mA}$. A current amplification of $0.98/0.02$ or 49 will then occur if a transistor circuit is arranged to use *base* current as the 'input' current. This is much more advantageous than using the emitter current as the input current; the ratio I_C/I_E is only 0.98 in this case (p. 238).

The most common type of amplifier circuit is thus the *common-emitter* (*CE*) circuit, so called because the emitter is common to the base and collector circuits, as shown in Fig. 13.7 (i), (ii). The input

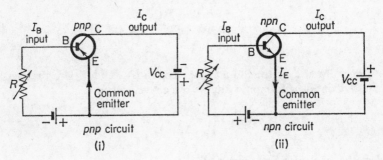

FIG. 13.7. Common-emitter (CE) amplifier

circuit is the base-emitter circuit; the output circuit is the collector-emitter circuit. The common-emitter circuit is widely used for a.f. or r.f. amplifiers or oscillators and will therefore be considered in some detail.

Characteristics

Fig. 13.8 shows a circuit for investigating the characteristic curves of a common-emitter arrangement. P and Q are potentiometers of 1 kΩ and 5 kΩ resistance respectively, for example, with 1·5 V and 4·5 V batteries across them. The voltmeter V_1 for measuring the base-emitter voltage V_{BE} should be preferably a d.c. valve-voltmeter type capable of reading p.d.s in steps of 50 mV. The current meter I_B should be a microammeter. The voltmeter V_2 for measurement of V_{CE}, collector-emitter voltage, should have a very high resistance; preferably, a d.c. valve voltmeter (p. 192) should be used. The current meter for measuring the collector current I_C should be capable of reading current in steps of 0·1 mA.

Before connecting the batteries, make sure that the potentiometers P and Q are turned to provide zero voltage initially.

I_C v. V_{CE} (I_B *constant*). Keeping I_B zero, vary V_{CE} from 0 to 4·5V in convenient steps of voltage and record each time the collector current, I_C. Tabulate the results. Repeat with I_B at 10, 20, 30 and 40 μA respectively. Draw the curves on graph paper of I_C v. V_{CE}, labelling

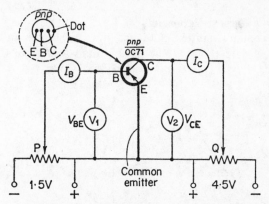

FIG. 13.8.   Circuit for common-emitter characteristic

each with the particular constant value of I_B. They are *output characteristics*.

I_B v. V_{BE} (V_{CE} *constant*), Make V_{BE} and V_{CE} both zero. Now increase V_{BE} to 0·25 V in steps of 50 mV, noting I_B at each setting. Repeat with V_{CE} at 4·5V. Draw the curves of I_B v. V_{BE} at $V_{CE} = 0$ and $V_{CE} = 4·5$ V respectively. Note the effect of V_{CE} on the I_B v. V_{BE} curve, which is an *input characteristic*.

I_C v. I_{BE} (V_{CE} *constant*). Set V_{CE} at 4·5 V. Increase I_B from 0 to 100 μA in steps of 20 μA and note each time the collector current I_C. Draw the graph of I_C v. I_B (V_{CE} constant), which is a *current transfer characteristic*.

Voltage and Current Gain

To obtain the order of magnitude of the current gain in the circuit of Fig. 13.8, set the potentiometer Q to give a maximum reading and connect a 2·2 kΩ–$\frac{1}{4}$ W resistor in series with the collector lead from the meter I_C to the potentiometer. Adjust I_B so that $I_C = 1$ mA and note the value of I_B. Increase V_{BE} by 20 mV and observe the new values of I_B and I_C. The ratio of the changes of current, $\Delta I_C / \Delta I_B$, is a measure of the current gain.

To obtain a measure of the voltage gain, (i) observe V_{CE}, (ii) reduce

V_{BE} by 20 mV and observe the increase ΔV_{CE} in V_{CE}. The ratio of the changes in voltage $\Delta V_{CE}/\Delta V_{BE}$, gives the order of the voltage gain.

The effect of *temperature change* on transistor operation can be shown by disconnecting the base in the circuit of Fig. 13.8 and using a microammeter for I_C. Grasp the transistor between the finger and thumb so that it becomes warm, and observe how the collector current suddenly increases. Transistors must be stabilized for temperature changes (p. 254).

Characteristic Curves. Parameters

Typical common-emitter characteristics are shown in Fig. 13.9. The input (I_B v. V_{BE}) and mutual (I_C v. V_{BE}) curves show the inherent

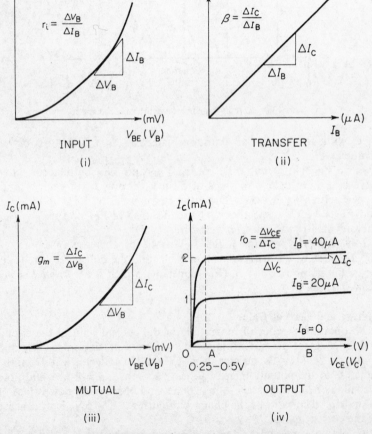

FIG. 13.9. Characteristic curves. Parameters

non-linearity of the transistor as a voltage operated device, Fig. 13.9 (i), (iii). The current transfer (I_C v. I_B) characteristic, however, is linear, Fig. 13.9 (ii). It shows that when used as an amplifier, the transistor should be driven from a constant current signal source.

The a.c. *input resistance*, r_i, is defined by the ratio

$$r_i = \frac{\Delta V_{BE}}{\Delta I_B} \ (V_{CE} \text{ constant})$$

As the input characteristic is non-linear, the magnitude of r_i depends on the particular voltage V_{BE}, and is of the order of kilohms, Fig. 13.9 (i).

A *mutual conductance* value, g_m, is given by the ratio

$$g_m = \frac{\Delta I_C}{\Delta V_{BE}} \ (V_{CE} \text{ constant})$$

and may be obtained from the mutual characteristic, Fig. 13.9 (iii).

When the transistor is operated as an amplifier, *the variations in output voltage are kept to the right* of the 'knee' of the output characteristics, Fig. 13.9 (iv), so as to provide an undistorted output. Observe that, when $I_B = 0$, some collector current flows. As I_B is increased, the collector current I_C increases for a given voltage V_{CE}. The a.c. *output resistance*, r_0, is defined by the ratio

$$r_0 = \frac{\Delta V_{CE}}{\Delta I_C} \ (I_B \text{ constant})$$

Thus if $\Delta V_{CE} = 4$ V and $\Delta I_C = 0.05$ mA, $r_0 = 4$ V/0.05 mA = 80,000 ohms.

Current Transfer Ratio

We have already seen that the base current, $I_B = I_E - I_C$ and that I_B is much less than I_E (p. 244). Thus the d.c. (and a.c.) input resistance in the common-emitter circuit is much greater than in the common-base circuit (p. 240). Values greater than 1 kilohm are common, and this is of particular importance in multistage amplifiers, as will be seen later. The a.c. output resistance, however, in the common-emitter circuit is lower than that obtained in the common-base circuit. Values may lie between 10 and 75 kilohms for smaller power transistors.

In a.c. operation, the *current transfer ratio*, β, is defined by

$$\beta = \frac{\Delta I_C}{\Delta I_B} \ (V_C \text{ constant})$$

The symbol h_{te} is also used for β and is another hybrid parameter (p. 260).

The current transfer ratio α, defined by $\alpha = \Delta I_C / I_E$ (p. 241), is simply related to β. Thus

$$\beta(h_{\text{fe}}) = \frac{\Delta I_C}{\Delta I_B} = \frac{\alpha \Delta I_E}{\Delta I_E - \Delta I_C} = \frac{\alpha \Delta I_E}{\Delta I_E - \alpha \Delta I_E} = \frac{\alpha}{1 - \alpha}$$

Taking $\alpha = 0.98$ (p. 241), then $\beta = 0.98/0.02 = 49$. Thus the common emitter can provide a current amplification of about 50 times that of the common-base circuit. In practice, β can vary between 20 and 200, depending on the type of transistor.

Voltage Amplification or Gain

As an illustration of the voltage amplification of a small signal, suppose a load R of 5 kilohms is used in the collector or output circuit of a common-emitter amplifier, Fig. 13.10. If we assume the a.c. input resistance of the common base circuit is 50 ohms, for example, then, roughly, the a.c. input resistance r_i of the common-emitter amplifier circuit is 50 times greater because the input current is about 50 times less, i.e. $\beta = 49$. Thus $r_i = 50 \times 50 = 2,500$ ohms. Hence a sinusoidal input signal of peak value 10 mV will produce a base current of peak value (see p. 243) given by

$$\Delta I_B = \frac{10 \text{ mV}}{2,500 \text{ ohms}} = 0.004 \text{ mA}$$

$\therefore$ collector current, $\Delta I_C = \beta \Delta I_B = 49 \times 0.004$ mA

$\therefore$ collector a.c. voltage peak, $\Delta V_O = \Delta I_C \times R$

$$= 49 \times 0.004 \text{ mA} \times 5,000 \text{ ohms} = 0.98 \text{ V}$$

$\therefore$ voltage amplification $A_V = \dfrac{\text{output voltage}}{\text{input voltage}}$

$$= \frac{0.98 \text{ V}}{10 \text{ mV}} = 98$$

This is a voltage amplification comparable with that obtained with the common-base amplifier (p. 243). However, it should be noted that the current gain is 49, so that the *power gain*, which is the product of current and voltage gain, is 49 $\times$ the A_V value, or about 4,800. The power gain in the common-base amplifier is 0.98 $\times$ A_V or 96, which is much smaller.

Generally, it can be seen from the above numerical calculation that, for the common-emitter circuit with a load R,

$$A_V = \frac{\text{output voltage}}{\text{input voltage}} = \frac{R \cdot \Delta I_C}{r_i \cdot \Delta I_B} = \frac{\beta R}{r_i} = \frac{h_{\text{fe}} R}{r_i}$$

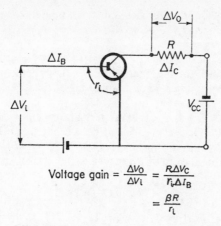

$$\text{Voltage gain} = \frac{\Delta V_0}{\Delta V_i} = \frac{R\Delta V_C}{r_i \Delta I_B}$$

$$= \frac{\beta R}{r_i}$$

FIG. 13.10.   Voltage amplification or Gain

Equivalent A.C. Circuit—CE Mode

Just as for a radio valve we can derive an equivalent a.c. circuit (see p. 228), so an equivalent a.c. circuit can be designed for the case of a transistor. This is illustrated in Fig. 13.11 for a transistor in the

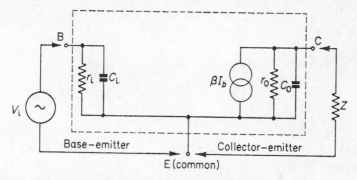

FIG. 13.11.   Equivalent a.c. circuit

CE (common-emitter) mode. In it, V_i represents the input voltage signal; and r_i, C_i the input a.c. resistance and capacitance respectively. On the output side, βI_b or $h_{te}I_b$ is the output current generator in the collector circuit; and r_0, C_0 represent the output a.c. resistance and capacitance respectively. Z is the collector load impedance. The input capacitance C_i represents the capacitance between the base and emitter (p. 243) and the output capacitance C_0 the capacitance between the collector and emitter.

Transistor equivalent circuits are generally more complex than valve equivalent circuits and reference must be made to more advanced books for further study.

Operating Point. Load Line

We now proceed to find the load line and operating point for a common-emitter amplifier when a small signal is applied in the base-emitter circuit.

Suppose the load R is 3 kilohms, the battery supply V_{CC} is 6 volts, Fig. 13.10, and the base current I_B at zero input signal is $20 \mu A$. The collector-emitter voltage, V_{CE}, is given by $V_{CE} = V_{CC} - I_C R$, where I_C is the collector current flowing when the transistor is operating.

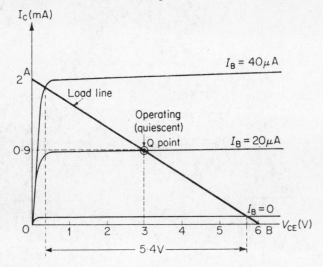

FIG. 13.12.　Load line

When $I_C = 0$, $V_{CE} = V_{CC} = 6$ V, and when $V_{CE} = 0$, $I_C = V_{CC}/R = 6$ V/3 kΩ = 2 mA. The two points A and B on the axes of I_C and V_{CE} of the characteristic curves can now be marked, and the line AB joining them is the load line, see Fig. 13.12. This is analogous to the way the load line was obtained in the case of the resistance load for a triode valve amplifier (p. 222).

The point Q where AB cuts the curve $I_B = 20 \mu A$ is the *no-signal* or *quiescent* operating point. Approximately, I_C and V_{CE} are then 0·9 mA and 3·0 V respectively. The product of these values, 0·9 × 3·0 or 2·7 milliwatts, gives the power dissipated at the collector. This should be less than the maximum allowed collector dissipation stated by the manufacturer. From the graph, if the input signal (ΔI_B) has a peak variation of $\pm 20 \mu A$, the peak output voltage (ΔV_C) is approximately 2·7 V.

Phase Relations

The phase relation between the output and input voltages should be noted. Consider a resistance load in a *common-emitter* amplifier. If the base of the transistor goes more negative, then V_{BE} is increased and an increase in collector current I_C is obtained. The voltage drop in the collector load resistance then increases. Thus V_{CE} falls, making the collector voltage more positive. Hence the collector voltage variations are in opposition in phase to the base voltage variations. This is also the case for the n-p-n transistor used as a common emitter amplifier.

Consider now a resistance load in a *common-base* amplifier. Suppose the emitter voltage goes more positive. Then the collector current I_C increases, making the collector more positive. In this case, therefore, the output voltage is in phase with the input voltage.

EXAMPLE

The data given in the Table refer to a transistor in the common emitter configuration.

Collector volts	Collector current (mA)			
	Base current			
	$-20\ \mu A$	$-40\ \mu A$	$-60\ \mu A$	$-80\ \mu A$
-3	$-0\cdot91$	$-1\cdot60$	$-2\cdot30$	$-3\cdot00$
-5	$-0\cdot93$	$-1\cdot70$	$-2\cdot50$	$-3\cdot25$
-7	$-0\cdot97$	$-1\cdot85$	$-2\cdot7$	$-3\cdot55$
-9	$-1\cdot00$	$-2\cdot05$	$-3\cdot00$	$-4\cdot05$

Plot the collector voltage/collector current characteristics for base currents of -20, -40, -60 and $-80\ \mu A$ and use these characteristic curves to determine (a) the current gain when the collector voltage is -6 V, (b) the output resistance of the transistor for $I_B = -60\ \mu A$.

The transistor is to be used as a common-emitter amplifier with a load resistor of 2,500 ohms and as a collector battery voltage of -10 V. Draw the load line and use this to find the base current for a collector voltage of -5 V. (*C. & G.*)

From the curves in Fig. 13.13,

(a) $\qquad \beta = \dfrac{\Delta I_C}{\Delta I_B} = \dfrac{2\cdot53}{60 \times 10^{-3}} = \dfrac{2\cdot53 \times 1,000}{60} = 42 \text{ (approx.)}$

(b) $r_0 = \dfrac{\Delta V_C}{\Delta I_C} = \dfrac{4}{0.47 \times 10^{-3}} = 8.5 \text{ k}\Omega$

(c) When $I_C = 0$, $V_C = V_{CC} = 10$ V; when $V_C = 0$, $I_C = \dfrac{10}{2.5} = 4$ mA

AB is the load line in Fig. 13.13.

At $V_C = -5$ volts, $I_B = 47\,\mu\text{A}$ (approx.)

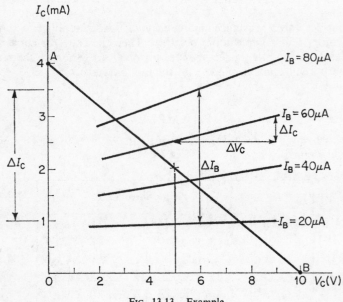

FIG. 13.13. Example

Leakage Current

If the emitter is disconnected in the *common-base* circuit, the current flowing in the collector circuit is that due only to *minority charge carriers*, which are thermally generated. This is the reverse current obtained when considering the junction diode (see p. 204), and it is the current also in this transistor case, since the collector-base is now reverse-biased. It is termed the *leakage current*, I_{CBO}, that is, it is the collector-base current at zero emitter current. During normal operation, the total direct current flowing in the collector circuit will be

$$I_C = \alpha I_E + I_{CBO}$$

The current gain α has a slight spread in transistor manufacture and the substitution by another transistor thus affects I_C slightly. The leakage current I_{CBO} also affects I_C. This increases when the transistor temperature rises, since the number of thermally generated carriers then rises. At moderature temperatures, the leakage current roughly doubles for every 8 deg C temperature. A typical I_{CBO} value for a small power transistor is $2\,\mu A$ at $25°C$ and $8\,\mu A$ at $40°C$. Fig. 13.14 (i)

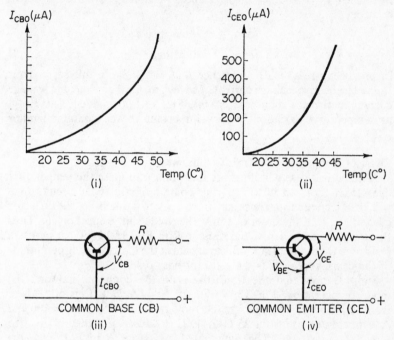

FIG. 13.14. Leakage current

shows the rapid rise with temperature of leakage current. Generally, however, since I_{CBO} is small, I_C is not much affected by temperature change.

If the d.c. collector current I_C changes, the d.c. collector voltage V_C changes, since V_C is the supply voltage less the voltage drop across the load resistor due to I_C. The operating point on the load line (p. 250) then shifts while the transistor is working and this may produce distortion in the output. It is not a serious problem in the common-base (CB) arrangement of a transistor because, as we have just seen, I_C is not much affected by a rise in leakage current, I_{CBO}.

Leakage Current in Common Emitter

As we shall see shortly, a different result is obtained in the case of the *common-emitter* (CE) arrangement. Here, the collector current, I_C, is made up of two components, the amplified input βI_B of the base current plus the leakage current I_{CEO}, the collector current at zero base current. Thus

$$I_C = \beta I_B + I_{CEO} = \beta(I_E - I_C) + I_{CEO}.$$

But when $I_E = 0$, $I_C = I_{CBO}$. Hence, putting $I_E = 0$ in the above relation,

$$\therefore I_{CBO} = -\beta I_{CBO} + I_{CEO}.$$

$$\therefore I_{CEO} = (\beta + 1)I_{CBO} \qquad (1)$$

In practice, β may be 49 and hence $I_{CEO} = 50 I_{CBO}$ in this case. Thus I_{CEO}, the effective leakage current, is *much* greater than I_{CBO}, the leakage current in the common-base circuit, Fig. 13.14 (ii). Hence attention to temperature variation is very important in the common-emitter (CE) circuit.

Effect of Temperature on D.C. Conditions

A numerical case will illustrate this point. Suppose the temperature rises from 25°C to 40°C. In the common base (CB) circuit, I_{CBO} will then increase four times, say from $2 \mu A$ to $8 \mu A$. Since the collector current, I_C, is of the order of 1 mA, the rise has little effect on I_C. Thus the potential drop across the resistor R in Fig. 13.14 (iii), or across a resistor in the emitter lead, will hardly affect the d.c. operating conditions of the transistor, such as the collector-base p.d., V_{CB}.

Suppose now that the transistor is in the common emitter (CE) mode of operation, Fig. 13.14 (iv). If β is 49, $(\beta + 1)$ is 50. Then, from (1) above, the leakage current $I_{CEO} = 50 \times 2 \mu A = 100 \mu A$. A temperature rise from 25°C to 40°C produces a change of I_{CEO} to 4×100 or $400 \mu A$. The potential drop across R in Fig. 13.14 (ii) is now appreciably changed, and this alters seriously the d.c. voltage V_{CE} between the collector and emitter. Further, changes in the base current I_B will cause variations in V_{BE}.

Effect of Lack of Stabilization

The effect produced by a lack of d.c. stability in the transistor CE arrangement is illustrated in Fig. 13.15. In (i) the ambient (surroundings) temperature is 25°C, AB is the load line, Q is the operating or quiescent point corresponding to $I_B = 60 \mu A$, and a peak-to-peak base-current input swing of $80 \mu A$ is applied. The base-current peaks occur at $I_B = 100 \mu A$ and $20 \mu A$ respectively. The variation in output current I_C is shown. It is an undistorted output.

Suppose now that the temperature rises to 45°C, Fig. 13.15 (ii). The I_C v. V_C curves are then roughly as shown, and the operating point may change to Q' since I_C increases. This is due to the increased voltage drop in R_L which makes V_{CE} less than before. Compare Fig. 13.15 (i), (ii). The collector current is now driven into the saturation region, on the left of the knee of the curves, for part of the input cycle. Hence the output is 'clipped', as shown, and so distortion occurs. Failure of a transistor to amplify when the collector voltage falls below the knee of the curves

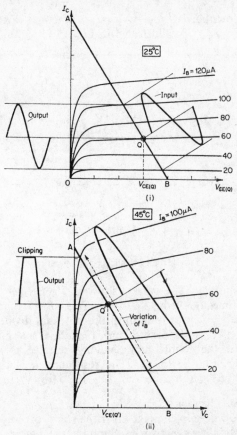

FIG. 13.15.   Effect due to lack of stabilization

is called *bottoming*. It should be noted that the base bias V_{BE} is altered with temperature rise, due to the increased base current, and 'clipping' occurs in a similar way.

It can now be seen that steps must be taken to stabilize the d.c. working conditions and operating point of the transistor in common-emitter operation, otherwise the transistor will not amplify correctly.

Stabilizing D.C. Operation

The usual method of stabilizing the d.c. working conditions is (i) to make the base potential practically independent of changes in base current, I_B, and (ii) to provide a counteracting voltage in the emitter circuit when the current alters with the temperature. The latter voltage is usually of the order of 1/5th to 1/10th of the battery supply voltage, V_{CC}.

The base potential is fixed by using a potential divider across the battery supply, V_{CC}. As illustrated in Fig. 13.16 (i), this is formed by

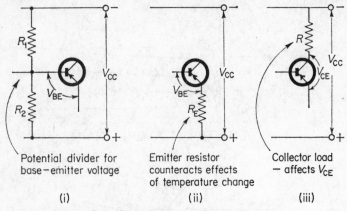

Potential divider for base—emitter voltage

(i)

Emitter resistor counteracts effects of temperature change

(ii)

Collector load — affects V_{CE}

(iii)

FIG. 13.16. Stabilizing d.c. operation

resistors R_1 and R_2. The current flowing, $V_{CC}/(R_1 + R_2)$, is usually made 5 to 10 times I_B, the base current. This ensures that any variation in I_B is a much smaller variation in the potential divider current and so reduces its effect on the base voltage, V_{BE}. R_E is the emitter resistance which provides the counteracting voltage referred to above, and is discussed later, Fig. 13.16 (ii). The resistance R is chosen so that V_{CE} is 0·3 to 0·5V_{CC} in most cases, Fig. 13.16 (iii).

Example on Stabilization

An example will help to make clear the steps involved in the design of the bias stabilizing network. Suppose the battery p.d., V_{CC}, is 6 volts; the required base biasing current, $I_{B(Q)}$, in the no-signal or *quiescent* condition is 50 μA, corresponding to a base-emitter voltage $V_{BE(Q)}$ of 0·1 V from the input characteristic, such as Fig. 13.9 (i); and the emitter current I_E is 1 mA, Fig. 13.17. Let $I_E R_E = 1$ volt, so that $R_E = 1$ kΩ.

Let the current through R_2 be 5I_B. Then, assuming $I_B = 50 \mu$A, the current flowing in R_2 is 5 × 50 or 250 μA, which is 0·25 mA. From the circuit, p.d. across $R_2 = V_{BE(Q)} + I_E R_E$

$$\therefore \quad \text{p.d. across } R_2 = 0·25 R_2 = 0·1 + 1·0 = 1·1 \text{ V}$$

$$\therefore \quad R_2 = \frac{1·1 \text{ V}}{0·25 \text{ mA}} = 4·4 \text{ k}\Omega$$

The current in $R_1 = 5I_B$ + current from transistor base = $6I_B$

$$\therefore \quad \text{current in } R_1 = 6 \times 50\,\mu\text{A} = 0.3 \text{ mA}$$

The p.d. across $R_1 = V_{CC} - 1.1 \text{ V} = 6 \text{ V} - 1.1 \text{ V} = 4.9 \text{ V}$

$$\therefore R_1 = \frac{4.9 \text{ V}}{0.3 \text{ mA}} = 16.3 \text{ k}\Omega$$

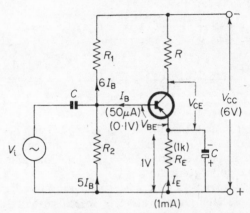

FIG. 13.17. Example on calculating components

Since $I_E R_E = 1$ V, then 5 V is available for R and V_{CE}. This may be divided equally, so that 2·5 V is the p.d. across R. As $I_C = I_E$ approximately $= 1$ mA, neglecting I_B, then

$$R = \frac{2.5 \text{ V}}{1 \text{ mA}} = 2.5 \text{ k}\Omega$$

In this way the magnitudes of R_1, R_2, R_E and R can be calculated.

Emitter Resistor

The action of the emitter resistance can be explained as follows. Suppose, due to temperature change, that the emitter current I_E increases. The p.d. across R_E then increases, so causing the potential of the emitter to decrease. If the base potential is fixed, then the base-emitter p.d. V_{BE} is reduced. The emitter current I_E is now reduced accordingly. Hence the effect of the temperature change is largely counteracted. *The emitter resistor thus stabilizes the d.c. operating conditions of the transistor.*

The capacitor C across R_E is large. It by-passes signal variations from R_E and hence prevents feedback of the signal. The reactance of C must be very small compared to R_E at the lowest frequency concerned. The series capacitor C in the base circuit ensures that any d.c. with the signal source V_i is blocked off. It also prevents short-circuiting of R_2 by the signal source.

A further point of note is that the input circuit is shunted by R_2 and R_1. From an a.c. point of view, R_1 is returned to the common

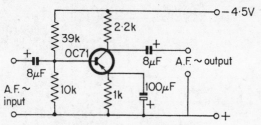

FIG. 13.18. A.f. Amplifier circuit

transistor line, running from the $+$ pole of the battery V_{CC} to one end of the signal source V_i, through the low resistance of V_{CC}. Hence R_1 and R_2 are in parallel across the transistor input and this reduces the effective a.c. input resistance.

Fig. 13.18 shows a p-n-p a.f. amplifier circuit using a Mullard transistor. It provides appreciable amplification of speech currents, obtained by using a microphone between the input terminals, for example.

Common-emitter Amplifier. *R–C* Coupling

A practical two-stage a.f. voltage amplifier circuit with resistance-capacitance (*R–C*) coupling is shown in Fig. 13.19. Each transistor circuit has a load resistance, a potential divider for biasing the base,

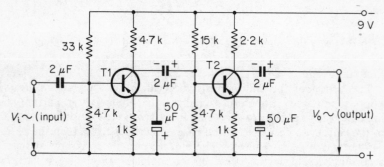

FIG. 13.19. Common-emitter (CE) amplifier. *R-C* coupling

an emitter resistor for temperature stabilizing with a by-pass electrolytic capacitor in parallel and the circuits are coupled by a $2 \mu F$ capacitor. The input is V_i, and the amplified voltage is V_o.

The transistor circuit of T2 is designed for larger currents than T1, since it will handle amplified signal current variations from T1. The $2\,\mu\text{F}$ capacitors are miniature electrolytic types, and their polarities should be noted. For example, the collector voltage of T1 will be more negative than the base of T2, so the positive terminal of the coupling capacitor is connected to the latter. At the input to the amplifier the signal source V_i will not have, in general, any d.c. polarity, so the base of T1 is the more negative in potential. The positive of the $2\,\mu\text{F}$ capacitor is hence connected to the input terminal and the negative to the base.

At medium frequencies in the a.f. band, 300 Hz to 3 kHz say, or at higher audio frequencies, the reactance of the coupling capacitor between the two stages is low and can be neglected. The capacitor does not then affect the amplifier frequency response. At low audio frequencies, however, say below 300 Hz, the reactance of the coupling capacitor increases as the frequency is lowered and becomes comparable to the magnitude of r_i. Since, from an a.c. point of view, the capacitor acts as a potentiometer with r_i, the gain of the amplifier is then appreciably reduced, as explained for a valve a.f. amplifier (p. 232).

Transformer Coupling

A transformer coupled amplifier is shown in Fig. 13.20. A step-down transformer with a turns-ratio $N\!:\!1$ is used to couple transistor T1 to transistor T2, so that increased current flows in the secondary towards the base of T2. The maximum gain is obtained by matching

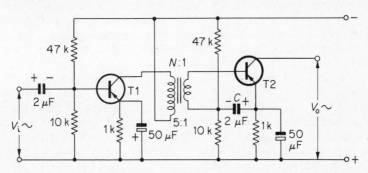

Fig. 13.20.   Transformer coupling

the output resistance r_0 of T1 to the input resistance r_{i2} of T2, that is, $N = \sqrt{r_0/r_{i2}}$ (p. 268). The capacitor C connects the bottom end of the secondary winding directly to the emitter for a.c., and it may be observed that the base (biasing) resistors do not shunt the input resistance of T2 in this circuit.

Although a greater gain than R–C coupling can be obtained with transformer coupling, the frequency response of the latter is not so good. This is due to the shunting effect of the primary inductive reactance at low frequencies, and the coil capacitance and leakage inductance at high frequencies.

Other Semi-conductor Devices

There are numerous semiconductor devices. The following are brief notes on some of the more important ones.

Photodiode. If a junction diode is reverse-biased, the leakage current flows (p. 204). When the junction is illuminated, the energy falling on it excites electrons. More then become free electrons, that is, electron-hole pairs are created. Thus the reverse current increases. The light-sensitive diode is called a 'photodiode'. *Solar cells* are unbiased silicon diodes with a large junction area—they can produce an e.m.f. of about half a volt when their junctions are illuminated.

Phototransistor. The phototransistor is a photodiode whose current, generated by light, is amplified by transistor action. It has an emitter, base and collector, as in the normal transistor. If the base is left disconnected, and the collector-emitter is reverse-biased as in a photodiode, a small leakage current flows in the dark. However, when the emitter is illuminated, a large current flows. It is larger than the current obtained in a photodiode for the same illumination, as the current from electron-hole pairs created in the emitter-base junction is amplified by transistor action.

Thermistor. The thermistor is a semiconductor material whose resistivity is sensitive to temperature. Thermistors may thus decrease in resistance when the current, and hence heat, in them increases. They are therefore used to compensate for the rise in collector current due to temperature rise in a transistor circuit, and to safeguard circuits where a surge of current is harmful.

Thyristor. The thyristor is a semiconductor device which can be used to control a.c. power supplied to lamps, heaters and motors, for example. It can handle currents ranging from tens of milliamperes to hundreds of amperes. Basically, it is made from four suitably doped silicon layers which may have a p-n-p-n or n-p-n-p structure, the first two layers acting as a diode. The thyristor is also known as a 'silicon controlled rectifier' (SCR).

Notes on Hybrid or *h*-Parameters

Hybrid or *h*-parameters are used in transistor theory. The following are brief notes on them. The 'short circuit' values of current-gain, that is, no resistance in the collector circuit, are given numerically by:

$$h_{\text{fb}} = \alpha = \frac{\Delta I_C}{\Delta I_E} \ (V_{\text{CB}} \text{ constant})$$

$$h_{\text{fe}} = \beta = \frac{\Delta I_C}{\Delta I_B} \ (V_{\text{CE}} \text{ constant})$$

Two h-parameters of importance are h_i and h_o. For common-base (CB) operation, they are denoted as h_{ib} and h_{ob} respectively. For common-emitter (CE) operation, they are denoted as h_{ie} and h_{oe} respectively.

h_{ie} is the value of the *a.c. input resistance* with V_C kept constant. As this is r_i, it is obtained from the input curve. Thus

$$h_{ie} = \frac{\Delta V_{BE}}{\Delta I_B} = r_i \ (V_{CE} \text{ constant})$$

h_{oe} is the *a.c. output conductance*. It is thus the reciprocal of r_o. Thus

$$h_{oe} = \frac{\Delta I_C}{\Delta V_{CE}} = \frac{1}{r_o} \ (I_B \text{ constant})$$

The unit of conductance is 'mho'. Similar formulae hold for h_{ib} and h_{ob}.

Internal feedback through the transistor occurs at all frequencies of operation. This is expressed in a parameter h_r, called the *voltage feedback ratio*.

Some typical values of the h-parameters for an a.f. transistor of low power are:

CB operation.

$$h_{ib} = 40 \ \Omega, \quad h_{ob} = 10^{-6} \text{ mho}, \quad h_{rb} = -0.98, \quad h_{rb} = 4 \times 10^{-4}$$

CE operation.

$$h_{ie} = 2{,}000 \ \Omega, \quad h_{oe} = 5 \times 10^{-5} \text{ mho}, \quad h_{fe} = 49, \quad h_{re} = 4 \times 10^{-4}$$

SUMMARY

1. In a transistor, the emitter-base is forward-biased and the collector-base is reverse-biased.

2. $I_E = I_C + I_B$ (d.c. conditions). $\alpha = \Delta I_C / \Delta I_E$ (V_C constant). $\beta = \Delta I_C / \Delta I_B$ (V_C constant). $\beta = \alpha/(1 - \alpha)$; if $\alpha = 0.98$, then $\beta = 49$.

3. The leakage current in common-emitter, $I_{CEO} = (\beta + 1)I_{CBO}$, where I_{CBO} is the leakage current in common-base. Stabilization of d.c. operating conditions is thus important in the CE amplifier, otherwise the transistor parameters and gain will vary and distortion is then produced.

4. In the CE amplifier, (i) an emitter resistor provides a counteracting voltage (negative feedback) to stabilize d.c. conditions for temperature, (ii) a potential divider 'swamps' any changes in base current.

5. Common emitter CE, common base CB, and common collector CC circuits (see p. 280) compare roughly as follows:

	CE	CB	CC
Current gain	High	1	high
Voltage gain	High	High	1
Input impedance	Medium	Low	High
Output impedance	Medium	High	Low
Power gain	High	Medium	Low
Cut-off frequency	Low	High	(depends on load)
Voltage phase change (a.f.)	180°	0	0

6. In a.f. amplifiers, R–C coupling and transformer coupling may be used. Although a greater gain with transformer coupling can be obtained, the frequency response is less uniform than R–C coupling.

EXERCISE 13

1. In Fig. 13A (i), (*a*) is this a p-n-p or n-p-n transistor? (*b*) name the terminals 1, 2, 3.

2. Fig. 13A (ii) shown an actual transistor. Name the terminals 1, 2, 3.

3. Fig. 13A (iii) shows a p-n-p transistor. (i) Name the terminals X, Y, Z, (ii) what is this circuit arrangement called? (iii) where may an 'earth' or 'chassis' connection to it be made?

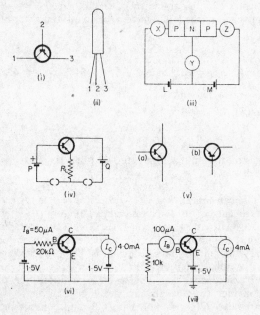

Fig. 13A

4. Fig. 13A (iv) shows a circuit *wrongly* connected; it is intended to be a common-emitter circuit with a resistance load R_L. Copy and re-draw the circuit correctly.

5. Name the transistors whose symbols are shown in Fig. 13A (v). Draw a circuit diagram showing how each is connected for (i) common-emitter, (ii) common-base circuits, showing clearly the positive pole of the batteries used and an 'earth' connection.

6. Fig. 13A (vi) represents a common-emitter circuit. With the currents shown, what are the magnitudes of (i) V_{CE}, (ii) V_{BE}, (iii) I_E, (iv) V_{BC}?

7. Fig. 13A (vii) shows a common-emitter circuit with a common 1·5 V battery and steady currents. (i) What current flows in the emitter lead, (ii) what is the value of β if a change of I_B from 50 to 70 μA produces a current change in I_C from 4·0 to 5·0 mA, (iii) what are the p.d.s V_{BE} and V_{CE} in the circuit shown? (iv) is the collector-base *reverse*-biased? Give a reason.

8. Is the transistor basically a *current* or a *voltage* amplifier? Draw a simple circuit in which a n-p-n transistor acts as an amplifier and explain how it functions by considering the movement of the carriers.

9. (i) Draw a sketch of a p-n-p transistor in the common-base (CB) and common-emitter (CE) arrangement. (ii) Write down the expression for the current gain, α and β, in the respective circuits. (iii) If $\alpha = 0.98$, calculate β. *Explain* any formula used.

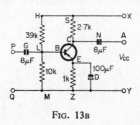

Fig. 13B

10. In a CE amplifier circuit, stabilization of d.c. conditions for temperature change is much more important than for the CB circuit. Explain the reason for this, and state how stabilization is arranged.

11. Answer the following questions about the amplifier circuit in Fig. 13B:

  (i) Where are the poles of the battery supply connected? Give a reason.
  (ii) Which are the output terminals?
  (iii) Which are the input (signal) terminals?
  (iv) Which is the resistor load?
  (v) What is the purpose of the 1 k resistor between E, Z?
  (vi) What type of capacitor is D and what is its purpose?
  (vii) What purpose do the 39 k and 10 k resistors serve?
  (viii) What is the purpose of the 8 μF capacitor G?

12. With the aid of a cross-sectional diagram, describe the construction of a germanium transistor.

Give a simple circuit for this transistor connected as an amplifier in common-base configuration, showing clearly the relative polarities of the bias voltages.

Sketch typical input (I_B/V_B) and output (I_C/V_C) characteristics for this transistor.   (*C. & G.*)

13. Sketch sets of characteristic curves for the following:

  (*a*) I_a against V_g for various values of V_a for a triode valve.
  (*b*) I_a against V_a for various values of V_g for a pentode valve.
  (*c*) I_C against V_C for various values of I_B for a transistor in the common-emitter connection.

(d) I_C against I_E for a given value of V_C for a transistor in the common-base connection.

State what information may be derived from the slope of the straight portion of each of these curves.

14. Sketch a test circuit for obtaining the collector current-collector voltage characteristics of a transistor. Give a brief description, with typical resulting curves, of an experiment determining these characteristics for a transistor connected in the following configurations:

(a) a common emitter, and (b) a common base.

Sketch a simple transistor amplifier circuit for either (a) or (b), showing the polarities of the battery connections. (C. & G.)

15. With the aid of sketches describe any one type of transistor, and explain briefly why it can act as an amplifier.

Give a circuit of a single-stage audio amplifier using a transistor.

What effect has temperature on the operation of such an amplifier?

(C. & G.)

16. The data given in Tables A and B refer to a transistor in the common emitter configuration.

TABLE A

Collector voltage V_C		−2	−4	−6	−8	−10
Collector current I_C (mA)	Base current −120 μA	−6·4	−7·0	−7·6	−8·2	−8·8
	Base current −80 μA	−4·4	−4·8	−5·2	−5·6	−6·0
	Base current −40 μA	−2·2	−2·4	−2·6	−2·8	−3·0

TABLE B

Collector voltage V_C = −4·5 V					
Base current I_B (μA)	0	−5	−10	−15	−20
Collector current I_C (mA)	−0·15	−0·45	−0·75	−1·1	−1·4

Use the data in Table A to plot the collector voltage/collector current characteristics for I_B = −40, −80 and −120 μA, and from the characteristic for I_B = −80 μA deduce the output resistance of the transistor. Use the data in Table B to plot the collector current/base current characteristic for V_C = −4·5 V and from the graph deduce the current gain. (C. & G.)

17.

Collector volts	Collector current (mA)			
	Base current −20 μA	Base current −40 μA	Base current −60 μA	Base current −80 μA
−3	−0·91	−1·60	−2·3	−3·00
−5	−0·93	−1·70	−2·5	−3·25
−7	−0·97	−1·85	−2·7	−3·55
−9	−1·00	−2·05	−3·0	−4·05

Plot the I_C/V_C transistor characteristics from the above table for the base currents shown. From the characteristics find (i) the current gain for a collector voltage of 8 V, (ii) the output resistance for base current of −40 μA.

If the transistor is used in a CE amplifier arrangement with a battery supply of 9 V and a load resistance of 2 kΩ, (a) draw the load line, (b) from the load line find the base current when the collector voltage is 6 V.

18. Draw circuit diagrams and briefly explain how a junction transistor may be used in a single-stage audio-frequency amplifier (a) with common-base connexion, and (b) with common-emitter connexion. Discuss the order of magnitude of the input and output impedance and the current gain characteristic for each type of amplifier.   (C. & G.)

19. Sketch a circuit and describe the operation of a two-stage R–C-coupled audio-frequency amplifier using transistors in the common-emitter configuration.

State approximate values of the load resistors and coupling capacitors.

Discuss any factors which affect the stage amplification.   (C. & G.)

20. A transistor operated in the collector-base (CB) mode has an emitter current of 2 mA and a base current of 0·04 mA. Calculate the value of the

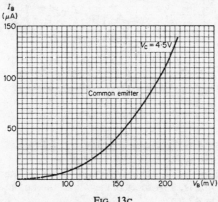

FIG. 13c

collector current and the approximate value of the transistor short circuit current gain factor α (h_{fb}).

21. If the transistor in Qn. 20 is operated in the common-emitter (CE) mode under identical conditions, find the value of β (h_{fe}).

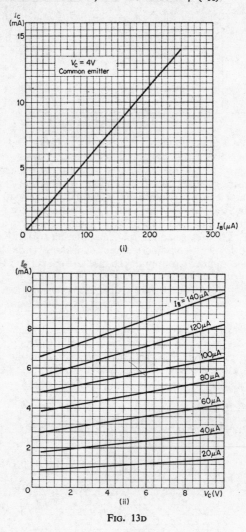

FIG. 13D

22. Use the OC71 input characteristic at $V_C = 4.5$ V to evaluate the input slope resistance $r_i(h_{ie})$ when $I_B = 40$ μA, Fig. 13c.

23. Use the average transfer characteristic (i) and the output characteristics (ii) of the OC71 in Fig. 13D to evaluate β and the output impedance r_o at $V_C = 4$ V and $I_B = 40$ μA.

24. The OC71 is used as a CE amplifier with a collector supply of 8 V and collector load resistor of 2 kΩ. Draw the load line. With a base biasing at 40 μA find the quiescent (no-signal) values of I_C and V_{CE} from the output characteristics, Fig. 13$_D$ (ii).

An input signal varies the base current by ± 20 μA. Deduce the total output voltage variation from the load line.

25. A transistor operated in the CE mode has quiescent currents $I_B = 40$ μA, $I_C = 2$ mA and quiescent voltage values, $V_{CE} = 3$ V, $V_{BE} = 0.15$ V when the supply voltage is 9 V. The emitter resistor has a potential drop of 2 V and the current through the base biasing resistor is $5I_B$. As on p. 257, calculate R_1, R_2, R_E and R.

26. A transistor CE amplifier has a collector resistor load of 3·3 kΩ, and the input is supplied by an a.f. signal source of internal resistance 2 kΩ which develops an e.m.f 20 mV. The transistor has an a.c. input resistance of 2 kΩ, an output resistance of 40 kΩ and β (h_{te}) = 40. Calculate the a.c. voltage developed across the collector load.

[*Hint*. The source e.m.f. and resistance are in series with the transistor a.c. input resistance. The a.c. voltage applied to the transistor is the p.d. across r_i. Note that 40 kΩ is much greater than 3·3 kΩ.]

14. A.F. Power Amplifiers

Impedance Matching

Audio-frequency (a.f.) amplifiers are used in radio receivers to operate a loudspeaker, Fig. 14.1 (i). For this purpose, the valve required is usually one which provides high *power*. It is essential that the power amplifier should have the optimum or suitable load value for maximum power delivery (see p. 38) and this is specified by the manufacturer. The load value also allows for a stated minimum distortion in the output.

The effective impedance of a loudspeaker while it is operating is

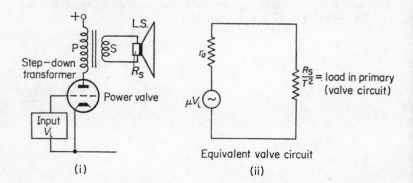

Fig. 14.1. Impedance matching

called its *dynamic impedance*. It is considerably greater than the d.c. resistance of the speech coil, as it includes the self-inductance of the coil while the varying a.f. currents flow in it and induction effects due to vibration in the field of the permanent magnet in the loudspeaker (p. 89). The dynamic impedance varies with frequency and a value at 1,000 Hz (1 kHz) is quoted by the manufacturer for reference purposes.

The dynamic impedance of a loudspeaker coil is very small, for example, less than 10 ohms. The power or output valve, however, has an a.c. resistance r_a of the order of thousands of ohms. For maximum power delivery, therefore, the load should also be of the same order of impedance. Now it was shown on p. 150 that, when a transformer is used, the reflected impedance in the primary is given by R_S/T^2, where T is the secondary to primary turns ratio, and R_S is the impedance in the secondary. Thus if a loudspeaker of 8-ohms impedance is used in the secondary of a *step-down* transformer of turns ratio $1:30$, then

$$\text{reflected impedance in primary} = \frac{R_S}{T^2} = \frac{8}{(1/30)^2} = 7{,}200 \ \Omega$$

This is illustrated in Fig. 14.1 (ii). *Thus a loudspeaker can be matched to the output or power valve by using a step-down transformer.*

Power Developed in Load

The power developed in the load while the output valve is working can be found from the *load line*. The method of drawing the load line was explained on p. 222, to which the reader may refer. Consider the

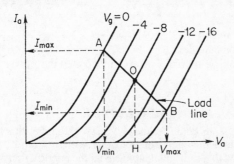

FIG. 14.2. Load line and power calculation

circuit shown in Fig. 14.1 (i). For all practical purposes, the d.c. voltage on the anode is the same as the h.t. supply voltage, since the primary coil between h.t. + and the anode has a relative low resistance. Suppose Fig. 14.2 represents the static anode characteristics of the power amplifier, and that the grid-bias is −8 volts. Then, if H corresponds to the h.t. voltage, O will be the operating point when an input is applied to the valve.

To draw the load line, another point is needed in addition to O. This may be found as follows: Take a suitable increase ΔI_a in I_a from that corresponding to O. Multiply ΔI_a by the optimum load resistance and subtract the voltage from the h.t. voltage. Mark the new anode voltage and current values on the graph, corresponding to a point above A, say (not shown). Join this point to O, thus obtaining the load line AOB.

The peak input to the valve must not exceed 8 volts in which case no grid current flows. Further, the grid swing must not make the valve operate on the curved portion of the static characteristic for $V_g = -16\,\text{V}$, otherwise distortion occurs. Thus for maximum power output, the grid swing of 8 volts about the operating point O takes place along the load line AOB where B is the beginning of the straight-line portion of the $V_g = -16$ V characteristic.

The a.c. power, P, developed in the load $= IV$, where I, V are the r.m.s. a.c. components of the output current and the voltage across the load.

$$\therefore \ P_{ac} = \frac{I_{peak}}{\sqrt{2}} \cdot \frac{V_{peak}}{\sqrt{2}} = \frac{1}{2} I_{peak} V_{peak} \tag{1}$$

If $I_{max.}$, $I_{min.}$ represent the maximum and minimum anode currents, and $V_{max.}$, $V_{min.}$, the corresponding quantities of anode voltage it follows that

$$I_{peak} = \frac{I_{max} - I_{min}}{2}, \ V_{peak} = \frac{V_{max} - V_{min}}{2}$$

$\therefore$ Power output, $P_{ac} = \frac{1}{8}(I_{max} - I_{min})(V_{max} - V_{min})$ from (1), and can now be calculated.

The following numerical example illustrates the power and efficiency obtained.

EXAMPLE

A valve used as an audio-frequency class A amplifier draws 30 mA anode current at an anode voltage of 200 volts with no input signal applied. When supplied with a sinusoidal input signal the anode voltage varies between 50 and 350 volts and the corresponding anode current change is 50 to 10 mA. Calculate (*a*) the power drawn from the h.t. supply, (*b*) the output power from the stage, (*c*) the efficiency of operation.   (*C. & G.*)

(*a*) Power drawn from h.t. supply,

$P_{dc} =$ mean anode voltage × mean anode current
$= 200 \times 30 \times 10^{-3} = 6$ watts

(*b*) A.C. Power output,

$$P_{ac} = \frac{(350 - 50)(50 - 10) \times 10^{-3}}{8} = \frac{300 \times 40}{8} \times 10^{-3} = 1 \cdot 5 \text{ watts}$$

(*c*) Efficiency $\quad \eta = \frac{P_{ac}}{P_{dc}} \times 100\% = \frac{1 \cdot 5}{6} \times 100\% = 25\%$

Note the relatively-low efficiency of a class A power amplifier.

Tetrode and Pentode Class A Power Amplifiers

Tetrode and pentode valves are discussed in the next chapter. Here we may say that tetrode and pentode amplifiers have a higher sensitivity, and give a higher anode efficiency, than triode valves. However, the operating conditions for obtaining a low percentage of harmonic distortion are more critical. Fig. 14.3 shows roughly how the power

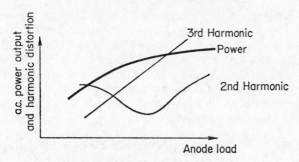

FIG. 14.3. Power and harmonic distortion

output and harmonic distortion both vary with the value of the anode load. A compromise load must therefore be chosen and this is obtained from the manufacturer.

Class A Push-pull Power Amplifier

By using two similar valves V1, V2 in a push-pull circuit (see p. 217) it is possible to obtain a greater a.c. power output and to reduce the distortion.

Fig. 14.4 shows the circuit required. The input and output transformers T_1 and T_2 are centre-tapped. The centre-tapping on T_1 ensures that the signal drive to one valve is 180° out of phase with that applied to the other valve. Then, as shown in Fig. 11.9, p. 218, the anode current of one valve increases as the other decreases. The manufacturer provides the required anode to anode load value. The turns-ratio of the output transformer T_2 is calculated by matching the loudspeaker dynamic impedance for maximum a.c. power (see p. 268).

Fig. 14.4 (i) illustrates the 1st, 2nd and 3rd harmonics in the anode current obtained from the valve V1. This is due to variations about the curved part of the dynamic characteristic. Fig. 14.4 (ii) illustrates the same harmonics produced in the anode current from valve V2. When the anode currents are added together to obtain the output in push-pull, the result is shown in Fig. 14.4 (iii). The second (even) harmonic has been eliminated, thus reducing the distortion.

Suppose the circuit is operating and a varying current flows in the primary of T_2. If the anode current of one valve increases by ΔI_a and the other decreases by ΔI_a, the resulting change in magnetic flux, ΔB, in each half of the primary is given by $\Delta B = k\Delta I_a$, where k is a constant, depending on the particular magnetic circuit. Thus the net flux change in the secondary $= k\Delta I_a - (-k\Delta I_a) = 2k\Delta I_a$, since the flux change in each half of the primary coil is in the opposite direction.

When there is no signal input and the two halves of the circuit are balanced electrically, equal and opposite steady anode currents flow in the two halves of the primary of T_2. The net d.c. magnetic flux linking the primary is then zero. This is also the case while the valves are working—the d.c. components of the anode current neutralise each other's influence. The d.c. magnetisation of the iron is hence zero. This is a considerable advantage as the incremental permeability of the iron is higher without permanent magnetisation, and distortion due to the B–H curve of the iron is reduced. Further, for a given a.c. power, the cross-sectional area of the iron used in the core can be reduced.

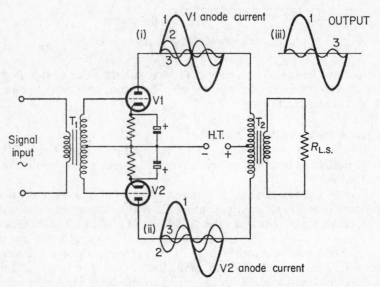

Fig. 14.4. Class A push-pull amplifier

The advantage of the push-pull power amplifier can be summarised as follows:

1. There is no even harmonic distortion.

2. For a given percentage of harmonic distortion, more than twice the power output of one valve is available.

3. Reduction in 'hum' output, that is, the sound output if the mains ripple comes through the loudspeaker—the 'hum' voltage on the high-tension line acts in phase on each valve, so that the net magnetic flux due to it in the output transformer is zero.

4. Less distortion in the output transformer and economy in the amount of iron used.

Transistor A.F. Power Amplifier

Transistors can also provide a.f. power amplification by using transformer coupling to the load, such as the impedance of a loudspeaker coil. As shown in Fig. 14.5 (i), practically the full collector voltage from the supply V_{CC} is then available at the collector because of the low transformer primary resistance.

The allowable collector current is governed by the maximum d.c. power which may be dissipated at the collector junction. Since power $= IV$, the maximum collector power dissipation curve, $P_{C\ max}$, is shown in Fig. 14.5 (ii) by the broken line and the quiescent operating point Q should lie to the left of it. Under this condition, the quiescent values

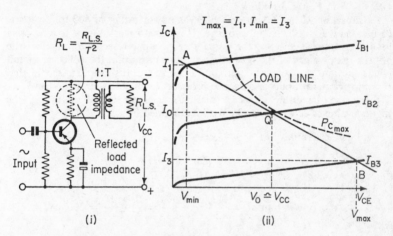

FIG. 14.5. Transistor power amplifier

V_0, I_0 are such that $V_0 I_0 \simeq V_{CC} I_0 < P_{C\ max}$. Further, since the knee of the I_C v. V_{CE} curve occurs at a fraction of a volt, the maximum allowable collector current peak swing may be taken as practically equal to I_0, where I_0 is the quiescent value. This is shown in Fig. 14.5 (ii). Likewise, the maximum peak swing voltage is approximately V_0, the quiescent value of collector voltage, or the supply voltage V_{CC}. Hence the maximum a.c. power output

$$= P_{ac} \simeq \frac{I_0 V_0}{2} = \frac{I_0 V_{CC}}{2}$$

Under these conditions, the required a.c. load, R_L, for the collector is given simply by $R_L = V_0/I_0 = V_{CC}/I_0$, a useful practical result. The load line construction, AB, is the same as that given on p. 269.

Generally, as in the case of the valve a.f. power amplifier, the a.c. power output and the d.c. power input are given respectively by:

$$P_{ac} = \tfrac{1}{8}(I_{max} - I_{min})(V_{max} - V_{min})$$

and $\qquad P_{dc} = I_0 V_0 \simeq I_0 V_{CC}$

The collector *efficiency*, η_C, of the circuit is given by

$$\eta_C = \frac{P_{ac}}{P_{dc}} \times 100\%$$

EXAMPLE

Class A A.F. Power Amplifier

A transistor with a maximum collector power rating of 500 milliwatts is to be used with a 10 V supply voltage. It is transformer coupled to a resistive load of 2 ohms. Neglecting the transformer winding resistances, calculate the approximate values of the maximum a.c. power output, the collector circuit efficiency, and the required output transformer turns-ratio. (Assume that the transformer primary inductance produces negligible shunting effect.)

Since the maximum collector dissipation power is 500 milliwatts, the highest value of I_0 which can be used is obtained from:

$$500 \text{ milliwatts} = I_0 V_0 \simeq I_0 V_{CC}$$

$$\therefore I_0 = \frac{500}{10} = 50 \text{ mA}$$

$$\therefore \text{ a.c. power output} \simeq \frac{V_0 I_0}{2} \simeq \frac{V_{CC} I_0}{2} = \frac{10 \times 50}{2} = 250 \text{ mW} \qquad (1)$$

$$\therefore \text{ efficiency} = \frac{P_{ac}}{P_{dc}} \times 100\% = \frac{250}{500} \times 100\% = 50\% \qquad (2)$$

This efficiency value is the maximum theoretical value possible under class A conditions. In practice, the efficiency is less than this but the fully driven transistor power amplifier is capable of giving efficiency values which closely approach the theoretical maximum. (See *Triode a.f. power amplifier*, p. 270).

The required a.c. load is approximately given by

$$\frac{V_0}{I_0} = \frac{10}{50} \times 10^3 = 200 \text{ ohms}$$

Thus the necessary step-down ratio T (primary to secondary turns ratio) is:

$$T = \sqrt{\frac{200}{2}} = 10:1$$

Class A Push-pull

The advantages of push-pull amplifiers (see p. 272) apply to transistors. If V_0 and I_0 are the quiescent values of collector voltage and current, then, when fully driven, the peak swing values are approximately equal to V_0 and I_0. The a.c. power output in this case is twice that for a single transistor. Hence

$$P_{ac} = I_0 V_0 = 2I_0^2 R_L$$

The required collector-to-collector load in this case is V_0/I_0, or $2R_L$, where R_L is the required load with one transistor.

Class B Push-pull

The class B push-pull amplifier is the more usual arrangement because of the economy in the use of the d.c. power input. The basic circuit is shown in Fig. 14.6.

The two transistors in push-pull are rarely biased to cut off. A driver stage by a transistor T is required. It feeds an input transformer S which has a turns-ratio smaller than that needed for impedance matching. This is necessary to 'swamp', to some extent, the variations in input

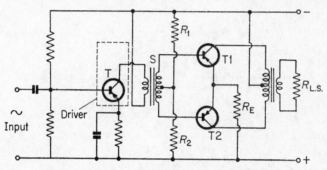

FIG. 14.6. Transistors in push-pull arrangement

resistance of the push-pull pair of transistors, T1, T2, which cause distortion of the signal input current.

The a.c. load value required by one transistor is V_{pk}/I_{pk} (p. 273). Now only one transistor operates at a time. Thus each half of the centre-tapped transformer can be considered as a separate unit. The step-down ratio from the total primary winding to each collector of the transistor is thus 2:1. Since the reflected impedance depends on the square of the turns-ratio, the reflected impedance is four times less for each transistor than for the collector-to-collector circuit. Thus the collector-to-collector load must be four times the value V_{pk}/I_{pk}. When the transistor is fully driven, $V_{pk} = V_{CC} - V_{min} = V_{CC}$ approximately.

The emitter resistor, R_E, in Fig. 14.6 cannot be decoupled owing to the large unidirectional currents which flow. These would charge up the decoupling capacitor, and produce exponential variations in the emitter voltage, with consequent severe distortion. R_E is of the order of 5 to 20 ohms and produces negative feedback. For a similar reason the resistor R_2 is not decoupled. It must have a relatively small value, such as 100 ohms, since it is in series with the signal applied between the base and the emitter.

EXAMPLES

Class B Push-pull Power Amplifiers

1. Two transistors with maximum collector current of 100 mA are to be used in a class B push-pull a.f. amplifier with a d.c. supply voltage of 6 V. Assuming a perfect output transformer, calculate the maximum a.f. power output obtainable and the required transformer turns-ratio to match a load impedance of 3 ohms.

As explained on p. 275, the peak voltage produced by each transistor is approximately equal to the supply voltage when fully driven, since $V_{pk} = V_{CC} - V_{min}$ and V_{min} is small. Thus the collector-to-collector load value

$$= \frac{4V_{pk}}{I_{pk}} \simeq \frac{4 \times 6}{0.1} = 240 \ \Omega$$

The turns-ratio $T = \dfrac{\text{total primary turns}}{\text{secondary turns}}$

$$= \sqrt{\frac{\text{collector-to-collector load}}{R_L}}$$

$$= \sqrt{\frac{240}{3}} = \sqrt{80} \simeq 9:1 \tag{1}$$

Maximum a.c. power output, P_{ac}

$$= \frac{V_{pk} \times I_{pk}}{2} = \frac{6 \times 0.1 \times 10^3}{2} \, \text{mW} = 300 \, \text{mW}$$

2. Two transistors having maximum collector dissipation of 60 mW each are used as a class B push-pull pair. $V_{CC} = 6$ V, the collector-to-collector a.c. load value is 240 ohms, and $V_{min} = 0.25$ V. Calculate the maximum a.c. power output when fully driven, and find the efficiency of the collector circuit.

The step-down ratio from the total winding to each collector of the transistor is 2:1. Since the reflected impedance depends on the square of the turns-ratio, the load for one transistor must be 2^2 or 4 times less than the collector-to-collector a.c. load value.

$$\therefore \text{ The load for one transistor} = \frac{240}{4} = 60 \ \Omega$$

$$\therefore I_{pk} = \frac{V_{pk}}{60} = \frac{6 - 0.25}{60} \times 10^3 \, \text{mA} = 96 \, \text{mA (approx.)}$$

Since the collector current flow is in the form of a half sine-wave, the resulting d.c.

$$I_{dc} = \text{average value} = \frac{2}{\pi} I_{pk} = \frac{2 \times 96}{\pi} = 61 \text{ mA}$$

Maximum a.c. power output, $P_{ac} = \dfrac{(V_{CC} - V_{min})I_{pk}}{2}$

$$= \frac{5 \cdot 75 \times 96}{2} \text{ mW} = 276 \text{ mW}$$

D.c. power supplied,

$$P_{dc} = V_{CC} \times I_{dc} = 6 \times 0 \cdot 061 \text{ W} = 366 \text{ mW}$$

$$\therefore \text{ efficiency} = \frac{P_{ac}}{P_{dc}} \times 100\% = \frac{276}{366} \times 100\% = 76\% \text{ (approx.)}$$

The theoretical maximum efficiency is $78 \cdot 7\%$. With valves, it is difficult to exceed 60% efficiency.

It should be noted that the collector power dissipation

$$= P_{dc} - P_{ac} = 366 - 276 = 90 \text{ mW}$$

Thus each collector is dissipating 45 mW as heat and this is within the maximum collector rating of 60 mW, as given in the question.

Feedback

When an amplifier functions normally, the input and output circuits are independent of each other. The performance of the amplifier, however, has been found to improve by feeding part of the output back to the input circuit. *Voltage feedback* and *current feedback* can be arranged.

If the feedback is in phase with the input signal, this is called *positive feedback*. The amplifier gain is then increased but a rapid build-up may lead to instability and to oscillations. So far as amplifiers are concerned, *negative feedback* has considerable advantages, as shown later. In this case the signal feedback is *opposite* in phase (antiphase) to the input signal. The gain is therefore reduced, but as the input can be increased to restore the gain, this is no drawback in practice.

Gain with Negative Feedback

Fig. 14.7 illustrates voltage negative feedback by a block diagram. V_i is the input signal, V_o is the output signal, and a fraction β of V_o is fed back to the input circuit using potential divider resistors R_1 and R_2. Together, R_1 and R_2 are much greater than the load R_L. Thus the fraction β fed back $= R_2/(R_1 + R_2)$ of V_o.

From Fig. 14.7, it can be seen that the voltage driving the amplifier is reduced from V_i to $(V_i - \beta V_o)$. In the absence of feedback, the output

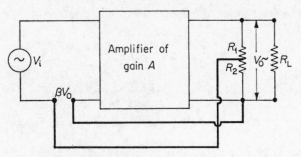

FIG. 14.7. Negative feedback

voltage $V_0 = AV_i$, where A is the gain of the amplifier. If V_0 is the new output voltage with feedback, then

$$V_0 = A(V_i - \beta V_0)$$

$$\therefore V_0(1 + \beta A) = AV_i$$

$$\therefore \frac{V_0}{V_i} = \frac{A}{1 + \beta A} = A_F$$

where A_F is the gain with negative feedback.

A_F is thus less than A by the ratio $1:(1 + \beta A)$. If the gain A is 180 and 5% of the output voltage is fed back, then $\beta A = 1/20 \times 180 = 9$. Hence $A_F = A/10 = 18$.

Effect on Harmonic Distortion

As explained on p. 216, the curvature of the dynamic characteristic of an amplifier valve introduces harmonic distortion into the output, that is, unwanted frequencies higher than the fundamental are introduced. Without negative feedback, suppose the amplitude of the voltage of the fundamental frequency is V_1 and that of a harmonic introduced is V_2, so that the proportion of the harmonic in the output is V_2/V_1.

With negative feedback, both V_1 and V_2 are reduced in the ratio $1:(1 + \beta A)$. The input signal, however, can be increased to restore the amplitude of the output voltage at the fundamental frequency to V_1. Consequently, the ratio of harmonic to fundamental voltage is now $V_2/(1 + A\beta) \div V_1$. Thus the ratio is reduced by $(1 + A\beta)$ and so harmonic distortion is reduced.

EXAMPLES

The following numerical examples illustrate the effect of negative feedback.

1. An a.f. voltage amplifier, delivering 10 V a.c. with 5% harmonic distortion, has a gain of 100. If 2% of the output voltage is fed back as negative feedback, NFB, find the input required to maintain the output at 10 V a.c. and the new value of harmonic percentage.

With negative feedback, NFB, gain A_F is given by

$$A_F = \frac{A}{1 + \beta A} = \frac{100}{1 + 100 \times 2/100} = 33 \cdot 3$$

Without NFB, the input V_i

$$= \frac{V_o}{A} = \frac{10 \text{ V}}{100} = 0 \cdot 1 \text{ V}$$

With NFB, the input required to restore the output to 10 V a.c. is given by

$$V_i = \frac{V_o}{A_F} = \frac{10 \text{ V}}{33 \cdot 3} = 0 \cdot 3 \text{ V}$$

The new percentage harmonic distortion is

$$\frac{5\%}{1 + \beta A} = \frac{5}{3} = 1 \cdot 7\%$$

2. An a.f. amplifier has a gain of 1,000 at 1 kHz and a gain of 100 at 50 Hz. Calculate the ratio of the gains at the two frequencies when NFB is applied, and comment on the effect produced on the frequency response curve of the amplifier, if β is 2%.

Without NFB,

$$\frac{\text{gain at 1 kHz}}{\text{gain at 60 Hz}} = \frac{1,000}{100} = 10$$

With NFB, (1) gain at 1 kHz

$$= \frac{1,000}{1 + \dfrac{2}{100} \times 1,000} = \frac{1,000}{21} = 47 \cdot 6,$$

(2) gain at 50 Hz

$$= \frac{100}{1 + \dfrac{2}{100} \times 100} = \frac{100}{3} = 33 \cdot 3$$

$$\therefore \text{ ratio of gains} = \frac{47 \cdot 6}{33 \cdot 3} = 1 \cdot 4$$

The gain ratio is thus reduced from 10 to 1·4 with negative feedback. This implies a more uniform frequency response of the amplifier circuit. Thus negative feedback improves the frequency response of an amplifier.

Advantages of Negative Feedback

If there are variations in the d.c. supply voltage or the valve characteristics while working, the amplification at a particular frequency may change from A_1 to A_2 say. With negative feedback, however, the change from A_1 to A_2 is considerably reduced. Negative feedback thus stabilizes the amplifier against variations in supply voltage or in valve characteristics.

To illustrate this point, suppose an amplifier has a gain A_1 of 1,000 and that this falls to 500, A_2, due to a drop in supply voltage. This is a ratio of gains, $A_2:A_1$, of 1:2. Now suppose, however, that negative feedback was applied so that $\beta = 0 \cdot 02$. Then

$$A_1 = \frac{1,000}{1 + 0 \cdot 02 \times 1,000} = \frac{1,000}{21} = 49 \text{ (approx.)}$$

and

$$A_2 = \frac{500}{1 + 0 \cdot 02 \times 500} = \frac{500}{11} = 45 \text{ (approx.)}$$

Thus $A_2/A_1 = 45/49 = 0 \cdot 9$ (approx.), or nearly 1. Hence the change in gain is considerably reduced with negative feedback.

Transistor Emitter-follower (or Common-collector Amplifier)

A circuit which utilises 100% negative feedback for a transistor amplifier is shown in Fig. 14.8. The load resistor, R_E, is placed in the emitter lead, so that (i) voltage feedback is obtained, (ii) the output is now taken from the emitter instead of the collector. It is called an

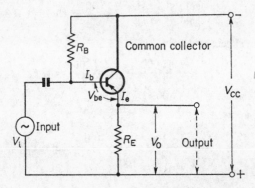

FIG. 14.8. Transistor common-collector amplifier

emitter-follower or *common-collector* amplifier; from an a.c. point of view, the collector is common to the input and output circuits *via* the low resistance of the supply, V_{CC}. Likewise, a *cathode-follower* valve circuit is one with a resistance load in the cathode lead.

Since R_E carries direct current, no bias stabilization circuit is required. Thus two base-biasing resistors (p. 256) need not be used. As can be seen from Fig. 14.8, only a resistor R_B is necessary, of the order of 100 kΩ. The high input resistance (see p. 281) of the transistor is then maintained. The value of $R_B = (V_{CC} - V_E)/I_B$.

As the whole of the output voltage is fed back, the voltage gain is less than one, but this is more than outweighed by the advantages of the circuit. These are (a) the input resistance is high and (b) the output resistance is low, which is useful for matching and isolating purposes.

Input resistance. With a.c. conditions, from Fig. 14.8 we have

$$V_{be} = V_i - I_e R_E, \quad \text{or} \quad V_i = V_{be} + I_e R_E$$

$$\therefore \text{ input resistance } r_i' = \frac{V_i}{I_b} = \frac{V_{be} + I_e R_E}{I_b} = \frac{V_{be} + (\beta + 1)I_b R_E}{I_b}$$

$$= r_i + (\beta + 1)R_E$$

Thus the input resistance r_i is increased by $(\beta + 1)R_E$ with 100% negative feedback.

If $(\beta + 1) = 40$ and $R_E = 4 \text{ k}\Omega$, $r_i' = r_i + 160 \text{ k}\Omega$, so that r_i' is of the order of $(\beta + 1)R_E$ and is high.

SUMMARY

1. If R_s is the dynamic impedance of a loudspeaker coil in the secondary of a step-down transformer, the reflected impedance in the primary circuit $= R_s/T^2$, where T is the turns-ratio. Maximum power is delivered by matching R_s/T^2 to the output valve or transistor.

2. The a.c. power developed in a load can be found by (i) drawing the load line, (ii) using $P_{ac} = (I_{max} - I_{min})(V_{max} - V_{min})/8$.

3. The efficiency of the circuit $= (P_{ac}/P_{dc}) \times 100\%$. Class A is relatively inefficient (less than 50%). Class B push-pull is much more efficient (theoretically over 70%) and eliminates even harmonic distortion.

4. With transistor a.f. power amplifiers, (i) the allowable collector current is governed by the maximum d.c. power which may be dissipated at the collector junction, (ii) the maximum allowable current peak swing may be taken as practically I_o, where I_o is the quiescent value, (iii) the maximum peak swing voltage is approximately V_o, the quiescent value, or V_{CC}, the supply voltage.

5. In negative feedback, the signal is fed back 180° out of phase with the input. This reduces harmonic distortion and produces a more uniform response. In the emitter-follower or grounded-collector (transistors), 100% negative feedback is provided. This leads to high input and low output impedance, which is useful for impedance matching.

EXERCISE 14

1. A loudspeaker has an impedance of 10 Ω, and is coupled to a power valve by a transformer of turns-ratio 1:50. Calculate the a.c. resistance of the valve r_a if it delivers undistorted maximum power to the loudspeaker when r_a is equal to the external impedance.

2. A loudspeaker has an impedance of 3 Ω and is coupled to a transistor a.f. power amplifier by a transformer with a turns-ratio 1:15. What is the impedance in the transistor circuit?

3. A valve used as an audio-frequency class-A amplifier draws 50 mA anode current at an anode voltage of 250 volts with no input signal applied. When supplied with a sinusoidal input signal the anode voltage varies between 50 and 450 volts and the corresponding anode current change is 90 to 10 mA.

Calculate: (*a*) the power drawn from the h.t. supply, (*b*) the output power from the stage, (*c*) the efficiency of operation.

4. Explain with the aid of a sketch the principle of operation of a moving-coil loudspeaker. What is the function of a baffle-board?

The optimum load of a particular output valve is 4,900 ohms. What turns-ratio is required in the output transformer to match the valve to a 4·0 ohm moving-coil loudspeaker? (*C. & G.*)

5. What is meant by the *load line* of a power valve? A triode has the following anode characteristics:

Grid volts = 0		Grid volts = −4 V		Grid volts = −8 V	
Anode volts	Anode current mA	Anode volts	Anode current mA	Anode volts	Anode current mA
50	12	—	—	—	—
75	25	175	10	300	7
100	43	200	23	325	17
125	65	225	38	—	—
—	—	250	58	350	28

If the grid bias is −4 V, the anode voltage supply 350 volts and the external load 6,000 ohms, calculate the power output when the grid swing has an amplitude of 4 V. (*C. & G.*)

6. The characteristics of a junction transistor are given below.

Collector voltage V_{CE}	Collector current I_C (mA)		
	$I_B = 0$	40 μA	80 μA
1·0	0·20	1·90	3·7
4·0	0·30	2·05	4·0
7·0	0·40	2·20	4·3

The transistor is connected in a common-emitter stage with a collector load of 1,500 Ω, a supply voltage of 6 V and a d.c. bias of 40 μA.

Plot the characteristics and draw the appropriate load line. Calculate the power dissipated in the transistor. (*C. & G.*)

7. A valve with a 15 kΩ resistor anode load has a battery supply of 200 V. A sinusoidal signal produces a sinusoidal anode current variation from 2 mA to 10 mA. Calculate the output power in the anode circuit.

8. When the load line is constructed on the output characteristics of a transistor CE power amplifier, it is found that $I_{max} = 46$ mA, $I_{min} = 2$ mA, $V_{max} = 11 \cdot 5$ V and $V_{min} = 0 \cdot 5$ V, under certain input signal drive conditions. Calculate (i) the value of the collector load resistance, (ii) the a.c. power output, (iii) the output transformer turns ratio required to match to a loudspeaker speech coil impedance of 5 Ω.

9. List the advantages of a class B push-pull amplifier compared to a class A amplifier.

10. A transistor class B push-pull amplifier requires a collector-to-collector load of 200 Ω. Calculate the transformer turns-ratio required to match to a loudspeaker of 2 Ω impedance.

When fully driven, each transistor passes a peak current of 80 mA. Find the a.c. power output and collector circuit efficiency if the supply $V_{CC} = 9$ V and the minimum voltage $= 0 \cdot 5$ V.

11. List the advantages of *negative feedback*. Draw a circuit to illustrate negative voltage feedback.

An a.f. amplifier, having a gain of 1,000 and an output distortion of 5%, is provided with negative voltage feedback. If the feedback fraction is $0 \cdot 02$, find the new values of the gain and of the distortion.

12. What are the advantages of an *emitter-follower*? Draw a circuit to illustrate the emitter-follower for a transistor.

13. A transistor having a value $\beta(h_{fe})$ of 50 is used in a common-emitter-follower stage with an emitter resistor of 5 kΩ and a power supply of 10 V. The collector current is to be 1 mA. Calculate the required value of base-biasing resistor and the effective input impedance. (V_{BE} is small enough to be neglected.)

15. R.F. Amplifiers

Inter-electrode Capacitance

There are three electrodes in a triode valve, anode, grid and cathode, and hence three inter-electrode capacitances. The most important when the valve is used is C_{ag}, the capacitance between the anode and grid. As shown in the block diagram in Fig. 15.1, this couples the output (anode) circuit to the input (grid-cathode) circuit. Thus a.c.

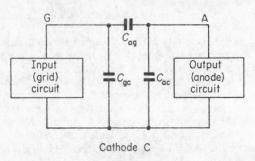

Fig. 15.1. Feedback

energy may be fed back from the output to the input circuit through C_{ag}, leading to distortion and circuit instability.

For a triode, C_{ag} is about 5 pF. At an audio-frequency such as 1,000 Hz, its reactance is 32 million ohms and feedback is thus negligible. At radio-frequency, however, the reactance is of the order of 30,000 ohms. Considerable feedback then occurs and thus the triode could not be used for r.f. amplification.

Tetrode Valve

The tetrode valve was introduced to reduce the anode-grid capacitance. This was done by placing an extra grid, S.G., between the grid, G, and anode, A, Fig. 15.2 (i). It is called a *screen grid* because it acts as an electrostatic shield between A and G, the control grid, and reduces the inter-electrode capacitance C_{ag} to an extremely low value, Fig. 15.2 (ii). The feedback from output to input circuits is then negligible at r.f. and thus stable r.f. amplification is obtained.

In practice, the screen grid is maintained at a high d.c. potential so that electrons continue to reach the anode after passing through it. The potential is obtained from the potential divider formed by R_1 and R_2 across the h.t. supply in Fig. 15.3. The screen grid must be *earthed to a.c.*, however, while the valve is operating and this is done by placing a decoupling capacitor C_1 between S.G. and the cathode C.

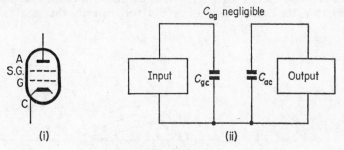

FIG. 15.2.   Tetrode valve

In Fig. 15.3, $C_1 = 0.1\,\mu\text{F}$. This has a low reactance of about 1 ohm to a.c. of radio-frequency 10^6 Hz (1 MHz) and effectively earths the screen to a.c.

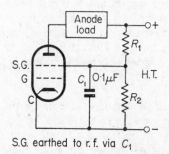

S.G. earthed to r.f. via C_1

FIG. 15.3.   Earthing screen grid to a.c.

Tetrode Characteristics

Typical tetrode characteristics are shown in Fig. 15.4. The *mutual characteristics* $I_a - V_g$, V_a and V_s (screen potential) constant, have about the same slope as the triode mutual characteristics, Fig. 15.4 (i). The mutual conductance, g_m, is hence of the same order. This is due to the fact that the control grid G is next to the cathode in each valve and has therefore similar effects on flow of anode current.

The curves, however, are closer together than in the triode, showing that changes of anode potential affect the anode current to a much smaller extent. This is due to the presence of the screen grid in front of the anode. It tends to shield the cathode from the influence of the anode. The r_a of the tetrode is thus much larger than the triode. If $r_a = 100,000\ \Omega$ and $g_m = 1.5$ mA per volt, then $\mu = r_a \times g_m = 300$. A high μ is an advantage of the tetrode valve.

Anode characteristics, $I_a - V_a$, V_g and V_s constant, are shown in Fig. 15.4 (ii). A dip or 'kink' appears between anode voltages of 15 to 72 V. This is due to a phenomenon called *secondary emission*. Above 15 V, the kinetic energy of the electrons reaching the metal anode

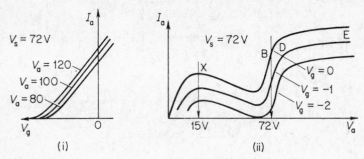

FIG. 15.4. Tetrode characteristics

plate is sufficient to knock out electrons from its atoms. These secondary electrons from the anode are then attracted to the screen grid, which has a higher positive potential than the anode. Beyond 72 V, however, which is the screen grid potential, the secondary electrons are attracted back to the anode. Thus the anode current rises from B to D, say, and a 'normal' anode current variation is then obtained.

Pentode Valve

The disadvantage of the tetrode valve lies in the irregular behaviour of I_a which may occur, owing to the 'kink' in the characteristic. Thus suppose that the valve is operating with an input V_1 and a load in the anode circuit. The actual anode potential then varies (see p. 222) and may become less than the screen-grid voltage for some portion of the input cycle. The secondary electrons then reach the screen grid, I_a behaves irregularly, and the result is distortion in the output circuit.

The pentode valve was designed primarily to overcome the secondary emission effect in the tetrode. In order to do this, the secondary electrons should return back to the anode from which they were ejected, and not be collected by the screen grid. A third grid, G_3, *earthed* by direct connection to the cathode, is therefore positioned between A and S.G. (Fig. 15.5). As A is always at some positive potential and G_3 is at zero potential, secondary electrons ejected from A will always be urged back to the anode. Thus no 'kink' is obtained in the I_a–V_a characteristic of a pentode. The new grid introduced is called a *suppressor grid* because it suppresses secondary emission effects in the anode circuit.

The pentode is thus a five-electrode valve containing three grids. In Fig. 15.5, G_1 is the control grid, G_2 is the screen grid. The intensity of the electrostatic field round C is still determined mainly by the potentials of G_1 and G_2. Thus variations of anode potential cause very little variation of I_a because A has an earthed grid, G_3, in front of it and is the farthest electrode from C. Nevertheless, as experiment shows, electrons

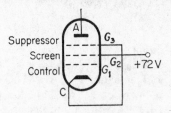

Suppressor earthed by direct
connection to C

FIG. 15.5   Pentode valve

reach the anode in large numbers. The electrons from C are accelerated as they approach the screen grid, and although the latter collects a number, many electrons pass through it. Between G_2 (+72 V say) and G_3 (0) the electrons are slowed down, but they are travelling fast enough to pass through G_3. They then immediately come under the action of the accelerating field from G_3 (0) to A (positive voltage) and reach the anode.

Pentode Characteristics

The *anode characteristics* of a pentode, I_a-V_a(V_g and V_s constant), are shown in Fig. 15.6 (i). There is no kink as in the tetrode. The small upward slope shows that the anode potential affects the anode current

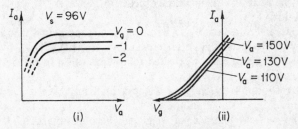

FIG. 15.6.   Pentode characteristics

slightly. The r_a is high. The actual magnitude depends on the geometry of the valve electrodes and the extent of the electrostatic shielding between anode and screen grid. The r_a of a pentode used for r.f. voltage amplification is very high, such as 1 megohm or more. The r_a of a power (output) pentode is much lower, such as 30,000 ohms.

The *mutual characteristics*, I_a–V_g (V_a and V_s constant) are shown in Fig. 15.6 (ii). The slope is about the same as for triode and tetrode valves. The characteristics are close together, as explained above. As r_a is generally high, it follows from $\mu = r_a \times g_m$ that μ is high. An amplification factor of 1,000 is common for a r.f. voltage amplifier.

R.F. Voltage Amplification

For r.f. voltage amplification, a resistance load, R_L say, is unsuitable owing to the circuit self-capacitance (p. 63). This would shunt the r.f. currents from R_L, since the reactance would be low at radio-frequencies. The only useful load for r.f. voltage amplification is the *tuned-anode load*, which is a parallel arrangement of coil (L, r) and capacitor (C)

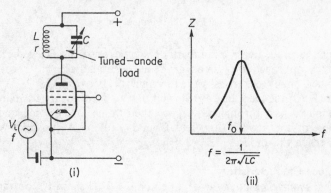

FIG. 15.7. R.f. voltage amplifier

tuned to the radio-frequency concerned, Fig. 15.7 (i). The advantages of such a load are:

(i) It has an impedance Z, and hence a voltage gain variation with frequency f which is highly selective, Fig. 15.7 (ii). Thus by tuning C, the desired signal can be selected for presentation to the detector in a radio receiver;

(ii) At resonant frequency, f_0 it has a high impedance, L/Cr ohms, and hence a high voltage gain.

(iii) The self-capacitance of the coil becomes part of the total capacitance required for tuning, which is mainly provided by C, and thus presents no problem.

Pentode as Constant Current Generator

Any generator with a very high internal resistance can be regarded as a constant current generator, since the current is then independent of the load. For this reason the pentode, which has a very high a.c.

resistance r_a, can be regarded as a constant current generator. We shall see later that the transistor amplifier can be considered as a constant current generator for the same reason. On the other hand, the valve triode amplifier has a relatively low a.c. resistance r_a, and is therefore best considered as a *voltage* generator in circuit analysis (p. 227).

To see what happens for an anode load in the pentode circuit, suppose Z_L represents the impedance of the tuned coil-capacitor. Then, as shown on p. 228 for the valve equivalent circuit, the output voltage V_0 is related to the input voltage V_i by

$$V_0 = \frac{\mu Z_L}{r_a + Z_L} V_i$$

But $\mu = g_m \times r_a$. Thus

$$V_0 = g_m V_i \times \frac{r_a Z_L}{r_a + Z_L} \tag{1}$$

Now $g_m V_i$ is the magnitude of the output alternating *current* obtained from the valve.

Hence, from (1), the valve acts as a current generator of magnitude $g_m V_i$, with the load given by $r_a Z_L / (r_a + Z_L)$.

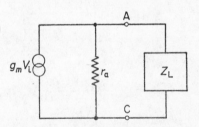

FIG. 15.8. Equivalent valve circuit

If S is the combined resistance of r_a and Z_L in parallel, then $1/S = 1/r_a + 1/Z_L$, from which $S = r_a Z_L / (r_a + Z_L)$. It therefore follows that the equivalent valve circuit can be represented as shown in Fig. 15.8. Thus the tuned circuit is directly damped by the a.c. resistance r_a of the valve.

EXAMPLE

What parallel tuning capacitance is required across a coil of 200 μH inductance, 20-ohm resistance to make it resonate to a frequency of 1,000 kHz? Calculate the impedance of this parallel circuit at 1,000 kHz, and find the voltage amplification obtained when it is used as a tuned-anode load with a pentode of $g_m = 2$ mA/V, $r_a = 500,000$ Ω.

Let C = the parallel tuning capacitance required in farads. Since

$$f_0 = \frac{1}{2\pi\sqrt{LC}}$$

$$\therefore \ 10^6 = \frac{1}{2\pi\sqrt{\dfrac{200}{10^6}C}}$$

$$\therefore \ 10^{12} \times 4\pi^2 \times \frac{200}{10^6}C = 1$$

$$\therefore \ C = \frac{1}{10^6 \times 4\pi^2 \times 200}\,\text{F} = 125\ \text{pF}$$

At resonance, the load Z reduces to a pure resistance of L/Cr ohms (p. 171).

$$\therefore \ Z = \frac{L}{Cr} = \frac{\dfrac{200}{10^6}}{\left(\dfrac{1}{10^6 \times 4\pi^2 \times 200}\right) \times 20} = 80{,}000\ \Omega\ \text{(approx.)}$$

Now   voltage gain, $A_V = \dfrac{\mu\,\dfrac{L}{Cr}}{r_a + \dfrac{L}{Cr}}$

where $\mu = R_a \times g_m = 1{,}000$.

$$\therefore \ A_V = \frac{1{,}000 \times 80{,}000}{500{,}000 + 80{,}000} = 138$$

Also, from our previous analysis for Fig. 15.8,

$$S = \frac{r_a Z_L}{r_a + Z_L} = \frac{500 \times 80}{580}\,\text{k}\Omega$$

so that $A_V = g_m S = 2 \times \dfrac{500 \times 80}{580}$

$$= 138,\ \text{as before}$$

Couplings

If more than one pentode is used, the couplings may be *R–C coupling*, Fig. 15.9 (i), or *transformer coupling*, Fig. 15.9 (ii). The maximum stage-gain is obtained when the load is tuned to the input frequency in Fig. 15.9 (i) and when the secondary circuit is tuned to the input frequency in Fig. 15.9 (ii). In the latter case, the voltage across the capacitor passed to valve 2 is Q times the induced e.m.f. in the secondary (see p. 160).

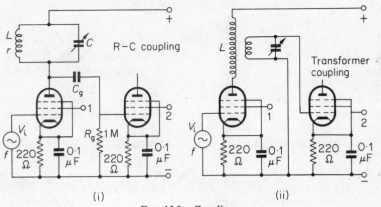

FIG. 15.9. Couplings

Band-pass Coupling

If a tuned-anode load is loosely coupled to a secondary circuit tuned to the same frequency (Fig. 15.10 (i)), i.e. $L_1C_1 = L_2C_2$, a *band* of radio-frequencies is evenly amplified. This is shown in the frequency-response curve (Fig. 15.10 (ii)). Consequently, when the circuit is

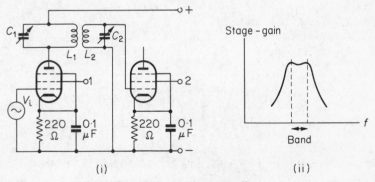

FIG. 15.10. Band-pass coupling

tuned to a transmitter sending out a narrow band of radio-frequencies, the same amplification of all the frequencies can be obtained. The single resonant circuit discussed in Fig. 15.9 (i) and (ii) is unsuitable for dealing with a band of frequencies. In a later chapter (see p. 310), it is shown that the transmission of sound (a.f.) frequencies from a broadcasting station occupies a band of radio frequencies. A circuit such as Fig. 15.10 (i) is therefore necessary to amplify the frequencies without distortion.

Transistor R.F. Amplifier

In the triode valve, internal feedback occurs from the output to the input circuit, largely by way of the inter-electrode capacitance C_{ag} (p. 284). Feedback is considerable for radio-frequencies, leading to instability. In a similar way, internal feedback occurs through a transistor *via* the collector-base capacitance. Thus a voltage produced at the output terminals when the transistor acts as a current generator will partly be fed back to the input, and this causes instability at r.f. if no counter measures are taken.

Another point of concern in r.f. amplification with transistors is the fall in gain with frequency. The α cut-off frequency, the frequency when the current gain falls to 3 dB of its low-frequency value, must be at least ten times the operating frequency to obtain the best transistor performance in the CE mode.

Previously, the use of the alloyed-junction type of transistor required a *neutralisation circuit*. This circuit provided a current feedback to the input (base) circuit which was 180° out of phase with that due to internal feedback from the collector circuit and neutralised it. Nowadays, with the use of alloy diffusion and planar-type transistors, the collector-base capacitance is reduced below 2 pF. Since these transistors have α cut-off greater than 100 MHz, they can be used at frequencies of 10 MHz, for example, without a neutralising circuit.

Tuned Collector R.F. amplifier

The transistor tuned r.f. amplifier circuit is shown in Fig. 15.11. T1 is the tuned collector amplifier, coupled to a following transistor T2

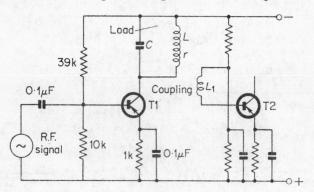

FIG. 15.11. R.f. amplifier—tuned collector

via the mutual inductance between L and L_1. A step-*down* ratio is used, for a reason we now explain.

Ferrite cups and cores are used for L and L_1, so that the coupling factor is close to 1 and impedance transformation formulae may be applied. Suppose T2 has a low input resistance r_i of $2k\Omega$ and $T =$ ratio of primary to secondary turns $= 10$. Then the reflected resistance across the tuned circuit $= T^2 r_i = 10^2 \times 2k\Omega$. The dynamic resistance of the tuned circuit may be say $80k\Omega$. Damping of the tuned circuit by the low resistance r_i, which would occur with direct coupling to T2 and would lead to a substantial reduction in Q-factor and selectivity, is thus avoided. Further, suppose the input capacitance C_i of T2 is 50 pF. Then the reflected capacitance across the tuned circuit $= C_i^2/T^2$ (p. 150) $= 50/10^2 = 0.5$ pF. Since the tuned circuit may require 100 pF, for example, to tune it, it can be seen that any variation of the transistor capacitance C_i will have a negligible effect during operation. This would not be the case with direct coupling.

EXAMPLE

A tuned transistor amplifier has a step-down ratio of 10:1 from the tuned circuit to the following transistor. Both transistors operate in the CE (common-emitter) mode and have input resistances of $2\,k\Omega$ at the operating frequency. The output resistances are high enough to have negligible effect. The β-value is 40. Calculate the voltage gain (base to base) at the resonant frequency, if the dynamic resistance of the tuned circuit is $200\,k\Omega$.

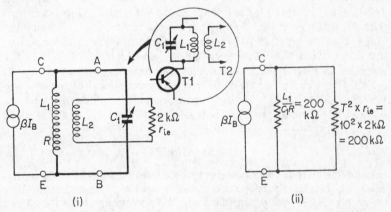

Fig. 15.12. Example

Fig. 15.12 (i) shows the equivalent circuit of the transistor with its tuned load L_1, C_1. L_2 represents the coupling coil to the second transistor, with its input resistance r_{ie} of $2\,k\Omega$. This is further simplified in Fig. 15.12 (ii). It shows the dynamic resistance L_1/C_1R of the tuned load (p. 288), in parallel with the reflected resistance from L_2 of $2\,k\Omega$. This is stepped-up by the square of the turns-ratio, T.

$$\therefore \text{ reflected resistance} = T^2 \times r_{ie} = 10^2 \times 2\,k\Omega = 200\,k\Omega$$

From Fig. 15.12 (ii), the effective load R' in the first transistor is that due to 200 kΩ in parallel with 200 kΩ. Hence $R' = 100$ kΩ,

$$\therefore \text{ voltage across load} = \beta I_B \times R' = 40 I_B \times 100 \text{ k}\Omega$$

This voltage is reduced 10 times to the following transistor since the step-down ratio is 10:1. Hence the base voltage $= 4 I_B \times 100$ kΩ. But the input voltage to the first transistor is $I_B \times 2$ kΩ

$$\therefore \text{ voltage gain} = \frac{4 I_B \times 100 \text{ k}\Omega}{I_B \times 2 \text{ k}\Omega} = 200$$

R.F. Transistor Cut-off Frequency

The transistor cut-off frequency, $f_{\alpha CO}$, is an important parameter which we have already met on p. 243. As we saw there, the current amplification factor α diminishes at high frequencies owing to the transit time taken by the carriers. $f_{\alpha CO}$ is defined as the frequency at which α_0, the low-frequency value, drops by 3 dB, or the frequency at which $\alpha = \alpha_0/\sqrt{2} = 0.71\alpha_0$. Thus the magnitude of $f_{\alpha CO}$ indicates the maximum frequency of usefulness of the transistor. The β cut-off frequency is related to the α cut-off frequency by $f_{\beta CO} = f_{\alpha CO}(1 - \alpha_0)$, so that $f_{\beta CO}$ is much smaller than $f_{\alpha CO}$.

Another important parameter of transistors intended for r.f. use is the frequency f_T at which β is reduced to unity. Approximately, $f_T = \beta_0 f_{\beta CO}$, where β_0 is the low-frequency value of β. Only transistors with suitable high values of $f_{\beta CO}$ or f_T should be used in an r.f. amplifier.

$f_{\alpha CO}$ is in the region of 10 Mc/s for alloyed junction type r.f. transistors but micro-alloyed diffused types have $f_{\alpha CO}$ as high as 250 MHz. The more recent planar silicon transistors may have $f_{\alpha CO}$ values as high as 1,500 MHz. These two types of transistors are typical of those which may be used up to 20 MHz in the common-emitter mode of operation, without any need to consider feedback.

SUMMARY

1. (*a*) The tetrode was developed to overcome the inter-electrode capacitance, C_{ag}, between the anode and grid of the triode, which makes the latter unsuitable for r.f. voltage amplification. (*b*) When in operation the tetrode has its screen grid at a positive d.c. potential but is earthed to r.f. (*c*) The I_a–V_g curves of the tetrode are similar to those of the triode, but the I_a–V_a curve has a 'kink' due to secondary emission effects. The tetrode may be regarded as a 'triode + extra anode', and has a high μ and r_a.

2. The *pentode* eliminates the effect of secondary emission by means of a suppressor grid, earthed by connection to the cathode, placed between anode and screen grid. The I_a-V_a curves thus have no 'kink'.

The I_a-V_g curves are similar to the tetrode.

The r_a and μ of pentodes are very high and they are widely used in r.f. amplifiers.

3. The dynamic characteristics of a tetrode and pentode of high R_a are almost identical with their static characteristics, and with a given input the valves may be considered as constant current a.c. generators.

4. In r.f. valve amplifiers, (i) a tuned load is used, (ii) transformer coupling may be used, (iii) band-pass coupling is obtained from two tuned circuits.

5. In a r.f. transistor CE amplifier, (i) a tuned collector is used, (ii) a step-down transformer is used for coupling. Internal feedback through the transistor is neglected in modern (e.g. planar) transistors.

EXERCISE 15

1. Explain as fully as you can why a triode valve is unsuitable as a r.f. voltage amplifier.

2. Draw a sketch showing the electrodes in (i) a pentode valve, (ii) a tetrode valve. Name the electrodes in each valve and, roughly, their usual d.c. potentials.

3. Draw the I_a–V_a and I_a–V_g characteristics of a *tetrode*, where I_a, V_a, V_g are the respective anode current, anode voltage and grid voltage. Account for (i) the small slope of the I_a–V_a curve, (ii) the 'kink' in the curve.

4. Explain the purpose and action of the *suppressor grid* in a pentode.

5. Draw several mutual and anode characteristics of an r.f. pentode voltage amplifier, and state how its constants r_a, g_m, μ compare with those of the triode. What effect, in general, has (*a*) a change in screen-grid potential, (*b*) a change in anode potential, on the anode current?

6. Explain the disadvantages of a resistance load, and the advantages of a tuned circuit load, for a r.f. amplifier.

7. Sketch a typical family of anode-current/anode-voltage characteristics for a pentode valve.

What are the fundamental reasons for: (i) the low value of r_a at low anode voltages, (ii) the high value of r_a at high anode voltages?   (*C. & G.*)

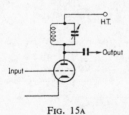

Fig. 15A

8. Explain, by reference to waveform diagrams, what is meant by (*a*) Class A, (*b*) Class B, and (*c*) Class C operation in a tuned transistor or valve amplifier.

State the drawbacks of using a triode valve in the radio frequency amplifier circuit shown in Fig. 15A. Draw an alternative circuit using a pentode valve and briefly explain how this avoids these drawbacks.   (*C. & G.*)

9. By reference to a sketch, explain the purpose of each of the three grids in a pentode valve.

Briefly discuss the reasons for using pentode valves rather than triode valves in the high-frequency stages of medium-wave radio receivers. (*C. & G.*)

10. Explain, by reference to a frequency response curve, how a tuned circuit may be used to provide selectivity in a radio frequency amplifier.

The measured response of a parallel tuned circuit is as shown in Table 1.

TABLE 1

Frequency in kHz	245	246	248	249	250	251	252	254	255
Voltage	35	55	83·5	96	100	96	83·5	55	35

Plot the response curve and use it to determine the bandwidth of the tuned circuit at the half-power (−3 dB) points.

Briefly comment on the suitability of such a circuit for use in a medium-wave broadcast receiver. (*C. & G.*)

11. With reference to a valve, define the terms:

(*a*) anode slope resistance (r_a), (*b*) amplification factor (μ), (*c*) mutual conductance (g_m).

A tuned-anode valve amplifier operates at resonance. For the valve, $\mu = 1,000$, $r_a = 500 \text{ k}\Omega$: the anode load consists of a 500-μH inductor (*L*) of 30-Ω resistance (*R*) with a parallel-connected tuning capacitor (*C*) of 450 pF.

Sketch the simple equivalent circuit of the amplifier and calculate its stage gain at resonance, given that the dynamic resistance of the resonant circuit is L/CR.

12. Draw a circuit diagram of a two-stage r.f. amplifier using transistors. Briefly explain the operation of the biasing arrangements.

Table 2 shows the voltage gain of an amplifier whose input and output impedances are equal.

TABLE 2

Frequency (kHz)	450	454	462	478	498
Voltage gain	100	92	60	31	17·5

Plot the gain-frequency characteristic on squared paper using scales of 3 dB/in. and 10 kHz/in. What is the 3-dB bandwidth of the amplifier? The gain-frequency characteristic may be assumed symmetrical about 450 kHz and the characteristic below resonance need not be plotted.

(*C. & G.*)

13. A valve amplifier consists of a valve having an internal anode circuit impedance of 30,000 ohms and an amplification factor of 25. An external impedance is placed in the anode circuit. What is the amplification obtainable with this arrangement if this impedance consists of (i) a resistance of 30,000 ohms, (ii) a coil of 5 millihenries and 25 ohms resistance shunted by a

capacitor of 0·001 microfarad, the amplifier in this case being operated at
the resonant frequency of this circuit?   (*C. & G.*)

14. Draw a diagram of band-pass coupling between r.f. amplifiers, and
sketch the frequency-response curves. What are the advantages of such a
coupling?

15. Draw a circuit diagram of a transistor CE tuned r.f. amplifier, showing
(i) the r.f. input, (ii) the load, (iii) the emitter resistor and decoupling
capacitor.

16. What do you understand by the terms: (i) transistor cut-off frequencies,
(ii) α_0 and β_0? A transistor intended for r.f. use is to be incorporated in a
CE tuned r.f. amplifier operating at 500 kHz. It has parameters of $\beta_0 = 50$
and α cut-off frequency $f_\alpha\text{co} = 120$ MHz. If the β cut-off frequency,
$f_\beta\text{co} = (1 - \alpha_0)f_\alpha\text{co}$, show that the transistor is suitable.

17. How are the effects of the input and output capacitance reduced in a
r.f. transistor amplifier?

The tuning capacitor in the tuned circuit of a CE transistor r.f. amplifier
is required to be 100 times the reflected capacitance from the preceding and
following transistors, T_1 and T_2 respectively. The output capacitance of T_1
is 10 pF and the input capacitance of T_2 is 200 pF. The step-up ratio from
the collector of T_1 is 2:1 and the step-down ratio to transistor T_2 is 10:1.
Calculate the value of the tuning capacitor.

16. Principles of Oscillators

Oscillations

If a charged capacitor C is discharged through a coil of inductance L and resistance R, an alternating current i is obtained whose amplitude decreases rapidly, Fig. 16.1 (i). This is often called an 'oscillatory discharge', Fig. 16.1 (ii). The frequency of the oscillations is approximately $1/2\pi\sqrt{LC}$. No oscillations are observed, however, when a

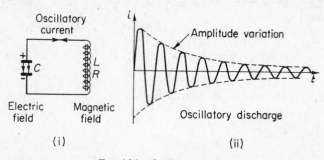

FIG. 16.1. Oscillatory circuit

charged capacitor is discharged through a resistor; the current then diminishes along an exponential curve, as shown in Fig. 4.19, p. 67.

The existence of oscillations of current when a charged capacitor C is discharged through an inductor L can be proved mathematically

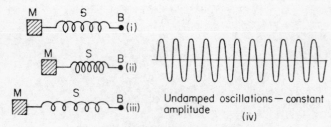

FIG. 16.2. Energy exchange in oscillations

but this is beyond the scope of this book. We can understand what happens, however, by considering a mechanical analogy. Fig. 16.2 (i) shows a spring S and a mass M attached to a fixed point B on a smooth horizontal plane. If M is displaced slightly in a horizontal direction and then released, the system oscillates to and fro along a horizontal

298

line. Examination of M and S, the two components, shows that
(i) when M is moving fastest, through its original undisturbed position
as in Fig. 16.2 (i), S is normal in length, (ii) when M is momentarily
at rest the spring S is either fully coiled up as in Fig. 16.2 (ii), or is
fully stretched out as in Fig. 16.2 (iii). The energy in the system is
alternating between the kinetic energy of M and the potential energy
of S. L and C in the above electrical system may be compared to M
and S in the mechanical system. *The energy in the electrical circuit is
stored alternately in the magnetic field of the coil and the electric field
of the capacitor.*

Energy Losses

The amplitude of the electrical oscillations diminishes, as shown in
Fig. 16.1 (ii), because energy is lost from the circuit. This occurs in two
ways: (i) The coil has some resistance, R, which gives rise to
I^2R losses, and (ii) electrical energy is lost into space outside the circuit,
especially when high-frequency a.c. flows, this phenomenon being
known as 'radiation'. These two losses may be added together, and the
total can then be considered due to some 'effective' resistance, R',
in the circuit.

The amplitude variations shown in Fig. 16.1 (ii) are known as *damped*
oscillations, and *are obtained when any electrical disturbance is started
in an L, C circuit*. In contrast, Fig. 16.2 (iv) shows continuous undamped
oscillations, which are of *constant* amplitude, and in order to obtain
them energy must be given continuously to the L, C circuit to make up
for the losses which inevitably occur. We proceed to discuss how this
can be done with the aid of a valve.

Simple Valve Oscillator

As an introduction to practical oscillators, consider the simple
valve circuit illustrated in Fig. 16.3. It is known as a form of *tuned-grid
oscillator*. In it the L, C circuit, known as the 'tank' circuit, is connected

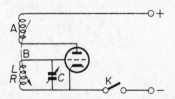

FIG. 16.3. Simple oscillator (tuned-grid)

between grid and cathode of a triode. The anode circuit contains a
coil A coupled to the coil B. Suppose that the circuit is completed
by the key K. An electrical disturbance is then caused in the tank
circuit, and the oscillations in it may die away. If, however, the coil

A is correctly wound and positioned relative to B, sufficient energy may be returned by electromagnetic induction to the tank circuit to make up for the losses. Once this has been brought about the oscillations will be undamped, and they will be continuous if energy from A is continuously making up that lost in the tank circuit. The electromagnetic coupling between A and B is represented by an arrow in Fig. 16.3.

So far we have been concerned with the coil A and the tank circuit. Suppose we now consider the action of the valve. When the circuit is made, the oscillatory current started in the tank circuit sets up an *alternating* voltage across the capacitor. This voltage between the grid and cathode in turn sets up an alternating current in the anode circuit. As B is coupled to A an alternating voltage is induced in B, and if this is *in phase* with the oscillatory current in the tank circuit the oscillations continue. In this way the valve circuit acts as a device which supplies energy continuously to the tank circuit. The source of energy, it should be noted, is the h.t. battery, which maintains the anode current. Thus the energy in the battery is consumed at a greater rate when the circuit is oscillating. The frequency of the oscillations in the tuned-grid circuit in Fig. 16.3 is given approximately by $1/2\pi\sqrt{LC}$.

Tuned-anode Circuit

The tank circuit may also be positioned in the anode circuit instead of the grid circuit (Fig. 16.4). More power is then obtained for the oscillatory circuit.

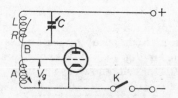

FIG. 16.4. Tuned-anode circuit

As before, an electrical disturbance is set up in the tank circuit when K is depressed, and an oscillatory current is obtained. An alternating voltage, V_g, is then induced in the grid circuit. In turn, V_g sets up an alternating current in the tank circuit by the amplifying action of the valve. If the coils are correctly wound and positioned relative to each other, this alternating current can be in phase with the oscillations in the tank circuit, so that power is supplied there to make up for the losses. The frequency of the oscillations is again given approximately by $1/2\pi\sqrt{LC}$.

The above considerations for maintaining oscillations is only a very general one. A rigorous treatment would require a study of the vector diagrams for the alternating quantities concerned. Further, the circuit in Fig. 16.4 is inefficient, as we see later.

Efficiency of Oscillator

All a.c. power, no matter which type of electronic device is used, is obtained by the conversion of the d.c. power supplied by the high-tension power unit. The *efficiency* of an oscillator is defined by:

$$\frac{\text{output power (a.c. power in tank circuit)}}{\text{input power (d.c. power from h.t. power unit)}} \times 100\%$$

The efficiency of a circuit depends on the type of bias employed, since this affects the anode current or power supplied. As we have seen, class A bias represents a maximum efficiency of 50%. There is a constant flow of anode current throughout the input cycle. Class B bias (p. 217) represents a higher efficiency since less anode current flows during the input cycle. Practical oscillators use class C bias, which produces the highest efficiency. In this case the valve is biased to an average negative d.c. potential beyond the cut-off value. Thus anode current may flow only for a short part of the input cycle, Fig. 16.5 (ii). If their phase and magnitude are correct, these pulses of current can supply just enough energy to make the oscillations in the tank circuit continuous. In an analogous way, the swing of a pendulum can be maintained by small impulses, correctly phased during the cycle.

Class C Bias

Any method by which class C bias is obtained must allow the oscillations to build up as soon as the valve circuit is made. A *fixed* battery-bias giving class C conditions is useless. The valve is then biased well beyond the cut-off point, and the valve is non-conducting when the circuit is made. No anode current and oscillations are then obtained.

A *C–R* combination or *grid leak* is used as a bias arrangement to ensure that the oscillator is self-starting, Fig. 16.5 (i). Since there is no current in *R* when the circuit is just made the grid-bias voltage is zero, the grid being then at the same potential as the cathode. The valve is now conducting, and oscillations build up. As it does so, the grid bias slides back automatically from zero until it is positive only for a very short part of the cycle, as shown. The power obtained or output power is now just able to maintain oscillations in the oscillatory circuit. In this way class C amplification is obtained automatically.

As can be seen from Fig. 16.5 (ii), the anode current flow settles down in the form of *pulses*. They occur on the positive half cycles

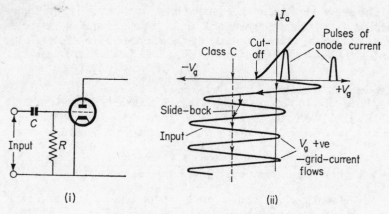

FIG. 16.5. Class C bias—high efficiency

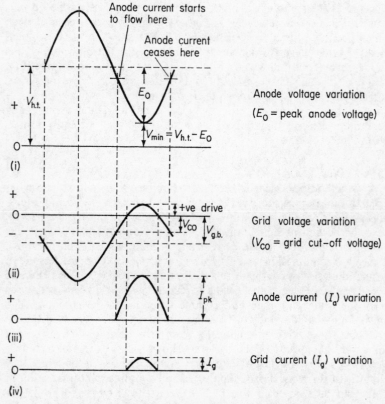

FIG. 16.6. Voltage and current variations in oscillator circuit

of the input voltage. Such a current waveform is a highly distorted version of the sine wave voltage driving the grid. However, as the anode load consists of a tuned circuit, a sine wave output of reasonably low harmonic distortion is obtained. The anode tuned circuit acts as a 'storage' circuit, storing energy between pulses, and is hence often called the 'tank circuit'. At the tank circuit resonant frequency, the pulses of anode current supply sufficient energy to maintain the oscillations. The efficiency increases when the pulses flow for a shorter time, but the a.c. power output then decreases so a compromise is necessary. To obtain maximum power output, the grid may be driven positive to the extent of about 10–15% of the h.t. voltage on the anode in power oscillators or amplifiers. Fig. 16.6 (i), (ii), (iii), (iv) show roughly the variations of anode voltage, grid voltage, anode current and grid current while the oscillator functions.

Practical Oscillators

The oscillator circuits shown previously in Figs. 16.3, 16.4 are inefficient. No provision for class C operation has been made in them. Automatic grid-leak bias is required for this purpose in practical oscillators, as we have seen.

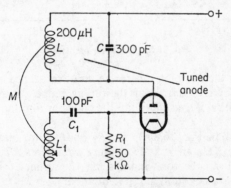

Fig. 16.7. Tuned-anode oscillator circuit

A form of *tuned-anode* oscillator is shown in Fig. 16.7. Feedback is obtained by mutual inductance M between the coils. When the tuned circuit is in resonance it acts as a pure resistance (p. 172), and the alternating voltage between the anode and cathode is then 180° out of phase with the alternating voltage between the grid and cathode (see p. 223). The feedback voltage is thus in the correct phase. The oscillator has the advantage that the tuned circuit is in the h.t. circuit where the anode current flows, so that it has a large a.c. output. Because of the power gain, it is also less susceptible to changes in the power supply voltages, and to variations in loading and valve parameters.

Transistor Oscillators

Using a transistor in place of a valve, the equivalent of the valve tuned anode oscillator is obtained by operating in the *common-emitter* mode and placing the tuning circuit in the collector lead, Fig. 16.8 (i). We have already seen that, in this case, the transistor input resistance is relatively low and its input capacitance relatively high. Consequently there must be adequate step-up from the base to the collector circuit,

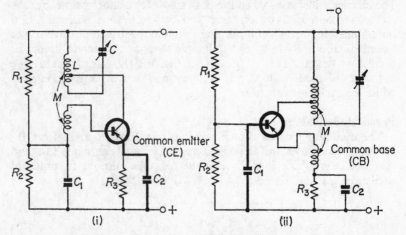

FIG. 16.8. Transistor oscillators

so as to reduce the damping due to the input resistance and to prevent the input capacitance restricting the tuning range. In the interests of frequency stability, it is usual to tap the collector into the tuned circuit, as shown.

In the circuit in Fig. 16.8 (i), R_1, R_2 and R_3 are bias stabilization components, C_1, C_2 are r.f. decoupling capacitors. The turns-ratio between base and collector windings may be about 1:15. Note that the emitter is at a common a.c. potential *via* C_2.

Fig. 16.8 (ii) shows a transistor oscillator in the *common-base* mode, with feedback from the emitter to the collector circuit. This gives a higher cut-off frequency, so the oscillator may operate at a higher frequency than in the common-emitter mode. It should be noted that the base is at a common a.c. potential *via* the decoupling capacitor C_1. Since the emitter-base input resistance is so low, the turns-ratio is greatly increased. A step-down ratio of 1:50 may be required,

Quartz Crystals

One important requirement of a radio transmitter is adequate frequency stability, and this depends considerably on the oscillator used in the circuit. So far, coils and capacitors have been used to provide control of the oscillation frequency, but, unless they are very carefully designed, the magnitudes of L and C are liable to vary slightly owing to temperature or humidity changes or to mechanical vibration. *Quartz crystals* have been used as the basic element of oscillators to provide very-high-frequency stability in transmitters and in electronic measuring equipment.

Quartz is a crystalline substance which can be cut in the form of a thin parallel-sided plate. If a mechanical stress is applied across two opposite faces between plates so that the dimensions of the crystal change slightly, electric charges appear on the plates. This is due to a displacement of ions inside the crystal structure. It is called the *piezo-electric effect*. Conversely, if a voltage is applied across the plates, the dimensions of the crystal change slightly. Thus if the voltage is alternating, the crystal *vibrates* owing to the continuous change in dimensions.

The frequency of vibration of the crystal depends only on the dimensions of the plate, such as its thickness, and is extremely stable. In a particular direction of cut of the crystal, the piezo-electric effect is a maximum. Silver vapour is condensed on opposite faces of the crystal plate for connections to be made and the plate is then mounted in an evacuated glass envelope like a radio valve.

Crystal Oscillator Circuits

A very simple form of crystal oscillator is the *Pierce* type shown in Fig. 16.9. Fig. 16.9 (i) shows a transistor oscillator and Fig. 16.9 (ii)

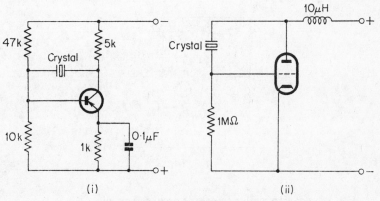

Fig. 16.9.   Crystal oscillator circuit

a valve oscillator. In the circuits, the quartz crystal acts effectively as a parallel-tuned circuit of high-frequency stability, with feedback arrangements as required in oscillators (p. 303).

SUMMARY

1. A transistor or valve maintains oscillations by acting as an amplifier providing its own input. It operates under class C conditions for maximum efficiency by means of a grid-bias arrangement, the source of power being the h.t. supply. Efficiency = (a.c. power/d.c. power supplied) × 100%.

2. In the tuned-anode valve oscillator, feedback is produced through mutual inductance between coils in the anode and grid circuit.

3. With a transistor oscillator in the CE mode, (i) the tuning circuit is the collector load, (ii) feedback is obtained between collector-base, (iii) bias may be applied by an emitter resistor and potential divider arrangement.

4. In the CB mode, (i) feedback is obtained between collector-emitter, (ii) the oscillator can operate at a higher frequency than the CE mode as the cut-off frequency is higher.

5. Quartz oscillators provide very high stability of frequency. Using transistors, they may be of the CE mode (Pierce).

EXERCISE 16

What are the missing words in the following statements 1–6?

In an oscillator:

1. The frequency is that of the . . . circuit and given by the formula . . .

2. Feedback to the input circuit should be . . . with the input signal. This is called . . . feedback.

3. The necessary bias is class . . . because it provides the greatest . . .

4. The source of energy of oscillations is the . . .

5. When the oscillator is switched on, the grid-bias in a valve is initially . . .

6. As the oscillations build up from zero, the grid-bias . . .

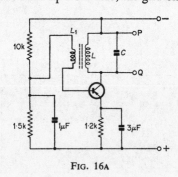

FIG. 16A

7. Fig. 16A shows a simple transistor oscillator circuit.

(i) If $L = 5$ mH, $C = 0 \cdot 05$ μF, what is the frequency of oscillations?

(ii) What is the purpose of L_1?

(iii) What is the purpose of the 10 k and 1·5 k resistors?

(iv) Why is the 1·5 k decoupled by the 1 μF capacitor?

(v) What is the purpose of the 1·2 k resistor?

(vi) Which are the output terminals?

8. Explain briefly how the transistor oscillator in Qn. 7 functions after it is switched on.

9. Describe the method of obtaining the class C bias in oscillator circuits. Explain why a grid-bias battery giving class C bias cannot be used.

10. A voltage amplifier usually functions under class A conditions, while an oscillator functions under class C conditions. Explain briefly the reason for the difference.

11. Draw a circuit diagram of a valve oscillator and describe how it works.

12. 'An oscillator can be considered as an amplifier providing its own input'. Explain this statement by taking the case of a practical oscillator. What is the source of energy of the oscillations and the *efficiency* of the oscillator?

13. Give a circuit diagram and briefly explain the action of *any* type of oscillator which uses a tuned circuit and either a valve or a transistor.

What factors influence the choice of the L/C ratio of the tuned circuit?

(*C. & G.*)

14. Draw a circuit diagram of (i) a tuned anode valve oscillator circuit and (ii) a tuned collector transistor oscillator circuit. Compare the action of the two circuits.

15. Explain the advantage of a *quartz crystal oscillator*. Draw a circuit diagram of such an oscillator using a transistor or a valve and explain how it functions.

16. Draw a circuit diagram of a transistor oscillator in the CE and CB arrangements respectively.

Explain why the possible frequency of oscillation is higher for CB than CE operation, and why the step-down ratios from the tuned circuit are so different in the two cases.

17. Modulation and Detection

Amplitude Modulation

The energy radiated from an aerial when the frequencies are below 15,000 Hz is practically zero. It is impossible, therefore, to send out audio-frequency (a.f.) electromagnetic waves directly from a transmitter. The latter will radiate, however, frequencies from, say, 15,000 Hz and

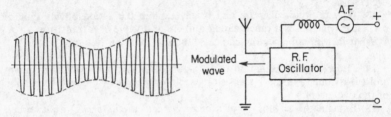

FIG. 17.1. Modulated wave

upwards, which are those we know as radio frequency (r.f.) electromagnetic waves.

Practical methods of radiating a.f. energy consist basically of 'imposing' it on an r.f. wave, which is called the *carrier wave*. The process is known as *modulation*, and the r.f. wave is said to be modulated. A simple method of doing this is illustrated by the diagram in Fig. 17.1.

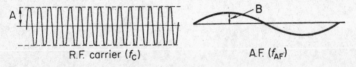

FIG. 17.2. Carrier and a.f. wave

If the a.f. voltage is supposed to be due to a single frequency from a microphone, the modulated wave radiated from the aerial, shown in Fig. 17.1, consists of an r.f. wave *whose amplitude varies with the same frequency as the a.f. voltage* in the circuit. This method is known as 'amplitude modulation'.

Without an a.f. voltage in the circuit, the oscillator generates an r.f. voltage of constant amplitude A (Fig. 17.2). Suppose that the a.f. voltage has itself a constant amplitude B, as shown in Fig. 17.2. Then the modulated voltage wave-form has an amplitude variation of exactly the same frequency as the a.f. voltage, and has a maximum amplitude $= (A + B)$, and a minimum amplitude $= (A - B)$ (see Fig. 17.3 (i)).

The *depth, m,* of the modulation obtained is defined as B/A, and the

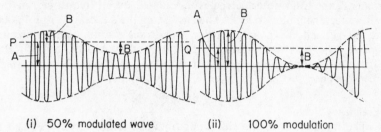

(i)   50% modulated wave   (ii)   100% modulation

FIG. 17.3.   Depth of modulation

percentage modulation as $B/A \times 100\%$. When $B = A$, the depth of modulation m is 100%. This is shown in Fig. 17.3 (ii). It is the maximum modulation obtainable. In Fig. 17.3 (i), if $B = A/2$, $m = 1/2$ or 50%.

Upper and Lower Side Frequencies. Sidebands

The analysis of the modulated wave shows that it consists of three different r.f. waves each of constant amplitude. They are illustrated in Fig. 17.4. This means that if the three waves are added together,

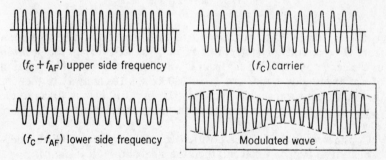

$(f_C + f_{AF})$ upper side frequency (f_C) carrier

$(f_C - f_{AF})$ lower side frequency   Modulated wave

FIG. 17.4.   Upper and lower side frequencies

the modulated wave is obtained. Further, each of the three waves can be detected separately.

If f_C is the carrier frequency and f_{AF} is the modulating audio-frequency, the frequencies of the r.f. waves are respectively $(f_C + f_{AF})$, f_C, and $(f_C - f_{AF})$. The highest frequency is called the *upper side-frequency*; the lowest is called the *lower side frequency*.

Suppose that a carrier C of 1 MHz or 1,000 kHz is modulated by a high a.f. of 10 kHz. Then the upper side frequency U has a frequency of 1,010 kHz and the lower side frequency L has a frequency of

990 kHz, Fig. 17.5 (i). Suppose the carrier is also modulated by the low a.f. of 50 Hz or 0·05 kHz. In this case the upper side frequency is 1,000·05 kHz and the lower side frequency is 999·95 kHz. Now, in general, the transmitter carrier is modulated by all frequencies in the a.f. range, from high to low. Thus assuming the a.f. range to be 10,000 to 50 Hz, all the possible upper and lower side frequencies are respectively in the two r.f. ranges 1,010–1,000·05 kHz and 990–999·95 kHz. These two bands of frequencies are called the *upper* and *lower sidebands* respectively.

Frequency Scale

The frequencies in the sidebands obtained with a given carrier of, say, 1,000 kHz may be registered along a scale shown in Fig. 17.5 (i),

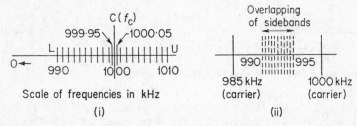

Scale of frequencies in kHz

(i)

(ii)

FIG. 17.5. Sidebands and width

with some origin O to correspond to zero frequency. Suppose 1 cm from O represents a change in frequency of 1 kHz. Then the position of the carrier, C, is 1,000 cm from O, or 10 metres away. The position of the lowest side frequency, L, of 990 kHz is 10 cm away to the left, that of the uppermost side frequency, U, of 1,010 kHz is 10 cm to the right. The *width* of the sidebands in terms of frequency is therefore 20 kHz.

Consider now the *relative* position from the carrier of all the sidebands. If O to C is 1,000 cm, then the sideband most distant from C, L or U, corresponds to a shift of 10 cm/1,000 cm, i.e. only 1%. With a carrier of 1,200 kHz all the sidebands are not more than 10/1,200 × 100% from it on a frequency scale, i.e. less than 1%. The separation between the carriers themselves, 1,000 kHz and 1,200 kHz, is, however, considerable. From this we may state that, in effect, the position of the *carrier* on a frequency scale is practically the position of the sidebands which accompany it. If we therefore tune to the frequency of a transmitting station, which is the frequency of the carrier, we may be sure of having tuned at the same time to all the side frequencies sent out by the modulation process.

If the separation between two transmitters is less than 20 kHz part of the sidebands of each have the same frequencies, and 'overlapping' occurs. This is illustrated in Fig. 17.5 (ii) for carrier frequencies of 985 kHz and 1,000 kHz, in which case 'interference' may occur from one transmitter when reception is required from the other. Since in practice two broadcast stations may be separated by about 9 kHz, this 'interference' takes place between two powerful stations. It can be heard on an old-fashioned (unselective) receiver set.

Frequency Modulation (F.M.)

In amplitude modulation (a.m.), the *amplitude* of the carrier waves is modulated by the audio-frequency. Thus if

$$e = E_C \sin \omega t = E_C \sin 2\pi f_C t$$

represents the carrier voltage, then E_C is modulated, as previously explained. Another way of modulating the carrier wave is to modulate its *frequency f_C*. This is called *frequency modulation* (f.m.). This has advantages over amplitude modulation, as we see later.

To gain some idea of what frequency modulation means, it is useful to imagine a variable capacitor in an oscillator circuit which provides the carrier wave frequency. If the movable plates are rocked to and fro by hand from some mean position, the frequency will vary continuously from a minimum to a maximum value. In practical oscillator circuits designed for frequency modulation, which need not concern us, the *amplitude* of the a.f. signal produces a proportional shift of the carrier frequency. For example, suppose the carrier frequency is 1 MHz or 1,000 kHz. The loudness or amplitude of an a.f. signal on one occasion may then produce a carrier with a frequency variation of $1,000 \pm 1$ kHz (a shift or deviation of 1 kHz), and on another occasion a carrier with a frequency variation of $1,000 \pm 2$ kHz (a shift of 2 kHz). In the latter case the amplitude is twice that in the former case. Deep modulation thus corresponds to a large deviation or swing of carrier frequency and low modulation to a small deviation or swing. This is illustrated in Fig. 17.6 (i), (ii), where f_S represents the frequency swing from the carrier frequency f_C.

Frequency

To understand how the *frequency* of the a.f. signal is imposed in F.M., consider again the imaginary oscillator circuit with a variable capacitor. If the movable plates are rotated very slowly through a given angle, a slow *rate of change* of frequency occurs in the given frequency shift. If the plates are rotated very quickly through the same angle, a rapid rate of change of frequency occurs in the same frequency shift. *The rate at which the carrier frequency varies is made to depend only on the modulating frequency.* Fig. 17.7 (i) and (ii) illustrate low frequency and high frequency modulation at a constant a.f. amplitude;

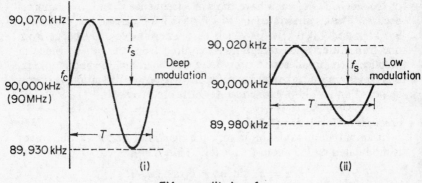

F.M. — amplitude $\propto f_s$

FIG. 17.6. Frequency modulation

the latter is shown by the same shift or deviation on the vertical frequency scale. In broadcasting practice, the carrier mean frequencies are in the region of 90 MHz and the maximum allowable frequency

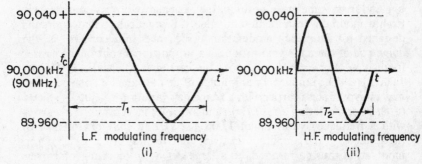

F.M. — frequency $\propto$ rate of change of f_s

FIG. 17.7. Variation of carrier frequency

swing, corresponding to 100% modulation, is 75 kHz; the latter is called the *frequency deviation, f_d*.

Summarizing, in FM (1) the modulating a.f. frequency is made to determine the rate at which the carrier frequency shifts, (2) the amplitude of the a.f. signal is made to determine the magnitude of the shift or deviation of the carrier frequency.

Sidebands

In amplitude modulation by a sine wave a.f. signal of frequency f_{AF}, two radio side frequencies are produced (see p. 309). In the case of frequency modulation, however, it can be shown mathematically that there are an infinite number of side frequencies for each sine wave modulating audio-frequency. Fortunately, it is found in practice that almost perfect reproduction of the modulating wave-form can be achieved by transmitting and receiving all the side frequencies contained in the band $2(f_d + f_{AF})$, since these contain the bulk of the available energy. Thus if the frequency deviation f_d is 75 kHz and f_{AF} is 15 kHz, the highest modulating frequency, then the bandwidth required is 2×90 kHz or 180 kHz, centred on the particular carrier frequency. This is a very wide bandwidth. To accommodate channels of such bandwidth, frequency modulation (FM) transmission is made on the higher carrier frequencies, or v.h.f. band of frequencies, such as 100 MHz.

Advantages of F.M.

FM has many advantages over AM. It achieves higher audio fidelity, a reduction in interference from adjacent channels, and an increased signal-to-noise ratio. 'Noise' is the inherent 'hissing' in a receiver due to electron random movement (p. 4). By design, a reduction in electrical interference from car ignition systems or electrical machinery can be achieved in FM receivers.

FM transmitters use available power more efficiently than AM transmitters.

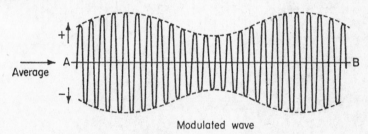

Modulated wave

FIG. 17.8. Symmetrical modulated wave

Detection

Detection is the name given to the method of separating out the a.f. energy carried by a modulated wave. The process is also known as 'demodulation'. Here we deal only with detection of amplitude modulated waves.

The r.f. voltage variations which a modulated wave represents are continuously symmetrical about the time-axis AB (Fig. 17.8). The average of all these variations over an appreciable period of time is therefore zero.

In order to obtain an a.f. output a modulated wave must be made non-symmetrical. Fig. 17.9 (i) shows one half of the modulated wave completely cut off, in which case there is an average positive value which varies as shown. Fig. 17.9 (ii) represents the unaffected positive half of a modulated wave together with a small negative portion. The average is therefore again some varying value, as indicated. Finally, Fig. 17.9 (iii) shows a distorted wave-form with positive half-cycles

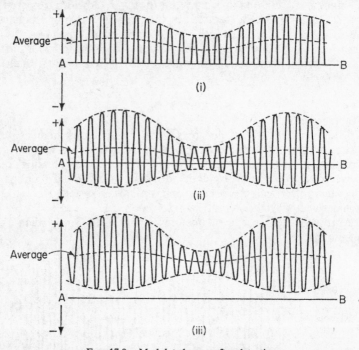

FIG. 17.9. Modulated wave after detection

of larger amplitude than the negative. The average is again a positive variation. It can therefore be seen that a non-symmetrical, or 'distorted', wave-form has always some average value.

When a modulated voltage is applied to a conductor obeying Ohm's law a current is obtained which is numerically the same for the negative as for the positive voltage variations, and a similar modulated wave-form of current is produced. It should therefore be clear that some device is required which has not the same response to voltages in opposite directions, i.e., it should not obey Ohm's law. A valve or semiconductor diode is therefore suitable. These are devices which have non-linear characteristics and in this application they are known as *detectors*. They also act as 'rectifiers', as explained on p. 189.

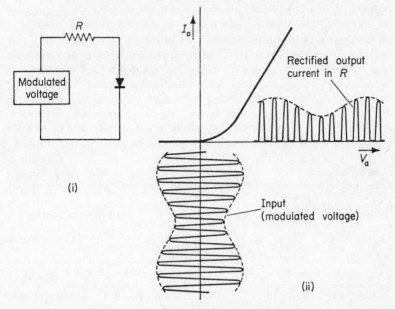

Fig. 17.10. Detection by diode

Analysis of the Rectified Output

Consider a modulated voltage applied to a diode with a resistance R as the load in the circuit (Fig. 17.10 (i)). The diode conducts only on the positive half-cycles, and the resulting anode current (Fig. 17.10 (ii)) causes a voltage across R which we may call a rectified output voltage, V_0 (Fig. 17.11 (i)).

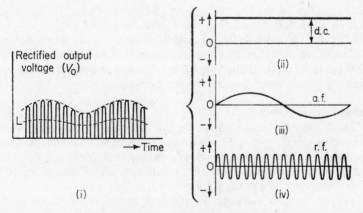

Fig. 17.11. Analysis of output

Analysis of V_0 shows that it consists of several voltage variations of constant amplitude which add up together and make the wave-form of V_0. The most important are shown in Figs. 17.11 (ii), (iii), (iv), and consist of an r.f., a.f., and d.c. voltage. It is not an easy matter to arrive at this analysis without actually going through the process of adding up these voltage graphs (or some harder mathematics), but it can be seen that (i) V_0 contains r.f. because it is itself an r.f. variation, (ii) V_0 has an average represented by the dotted line L, which is an a.f. because it follows the variation of the amplitude, (iii) V_0 contains d.c. because its variations are all in the same direction.

Diode Detection

In order to obtain only the a.f. signal, the r.f. must be separated from the a.f. in the rectified output. Thus in place of R a *capacitance* (C)-*resistance* (R) combination is needed, Fig. 17.12 (i). With suitably

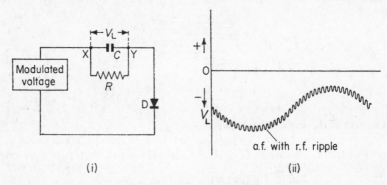

FIG. 17.12. Diode detection

chosen values of C and R, the r.f. component may be by-passed through C, leaving the a.f. and d.c. components through R.

Suppose C is about $0.0002\,\mu\mathrm{F}$ and R about $0.5\ \mathrm{M\Omega}$. The reactance of C to r.f. of 10^6 Hz is then $800\ \Omega$ (approx.) but its reactance to a.f. of $1,000$ Hz is $0.8\ \mathrm{M\Omega}$. Thus very little r.f. flows through R. This now carries most of the a.f. and all the d.c. components.

Voltage Across Load

The voltage V_L developed across the load can be observed on the cathode-ray oscillograph. This is similar in appearance to that shown in Fig. 17.12 (ii). It consists of an a.f. voltage with a r.f. 'ripple'. The voltage V_L is mostly a.f. because the reactance X_C of the capacitor to r.f. is very low, and the r.f. voltage = r.f. current in $C \times X_C$.

Suppose we now consider the physical action of the diode as the action continues. With a capacitor alone as a load, electrons reach the right-hand plate of C and charge it up to a voltage $V = Q/C$. This voltage is a negative bias, as we have seen in the case of a diode valve-voltmeter (p. 192). If a modulated voltage is applied the capacitor becomes rapidly charged to the voltage of the biggest amplitude, and the electron flow ceases. When a C–R combination is used, however, the capacitor becomes charged on the positive half-cycle of the modulated voltage, but on the negative half-cycle the electrons leak away through the path R now open to them. This action settles down in a very short time, with the result that the voltage, V_L, across the load is a *varying negative* voltage at the anode (see Fig. 17.12 (ii)), but

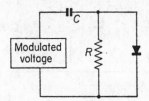

Fig. 17.13. Diode detection

throughout its variation V_L is numerically less than the voltages reached on the peaks of the applied modulated voltage V. Electrons thus continue to reach C by small bursts of current on the positive half-cycles of V, and make up for the charge on C which has leaked away through R.

It can now be seen that the values of C and R must be chosen so that the time constant CR is large compared with the period of the r.f. carrier but small compared with the modulating a.f. The current in R will then practically follow the a.f. variation but not the r.f.

A C–R combination can also be arranged as in Fig. 17.13 to separate the r.f. from the a.f. and d.c. components of the rectified output. The action is similar to the C–R combination in Fig. 17.12 (i).

Diode Plus Class A Amplifier

The disadvantage of the diode detector is that it is insensitive by itself. It is therefore usual to hand on the a.f. voltage variation to a class A amplifier. One method of doing this in a valve circuit is illustrated in Fig. 17.14. Additional r.f. filtering is provided by R_1 and C_1, and the d.c. is eliminated by the capacitor C_g which, however, allows the a.f. voltage to be developed across the resistor R_g.

It should be noted that the d.c. load is provided by R. So far as the a.f. variation is concerned, however, the a.c. load resistance consists of R and R_g in parallel. R and R_g should be chosen so that the difference between the a.c. and d.c. load values is as small as possible. Otherwise, the a.f. wave will tend to be 'clipped' at the higher modulation depths.

The grid resistor of the a.f. amplifier valve has an upper limit of 1 to 2 MΩ. Thus R should be 100 to 250 kΩ for a suitable compromise.

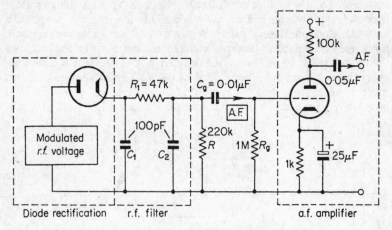

Diode rectification   r.f. filter   a.f. amplifier

Fig. 17.14.   Diode and Amplifier

Point Contact Diode Detector

Although the valve diode has nearly infinite reverse resistance, it does have an appreciable capacitance. This reduces its performance at the higher frequencies. Further, as it usually has an a.c. heater supply, pick-up 'hum' may tend to occur since a.f. amplification follows the detector stage. In addition, the r.f. voltage input to the detector is often of the order of volts, and it can be a source of r.f. harmonics of relatively high amplitude which may radiate from the detector wiring. The valve diode is also bulky.

The *point contact diode*, a semi-conductor diode, is nowadays always used as a detector. It consists of a small wafer of germanium or silicon, having a tungsten wire with a fine point pressing against it. The assembly is enclosed in an envelope of glass or ceramic. It is so small that it can be housed in the screening can of the tuned circuit feeding it. Its capacitance is of the order of 1 pF, and it does not have a heater supply. On this account it is far superior as a detector to the diode valve. Point contact diodes are usable at frequencies up to thousands of MHz.

Point Contact Diode and A.F. Amplifier

When the point contact diode is used in a transistor receiver, the a.f. amplifier which follows is usually operated in the common-emitter mode. The input resistance may then be only 2 kΩ at most and if serious a.f. 'clipping' is to be avoided, the diode load resistor must be drastically reduced. However, an appropriate time constant must be maintained, as explained on p. 317, and so the load capacitor C is proportionately increased.

A typical diode detector and transistor a.f. amplifier is shown in Fig. 17.15. Since the detector circuit now has such low impedance, a step-down transformer is needed from the tuned circuit. The series 4·7 kΩ resistor in the input a.f. amplifier circuit may be considered to

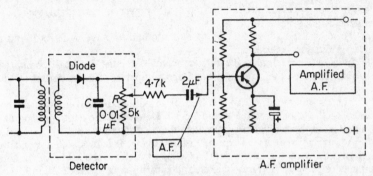

FIG. 17.15. Diode and transistor amplifier

have two functions. In conjunction with the transistor input capacitance it provides additional r.f. filtering, and it also raises the value of the a.c. load. Some loss of a.f. voltage occurs as the 4·7 kΩ resistor and the input resistance act as a potential divider. However, the gain is usually sufficient. By making R a potentiometer, a volume control is obtained, which is a further advantage. Reception is mostly from local or home broadcast stations, so in general the tap is at a relatively low position. This ensures minimum loading of R and least 'clipping'.

SUMMARY

1. The amplitude of a modulated wave varies as the a.f. (f_{AF}) which modulates the r.f. carrier (f_C). The modulated wave is an r.f. wave, and may be analysed into the carrier and upper ($f_C + f_{AF}$) and lower ($f_C - f_{AF}$) side frequencies. The sidebands contain the sound energy.

2. In frequency modulation (FM), the modulating a.f. is made to determine the rate at which the carrier frequency shifts, and the amplitude determines the magnitude of the shift or deviation.

3. A non-symmetrical wave-form (rectified output) is obtained in detection, and consists of r.f., a.f. and d.c. The r.f. and d.c. are 'filtered' from the a.f. The CR time-constant is important in detection.

4. A diode valve is a 'linear' detector as it gives practically no distortion of the a.f., and is followed by a class A amplifier.

A point contact diode followed by a transistor a.f. amplifier in the CE mode is superior to the diode valve and valve amplifier.

EXERCISE 17

What are the missing words in the statements 1–6?

1. Amplitude and frequency modulated waves are radiated considerable distances from an aerial since they are . . . waves.

2. In an amplitude modulated wave, the amplitude varies at . . . -frequency.

3. In a frequency modulated wave, the . . . varies at a rate depending on the audio-frequency.

4. In both types of modulation, the a.f. power is carried in the . . . - frequencies.

5. To obtain the a.f. signal carried by a modulated wave, a detector and a . . . combination is required.

6. In a detector circuit, the time-constant CR must be small compared with the period of the . . . wave but large compared with the period of the . . . wave.

7. The amplitude of a 205-kHz wave is modulated sinusoidally at a frequency of 3 kHz between 0·5 V and 1·5 V. Determine the depth of modulation and state the frequencies present in the modulated wave.

8. A carrier wave has a frequency of 700 kHz. It is modulated by a sine wave frequency of 4 kHz to a depth of 60%. Calculate the values of the side frequencies produced. Draw a sketch illustrating a 60% modulation.

9. A diode detector employs a C–R combination of 200 pF and 150 kΩ. It is fed by a 1 MHz signal amplitude modulated at 1 kHz. Show that the CR time-constant is small compared with the period of the modulating wave but large compared with that of the carrier wave. What is the reactance of C at the r.f. and the a.f. values given?

Explain fully, with diagrams, the action of the diode detector in the above case.

10. A semiconductor diode uses a capacitor of 0·01 μF and a 5 kΩ resistor as its load. Show that the time constant is satisfactory for the modulated signal in Qn. 9.

What are the advantages and disadvantages of a diode valve and a semiconductor diode in detection?

11. With reference to amplitude-modulation explain the terms *modulation envelope* and *depth of modulation* and distinguish between *side frequencies* and *sidebands*.

The amplitude of a 310-kHz wave is modulated sinusoidally at a frequency of 5 kHz between 0·9 V and 1·5 V.

Determine the amplitude of the unmodulated carrier, the depth of modulation and the frequency components present in the modulated wave. *(C. & G.)*

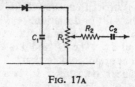

Fig. 17A

12. Fig. 17A shows the circuit of a germanium diode detector. Describe, by

reference to current and voltage waveforms, its use for demodulation of an amplitude-modulated signal.

Explain clearly the function of each component, including the diode detector. State suitable values for C1, C2, R1 and R2. (*C. & G.*)

13. Explain the need for a detector in a radio receiver.

Describe, with the aid of a diagram, the operation of a semi-conductor diode in the detection of an amplitude-modulated wave.

What are the relative merits of thermionic and semi-conductor diodes for this purpose? (*C. & G.*)

14. A transmitter is modulated by a number of frequencies up to 8 kHz. What is the total sideband width? If the carrier frequency is 1·6 MHz, what should be the minimum value of the Q-factor of a single receiving tuned circuit? (*Hint*. Consider the 3 dB bandwidth.)

15. An oscillator has a mean frequency of 10 MHz, which is varied to produce FM. The modulating frequency is 5 kHz and the frequency deviation is 25 kHz. Calculate the maximum and minimum frequencies of oscillation, and the required bandwidth of a FM receiver, for the reception of the signal with negligible distortion. What is the rate of variation of the oscillator frequency?

18: Transistor in Switching Circuits—Logical Gates. Pulse Circuits

LOGICAL GATES

In addition to its applications in radio, transistors are used in computer circuits. N-p-n transistors, usually silicon, are widely employed in high-frequency switching circuits. In these transistors the majority carriers are free electrons. These have a greater mobility than holes, the majority carriers in p-n-p transistors, and hence respond more quickly to high frequency pulses. An n-p-n transistor, biased in the common-emitter (CE) mode, is shown in Fig. 18.1. Note that the

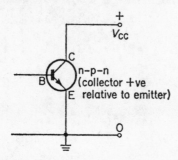

Fig. 18.1. N-p-n transistor (common emitter)

collector C in the n-p-n transistor is *positive* (the collector polarity is always indicated by the middle letter of its type, 'P' in this case.)

A typical family of common-emitter output characteristics, I_C (collector current) against V_{CE} (collector-emitter p.d.), shows that, unless V_{CE} is greater than about 0·2V, very little collector current flows (see p. 246, Fig. 13.9 (iv)). Above this p.d., the collector current soon rises to a value practically independent of V_{CE}, as shown by the flat or 'saturation' part of the characteristic.

The transistor amplifies base current, I_B. Base current flows only when the base-emitter p.d., V_{BE}, is greater than about 0·5V. The base current can then be varied over a large range, the base-emitter p.d. remaining practically constant at about 0·5 V.

Transistor switching

Consider the simple common-emitter circuit in Fig. 18.2, in which the collector C of the n-p-n transistor is joined to the positive pole of the d.c. supply V_{CC} through a resistance R. If a current I_C flows, the *output voltage V_0* at C is given by

$$V_0 = V_{CC} - I_C R.$$

Note that $V_0 = V_{CE}$, the voltage between the collector and emitter.

If I_C changes, V_0 or V_{CE} follows a variation given by $V_0 = V_{CC} - I_C R$ (see 'load line', p. 250). When the base current I_B is very low or practically zero, then I_C is practically zero. It then follows, from $V_0 = V_{CC} - I_C R$, that $V_0 = V_{CC}$, and in this state the transistor is said to be *cutoff*. If I_B is now increased, then I_C increases and hence the

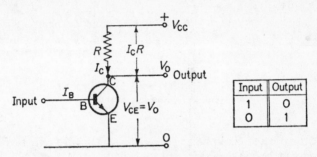

FIG. 18.2.   Transistor switching

potential drop $I_C R$ across R also increases. When $I_C R$ approaches V_{CC} in magnitude, V_0 approaches zero. Below a p.d. V_{CE} of about 0·2 V no further increase of I_C occurs. Hence the transistor is *saturated* at high base current.

We thus see that a transistor may have one of two states: (1) *Cutoff* (I_C practically zero and $V_0 = V_{CC}$), (2) *Saturation* (I_C high and $V_0 = 0$ practically). In computer circuits, as seen later, a transistor can be made to *switch* from one state to the other.

Basic NOR gate

Consider the circuit in Fig. 18.3. This has two resistors r_A and r_B connected to the base of the n-p-n transistor, and a load R. Suppose input voltages are applied to the terminals A and B. If both A and B and B are set to zero volts (or left disconnected), no base current flows. The transistor is then *cutoff*. Neglecting any small collector current, V_0 is equal to V_{CC}.

Suppose, however, that either or both of the input terminals A and B are set to a voltage equal to V_{CC}, so that a heavy base current flows. As previously explained, $I_C R$ then approaches V_{CC} in magnitude, and when the transistor is saturated, $V_0 = 0$ practically.

The output thus has two distinct states, namely $V_0 = V_{CC}$ (cutoff) or $V_0 = 0$ (saturation), depending on the state of the input. If both inputs at A and B are at 0 volts, then $V_0 = V_{cc}$; if either input, or both, is at V_{cc} volts, then the output V_0 is equal to zero. Similar results follow if there are more than two inputs. As now explained, the circuit in Fig. 18.3 is a 'NOR gate'.

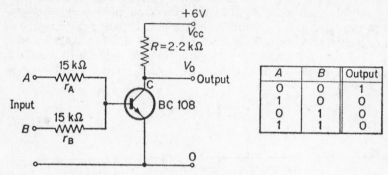

A	B	Output
0	0	1
1	0	0
0	1	0
1	1	0

FIG. 18.3. NOR gate circuit

Logical gates

Since the transistor can be operated as a switch with only two states, the latter can be used to represent two digits, say '1' and '0'. This is the basis of the *binary code*, in which all numbers are represented by 1 and 0. Suppose the voltage level V_{cc} in Fig. 18.3 is represented by 1 and the voltage level of zero is represented by 0. Then, since $V_0 = V_{cc}$ at cutoff and $V_0 = 0$ at saturation, we can write:

binary code	output voltage V_0
1	V_{cc}
0	0

A *truth table* is a convenient way of showing the output obtained for a given input. In Fig. 18.3, for example, suppose each of the inputs A and B can have only one of two possible values—'0', which corresponds to zero base current, and 1, which corresponds to high base current. Recalling that, in the output, 0 means $V_0 = 0$ and 1 means $V_0 = V_{cc}$, the truth table for the circuit can be written as follows:

Input A	Input B	OUTPUT
0	0	1
1	0	0
0	1	0
1	1	0

From the table, we see that the output is '0. if either input A *or* input B *or* both is '1'; and that the output is '1' if neither input A NOR input B is '1'. The circuit in Fig. 18.3 is hence known as a NOR gate. It is an example of a *logical gate*. Logical gates are the building blocks of computers.

Inverter. Symbols

By having only one input, the circuit in Fig. 18.3 can also be used as a *inverter* (or *negator*). Thus suppose one input A is removed, leaving only input B, Fig. 18.4. When input B is 1, the output is 0; if input B is 0, the output is 1. The input has thus been 'inverted'.

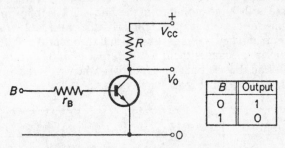

B	Output
0	1
1	0

FIG. 18.4.   INVERTER circuit

The NOR gate and the inverter are two important building blocks for logical circuits. They are represented symbolically in Figs. 18.5 and 18.6. A 'D'-shaped symbol represents any gate and a 'o'-shaped

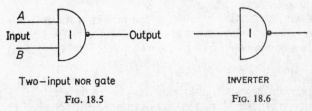

Two–input NOR gate   INVERTER

FIG. 18.5   FIG. 18.6

FIG. 18.5,6.   NOR gate and INVERTER symbols

symbol represents an inversion. The '1' inside the 'D' of the NOR gate means that only *one* of n inputs needs to be 1 to produce an output 0. Only the input and output connections are shown in symbols.

OR gate

The NOR gate and inverter can be connected in a variety of ways to form other types of logical gates. Fig. 18.7 (i) shows the principle of an OR gate symbolically. This is simply a NOR gate followed by an inverter.

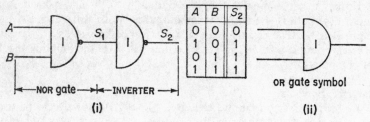

FIG. 18.7. OR gate

The truth table for the NOR gate on p. 324 shows that when the inputs A and B are both 0, the output from the gate is 1. The following inverter changes this to an output of 0. Similarly, the truth table for the NOR gate shows that when the input A is 1 and the input B is 0, the output is 0; the inverter changes the 0 to an output of 1. The truth table for the OR gate can thus be built up as follows, where S_1 is the output from the NOR gate and S_2 that from the INVERTER:

NOR gate		
A	B	S_1
0	0	1
1	0	0
0	1	0
1	1	0

→

INVERTER	
S_1	S_2
1	0
0	1

→→

OR gate			
A	B	S_1	S_2
0	0	1	0
1	0	0	1
0	1	0	1
1	1	0	1

The OR gate is so-called because, as can be seen from the truth table, it gives an output 1 when either A or B or both is 1. The OR gate symbol is; when any one of n inputs is 1, the output is 1 in Fig. 18.7 (ii).

AND gate

Other main types of gates can now be easily built up. Fig. 18.8 shows the principle of an AND gate symbolically, so-called because it gives a '1' output only when input A AND input B are '1'. The associated truth table can be represented as follows:

INVERTER	
A, B	S_1, S_2
0	1
1	0

→

NOR gate		
S_1	S_2	S_3
0	0	1
1	0	0
0	1	0
1	1	0

→→

AND gate				
A	B	S_1	S_2	S_3
0	0	1	1	0
0	1	1	0	0
1	0	0	1	0
1	1	0	0	1

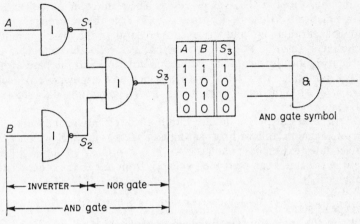

FIG. 18.8   AND gate

PULSE CIRCUITS

Multivibrator circuit. Bistable or flip-flop

In addition to circuits performing logical operations with binary digits, it is necessary in computers to have circuits which can (a) store binary digits, or (b) delay a binary digit, i.e., a pulse, by a fixed time, or (c) generate a train of pulses. This can be done by using a form of *multivibrator* circuit, due originally to Eccles and Jordan.

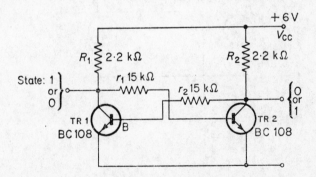

FIG. 18.9.   Multivibrator circuit. Bistable or Flip-flop

A basic multivibrator circuit is shown in Fig. 18.9. It consists of two transistors, TR1, TR2, each with a collector load R_1 or R_2. The special feature of the circuit is the connection from the collector of one transistor to the base of the other through a resistor r_1 or r_2, so that the output of one transistor is fed to the input of the other.

Initially, suppose that TR1 is *cutoff*. The voltage at its collector is then practically equal to V_{CC} (see p. 323). The base current to TR2 is supplied through r_2, and r_2 is chosen so that the base current is sufficient to saturate TR2 with TR1 cutoff. The collector voltage of TR2 is then practically zero. This voltage is connected to the base of TR1 *via* r_2, and since it is too low to produce any appreciable collector current in TR1, then TR1 remains cutoff. The circuit is thus stable in this state.

If TR2, and not TR1, is initially cutoff, then, by similar reasoning, the circuit is again stable with TR1 saturated and TR2 cutoff. Since only two stable states exist, the circuit is known as a *bistable* or *flip-flop*, after the way the states can be made to change from one to the other as now explained.

Change of state

When the multivibrator circuit is first switched on, it will fall immediately into one of these two stable states. The particular state depends on the small differences in symmetry of the transistors and resistors used.

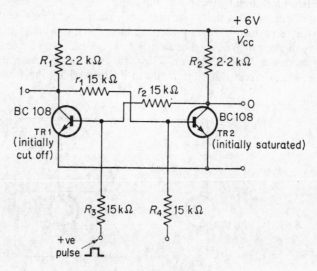

FIG. 18.10. Multivibrator action

Suppose that a positive pulse is now applied to the base of the cut-off transistor, say TR1, by means of a suitable resistor R_3, the transistor TR2 being saturated. Fig. 18.10. As soon as the pulse amplitude rises to a value greater than $0.5\,V$, base current for TR1 is drawn through R_3. Collector current then starts to flow through TR1, and this lowers the voltage at the collector of TR1. The base current flowing into TR2 is hence lowered. Since the base current in TR2 is reduced, so too is its collector current. The voltage of the collector of TR2 now begins to rise, since the voltage drop of R_2 is lowered. The rise in collector voltage of TR2 provides further base current for TR1 *via* r_2, thus increasing the effect of the pulse. This so-called *positive feedback* between the transistors increases rapidly, until TR1 is fully conducting and TR2 is cutoff. Thus the bistable has changed state.

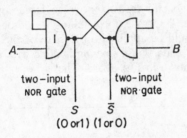

FIG. 18.11.   Bistable as NOR gates

Note that (i) the triggering pulse only initiates the onset of the positive feedback which occurs during the change of state, (ii) R_3 must be sufficiently low to make the base current large enough to saturate TR1, (iii) the circuit can be redrawn as either two two-input NOR gates connected together as shown in Fig. 18.11, or as a two-stage transistor amplifier which shows the presence of the positive feedback more clearly, Fig. 18.12.

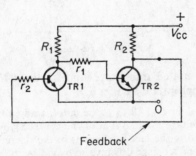

FIG. 18.12.   Positive feedback

Bistable as Store

The bistable can be used to 'store' a single binary digit, since it remains in one of its stable states until a triggering pulse is received. For example, suppose we take the voltage of TR2 collector in Fig. 18.10 as the 'output' of the bistable. Then when TR1 is saturated and TR2 is cutoff, the voltage of TR2 collector is practically equal to V_{cc}. In this case the output, or stored digit, is a '1'. Conversely, if TR1 is cutoff and TR2 saturated, then the TR2 collector is practically zero volts, ie. the output is a '0'. It may be noted that the voltage on the collector of TR1 is always the inverse of that of TR2. Thus the inverse of the digit stored in the bistable is automatically available from the same circuit if required, without the use of an additional inverter.

Pulse steering

In circuit operation, a positive input pulse should be applied to the base of the multivibrator transistor which is cut off and not to the saturated transistor, otherwise no switching would occur. Alternatively, a negative pulse could be applied to the base of the 'ON' transistor to push it to the 'OFF' state. *Pulse steering* is done with the aid of steering diodes, X, Y, as shown in Fig. 18.13. These diodes are used to 'sense'

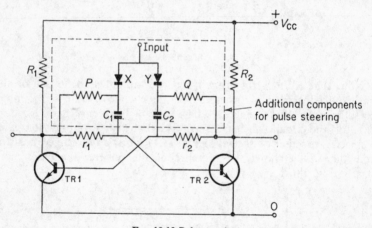

FIG. 18.13 Pulse steering

the cutoff and saturated transistors, and to direct the input pulse to the base of the appropriate transistor.

Action. Suppose TR1 in Fig. 18.13 is the cutoff transistor. The collector of TR1 is then at the voltage V_{cc} and that of TR2 is practically zero. If a positive pulse is now applied to the junction (input) of the steering diodes X and Y, diode X will not conduct since it is reverse-biased by the voltage V_{cc} on the TR1 collector through P. On the other hand, diode Y will conduct, because it is forward biased by the voltage (practically zero) at the collector of TR2 through Q. Thus the input pulse passes only through diode Y, and is hence applied to the base of TR1, the cutoff transistor, *via* the capacitor C_2. The bistable thus changes its state. If a further input pulse is applied, the opposite effect occurs—diode Y is reverse-biased since TR2 is now cutoff, diode X conducts, and the pulse is directed to the base of TR2. Thus the 'steering' circuit automatically directs the input pulses to the base of the cutoff transistor.

The steered bistable is shown in logical form in Fig. 18.14. Basically it consists of two NOR gates (see Fig. 18.11) together with two AND gates comprising the two steering circuits. Input pulses at C may be counted as binary digits, 1 or 0, at S or $\bar{S}$.

Fig. 18.15 shows a practical form of steered bistable, with component values.

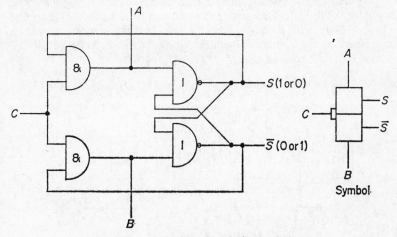

FIG. 18.14.   Steered bistable—logical equivalent

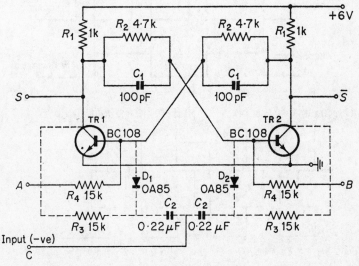

FIG. 18.15.   Steered bistable (steering circuit, shown by broken lines, are AND gates; capacitors C_2 shorten input pulse duration to a value less than switching times of TR1, TR2, which depends on C_1R_2)

Binary counter

The bistable or flip-flop provides a useful counting and storage unit for electronic computers. In practice, provision is made for such items as fast switching time, fast counting rate, 'set' input pulses (which set the output to 1), 'reset' input impulses (which set the output to 0), and toggle input pulses (which cause the bistable to change state).

To illustrate the basic principle of a binary counter, suppose four bistables A, B, C, D are arranged as shown in the block diagram of Fig. 18.16 (i). The bistables are in series, and the output of each is connected to the input of the next. Initially the outputs of all the bistables are set to read zero.

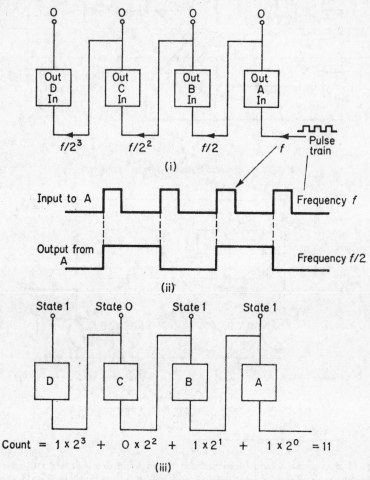

$$\text{Count} = 1 \times 2^3 + 0 \times 2^2 + 1 \times 2^1 + 1 \times 2^0 = 11$$

(iii)

FIG. 18.16. Binary counter principle

Suppose that a pulse train is now applied as an input to the bistable A. Every input pulse causes the bistable to change state, so that two successive input pulses produces an output of '1' followed by '0', which is one output pulse. Thus, as illustrated in Fig. 18.16 (ii), the output from bistable A is a train of pulses which is *half* the frequency of the input pulses.

Similarly, if the output of bistable A is fed to the input of bistable B, the output of B will be a train of pulses of 1/2 the frequency of the input pulses, or $1/2^2$ (1/4) of the frequency of the input pulses at A. It can now be seen that the states of the bistables A, B, C, D provide a number in binary code of the total number of pulses received at the input of A. Bistable A records the number of 2^0, B the number of 2^1, C the number of 2^2, and D the number of 2^3.

Fig. 18.16 (iii) shows the states of the bistables after 11 pulses have been received at the input of A. In this case:

(state of D) $\times 2^3$ + (state of C) $\times 2^2$ + (state of B) $\times 2^1$ +
(state of A) $\times 2^0$

$= 1 \times 2^3 + 0 \times 2^2 + 1 \times 2^1 + 1 \times 2^0 = 8 + 0 + 2 + 1 = 11$

This principle can be extended to large arrays of bistables, so that large numbers can be stored in binary code in computers.

Monostable multivibrator. Pulse shaping circuit

The *monostable* is a multivibrator which has only one stable state; the other state is unstable.

Fig. 18.17(i) shows the circuit of a simple monostable. Normally, transistor TR2 is cutoff, and TR1 is saturated through base current supplied *via* the resistor R. Suppose now that a short positive pulse is applied to the base of transistor TR2 *via* the resistor R. Base current is then supplied to TR2 through R, and thus TR2 starts to conduct. The flow of collector current in R_2 now causes the voltage of the TR2 collector to fall. The voltage drop is conveyed through the capacitor C to the base of TR1, and hence TR1 tends to become cutoff. The voltage at the TR1 collector thus rises. Further base current for TR2 is then supplied through resistor P, and this adds to the effect of the applied pulse. The circuit thus rapidly switches to a state where TR1 is cutoff and TR2 is saturated.

When this state is reached, C starts to charge up through resistor Q. The voltage of the base of TR1 now starts to rise at a rate determined by the time-constant CQ. When the voltage of the TR1 base is just sufficient to allow base current to flow, TR1 starts to conduct. The collector of TR1 therefore falls in voltage, leading to cutoff of TR2. Thus a sudden switch back occurs to TR1 saturated and TR2 cutoff.

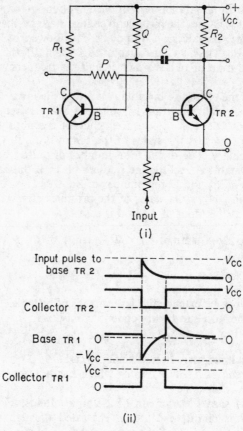

FIG. 18.17.   (i) Monostable circuit (ii) voltage variations

The circuit thus has only one stable state. Fig. 15 (ii) shows roughly the variation of voltage at the base and collector of T_1 and T_2.

The length of time for which TR1 is 'off' and TR2 is 'on' depends on the time constant CQ. Hence, for an input of any wave shape, the output is a rectangular pulse of constant width. This width can only be varied by altering C and Q. The monostable circuit is hence used as a *pulse-shaping* circuit. Further, as the output changes state at a definite time after the input pulse is applied, the circuit can also be used as a *delay circuit*.

Astable multivibrator. Pulse generating circuit

An *astable* is a multivibrator which has no stable states; it provides continuous oscillations. Fig. 18.18 shows a basic form of circuit. The

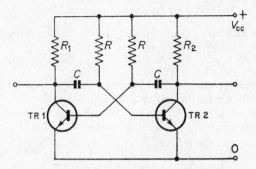

Fig. 18.18.   Astable. Pulse generator

action follows similar lines to that already discussed in multivibrator circuits, but here the circuit switches continuously between a state when TR1 is cutoff and TR2 is saturated, to a state when TR1 is saturated and TR2 is cutoff. The rate of this switching depends on the time-constant of the capacitors C and charging resistors R. On account of the continuous oscillations produced, the astable circuit is used to generate pulses. These may be required, for example, as input pulses for a binary counter (p. 322). The duration or width of the pulses depends on the time for which the transistors remain saturated, and this may be varied by altering the time constant value CR.

SUMMARY

We may summarise the multivibrators discussed as follows:

(i) *Bistable* (*Flip-flop*). The transistors are coupled by resistors. This has two stable states. The circuit is used in binary counters.

(ii) *Astable*. The transistors are coupled by capacitors. This has no stable states—it produces a continuous train of rectangular pulses. The circuit is used as a pulse generator.

(iii) *Monostable*. One coupling component is a resistor, the other is a capacitor. This has only one stable state. It may be used as a pulse shaping circuit or as a delay circuit.

Further details of logical gates and associated electronic circuits must be obtained from specialist textbooks on the subject, such as *Transistor Switching and Sequential Circuits* by J. J. Sparkes (Pergamon Press).

EXERCISE 18

1. Draw a sketch of a n-p-n transistor in the common emitter mode, with a load resistance R and a d.c. supply V_{CC}.

State if the collector current is low or high in the following cases: (i) $V_{BE} = 0$, (ii) $V_{BE} = + 1V$, (iii) $V_{CE} = 0.1$ V.

2. In the circuit of question 1, write down an expression for the collector voltage V_{CE} when a collector current I_C flows.

The base current is made (i) low and then (ii) high. What are the relative collector voltages V_{CE} in each case? Explain how a *transistor switch* functions.

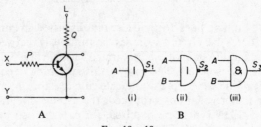

Fig. 18A, 18B

3. Fig. 18A illustrates a n-p-n transistor used in a logical gate. (i) Name typical component values for P and Q and for the supply L. (ii) If a positive input (1) and then a negative input (0) is applied between X, Y, state the output obtained in each case and explain your answer. What logical gate is obtained from Fig. 18A?

4. What logical gates are represented respectively by the symbols in (i), (ii) and (iii) of Fig. 18B? Show the outputs obtained, S_1, S_2 and S_3, in a truth table.

Draw a *transistor circuit* to illustrate each of the gates in (i), (ii), (iii) and show clearly on it the input and output terminals.

5. Fig. 18C shows a NOR gate with inputs P and Q. (i) Make a table showing all the possible output voltages V_0 when P and Q have binary values 1 or 0. (ii) Write down the meaning of a 'NOR gate'.

6. A NOR gate followed by an INVERTER is logically equivalent to an OR gate. Draw a sketch of this statement in symbolic form and explain why the statement is true.

7. In Fig. 18D, A and B represent a train of positive pulses applied to a two-input (i) AND gate, (ii) OR gate. Draw a sketch showing the output obtained in each case.

8. Fig. 18E represents an *incomplete* bistable or *flip-flop* circuit. (i) Complete the circuit. (ii) If a positive pulse is applied at S, explain how the outputs of TR1 and TR2 may be 0 and 1 respectively. (iii) What components are needed to speed up the switching action of the circuit, and where are they placed?

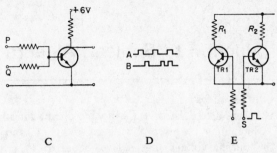

C   D   E

FIG. 18c, 18d, 18e

9. What is the difference between a *monostable* and an *astable*? Explain, with a circuit diagram, how one of these circuits can be used as a *pulse generator*.

10. What is a *binary counter*? Explain the principle of a binary counter.

19: Introduction to Boolean Algebra

Functions with two values

As we have seen, a transistor in a switching circuit can have one of two states, which may be given the binary digits '1' and '0'. Thus when V_0, the output voltage, has a level equal to V_{CC}, the supply voltage, this may be given the value '1'. If V_0 falls to zero, it is given the value '0'. (Conversely, the value '1' may be given to $V_0 = 0$ and the value '0' to $V_0 = V_{CC}$.) No other values than '1' or '0' can be obtained from the transistor switch.

Boolean algebra, named after George Boole, an English mathematician of the nineteenth century, deals with variables which can have only one of two values. These could be switches which are either 'on' or 'off', statements which could be 'true' or 'false', or, as we have used, the two possible states of a transistor, '1' or '0'. If a variable voltage A can have only one of the two states represented by 1 and 0, then a voltage $X = A$ is one in which $X = 1$ when say $A = 1$, and $X = 0$ when $A = 0$. No other values of X are possible.

Negation or complementary function

A variable which is 'not-A', or the *negation* of A, is written $\bar{A}$. It is also called the *complement* of A.

$$\text{Complement or negation of } A = \bar{A}$$

If A represents a switch when 'ON', then $\bar{A}$ represents the switch when it is 'OFF'. If $X = A$ represents a voltage X, then $X = 1$ when $A = 1$ and $X = 0$ when $A = 0$. If another voltage is represented by $X = \bar{A}$, then $X = 1$ when $A = 0$ ('not-0' is '1'), and $X = 0$ when $A = 1$ ('not-1' is '0').

Arithemetic rules

In Boolean arithmetic, there are two main rules. These may be expressed as follows:

(1) *Logical Addition* (OR) $X = A + B$ (1)

The 'plus' sign between A and B is read as 'or'. Thus the statement reads 'X equals A or B'. This means that if A or B or both is 1, then $X = 1$. In the form of a table:

A	B	X
1	0	1
0	1	1
1	1	1
0	0	0

An electronic or gate provides addition in logical circuits. Here the output X is 1 when A or B or both is 1, as in the above table (see p. 326).

Adding *logically* the values of A and B in the table, the following results are obtained:

$$1 + 0 = 1, \quad 0 + 1 = 1, \quad 0 + 0 = 0, \quad 1 + 1 = 1$$

Thus the logical addition agrees with the values of X obtained arithmetically from $X = A + B$, with the exception of $1 + 1$. In electronic circuits, however, '$1 + 1$' may represent a switch, for example, which is 'on or on', that is, 'on'. Hence in logical addition, remember that '$1 + 1$' always equals '1'.

(2) *Logical Multiplication* (AND) $X = A \cdot B$ (2)

The 'multiplication' sign between A and B is read as 'and'. Thus the statement reads 'X equals A and B'. This means that if *both A and B* are 1, then $X = 1$. Since $X = 0$ when either A or B is 0, then, in the form of a table, we may write:

A	B	X
1	0	0
0	1	0
1	1	1
0	0	0

An electronic and gate, discussed on p. 326, provides multiplication in logical arithmetic.

Multiplying arithmetically the values of A and B in the table, we obtain the following results:

$$1 \times 0 = 0, \quad 0 \times 1 = 0, \quad 1 \times 1 = 1, \quad 0 \times 0 = 0$$

This agrees with the values of X obtained by logical multiplication in the table in each case.

All statements in Boolean algebra can be checked by substituting the two possible values '1' and '0' in one side of the statement, and calculating the result in a table. For example, suppose the following statement is made:

$$A + \bar{A} = 1 \qquad (3)$$

Then, in a table, since $\bar{A}$ is 'not-A':

A	$\bar{A}$	$A + \bar{A}$
1	0	1
0	1	1

Thus $A + \bar{A} = 1$. Likewise, consider the statement:

$$A \cdot \bar{A} = 0 \qquad (4)$$

Then, in a table:

A	$\bar{A}$	$A \cdot \bar{A}$
1	0	0
0	1	0

Thus $A \cdot \bar{A} = 0$.

OR, NOR, AND, NAND logical functions

The OR gate has inputs A and B and an output X which is given by the following table (see p. 326):

A	B	X
1	0	1
0	1	1
1	1	1
0	0	0

This is the same as the table on p. 339. Hence the OR logical function is expressed by:

$$X = A + B$$

In the case of the NOR gate, the inputs A, B and the output X are given by the following table (see p. 324):

A	B	X
1	0	0
0	1	0
1	1	0
0	0	1

The output (0, 0, 0, 1) of the NOR gate is thus the complement or negation of the output (1, 1, 1, 0) of the OR gate. The NOR logical function can hence be expressed as the complement of the logical OR:

$$X = \overline{A + B}$$

The expression may be read 'X is not equal to A or B (neither A nor B)'.

The inputs A, B and the output X for an AND gate are expressed in the following table (see p. 326):

A	B	X
1	0	0
0	1	0
1	1	1
0	0	0

This is the same as the table on p. 339. Hence the logical function for the AND gate is expressed by $X = A \cdot B$.

The NAND function is the complement (negation) of the AND function. In the form of a table, if A, B are inputs and X is the output:

A	B	X
1	0	1
0	1	1
1	1	0
0	0	1

Thus $X = \overline{A \cdot B}$ in this case, which is read 'X is not equal to A and B'.

The INVERTER gate converts an input 1 to an output 0, or an input 0 to an output 1 (see p. 325). Hence if $X = A$ is the input function, then $X = \bar{A}$ is the output function.

SUMMARY

The following table summarises the four gates discussed:

Inputs		Output			
A	B	OR $(A + B)$	NOR $\overline{(A + B)}$	AND $(A \cdot B)$	NAND $\overline{(A \cdot B)}$
1	0	1	0	0	1
0	1	1	0	0	1
1	1	1	0	1	0
0	0	0	1	0	1

EXAMPLES

1. By constructing a truth table, verify that $\overline{A.B} = \bar{A} + \bar{B}$ (de Morgan's theorem).

Taking all the combinations of the two values 1 or 0 for A and B, we have:

A	B	$A.B$	$\overline{A.B}$	$\bar{A}$	$\bar{B}$	$\bar{A} + \bar{B}$
1	0	0	1	0	1	1
0	1	0	1	1	0	1
1	1	1	0	0	0	0
0	0	0	1	1	1	1

Hence, from the table, $\overline{A.B} = \bar{A} + \bar{B}$.

2. By using de Morgan's theorem, simplify $F = A.B + \overline{A.B} + A + B$

We have
$$\overline{A.B} = \bar{A} + \bar{B} \text{ (see Example 1)}$$

$$\therefore \quad F = A.B + \bar{A} + \bar{B} + A + B \tag{i}$$

But, from equation (3), p. 340, $\bar{A} + A = 1$ and $\bar{B} + B = 1$

$$\therefore \quad F = A.B + 1 + 1 = A.B + 1$$

Now $A.B$ has values of 1 or 0 for binary values of A and B.

$$\therefore \quad F = 1$$

Further details of Boolean algebra are outside the scope of this book and may be obtained from *Electronic Computers* by H. Jacobowitz (W. H. Allen).

EXERCISE 19

By using truth tables, or otherwise, prove the following identities:

1. $A + A = A$
2. $A + 1 = 1$
3. $A + A.B = A$
4. $A + \bar{A}.B = A + B$
5. $A.0 = 0$
6. $A.A = A$
7. $A.1 = A$
8. $A(A + B) = A$
9. $A(\bar{A} + B) = A.B$
10. $\overline{A + B} = \bar{A}.\bar{B}$ (de Morgan's theorem)
11. $A.(B + C) = A.B + A.C$

12. $(A + B) . (A + C) = A + B . C$

13. In Fig. 19A (i), what are the outputs S_1 and S_2 respectively? By using de Morgan's theorem, $\overline{A + B} = \bar{A} . \bar{B}$, show that the same output S_2 is obtained in Fig. 19A(ii).

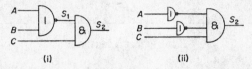

(i)   (ii)

FIG. 19A

14. In Fig. 19B, what are the outputs S_1, S_2, S_3 respectively if the two inputs are A and B?

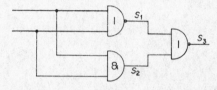

FIG. 19B

15. By using de Morgan's theorem, show that $\overline{A . B(A + B)} = A . \bar{B} + \bar{A} . B$.

20. Appendix: Field Effect Transistor. Differential Amplifier

Field Effect Transistor

Construction of f.e.t.

So far we have met a transistor which operates by the movement of two types of charge carriers, electrons (negative charges) and holes (positive charges). This may be called a 'bipolar' transistor.

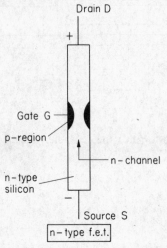

FIG. 20.1. Field effect transistor (f.e.t.)—basic construction

The *field effect transistor* ('f.e.t.' or 'FET' for short) uses only one type of charge carrier when working. It is thus a 'unipolar' transistor. Fig. 20.1 shows the basic construction of the early f.e.t. It consists of a bar of n-type silicon (p-silicon could also be used), with a voltage V_{DS} between one end marked *source* S and the other end marked drain D. The voltage of D can be varied positively with respect to the source S.

Alloyed into the bar on each side is an electrode called the *gate* G. This consists of a heavily doped p-region, which forms a p-n junction with the n-bar. Usually G is kept at a few volts *negative* relative to the source S. The modern way of making the f.e.t. is by diffusion of impurities into a silicon base.

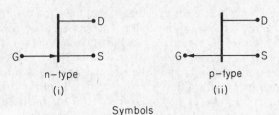

Symbols

FIG. 20.2. F.e.t. symbols

The symbol for a 'junction field effect transistor' (f.e.t.), as this is called, is shown in Fig. 20.2(i). The symbol for a p-type f.e.t., in which voltages are reversed compared to the n-type, is shown in Fig. 20.2(ii).

Action of f.e.t. Output and input characteristics

Consider the n-type f.e.t. in the circuit shown in Fig. 20.3. The region of the gate is a p-n junction. Further, the negative voltage V_{GS} makes it *reverse-biased*. Consequently, as shown in Fig. 20.4(i), a 'depletion region' is obtained round the gate G whose width depends on the magnitude of the voltage V_{GS}. See p. 204. When V_{GS} is made more negative, the depletion region spreads further into the silicon bar. Fig. 20.4(ii).

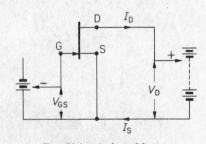

FIG. 20.3. Action of f.e.t

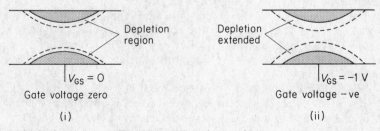

FIG. 20.4. Effect of gate voltage

The current I_D which flows in the bar from the source to the drain is called the 'drain current'. The charge carriers here are electrons, the majority carriers in the n-bar. When the drain voltage V_D is increased from zero, and V_{GS} kept constant at zero voltage, the drain current I_D at first increases linearly because the bar acts as an ohmic conductor. Thus the inclined part L of the characteristic is obtained. Fig. 20.5 (i).

When the voltage V_D is increased, the bar in the region of the gate becomes more positive relative to the source. This means that the p-n junction at the gate becomes *more reverse-biased*. The width of the depletion region at the gate thus increases. This narrows the channel through which the charge carriers flow along the bar, and so I_D begins to increase at a slower rate. The effect on the characteristic is shown in Fig. 20.5(i). The point at which the current I_D levels off is called the

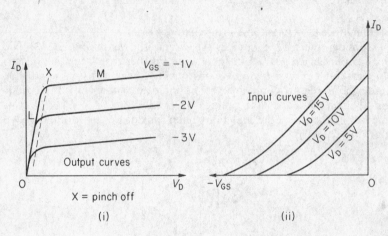

FIG. 20.5. Output and input characteristics of f.e.t.

'pinch off' point. After this, the increased voltage V_D is just able to overcome the effect of the narrow channel and the current I_D now increases regularly along the straight line M, which is inclined at a small angle to the horizontal.

The current I_D is of the order 5 mA when the drain voltage V_D is about 30 V positive relative to the source and $V_{GS} = 0$. It may be noted that I_D is practically equal to the source current, as only a very small leakage current, due to minority carriers, flows in the reverse-biased p-n gate.

When the gate voltage V_{GS} is made more negative, the reverse-bias is increased. The characteristic curves are thus similar in shape to before, but the current I_D is now smaller, as shown in Fig. 20.5(i). Fig. 20.5(ii) shows some input curves for the transistor.

From what we have said, it can be seen that the 'source' acts like the cathode of a valve, the 'drain' acts like the anode, and the 'gate' acts like the grid. In fact, the f.e.t. characteristics in Fig. 20.5(i) are similar to those of the anode characteristics of a pentode valve (see p. 287). The normal operating region of the transistor is along the straight line M. Since this line has a small slope, it follows that the transistor has a high a.c. impedance, which is an advantage for r.f. amplifiers.

Equivalent a.c. circuit. Parameters of f.e.t.

The equivalent a.c. circuit for the f.e.t. is usually the constant *current* generator form. Fig. 20.6. This is the case for the pentode valve, as shown on p. 289. In Fig. 20.6, R_L is the 'load' connected between the drain D and source S of the f.e.t., V_{gs} is the input varying voltage, and g_d is the 'transfer coefficient', defined by

$$g_d = \frac{\Delta I_D}{\Delta V_{GS}} \quad (V_D \text{ constant})$$

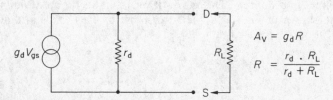

FIG. 20.6. F.e.t. equivalent a.c. circuit and parameters

The parameter g_d for the f.e.t. is analogous to the parameter g_m for the mutual conductance of a valve.

The 'a.c. output resistance', r_d, in Fig. 20.6 is defined by

$$r_d = \frac{\Delta V_D}{\Delta I_D} \quad (V_{GS} \text{ constant})$$

It corresponds to the a.c. resistance r_a of the valve.

Roughly, g_d is in the range 0·5 to 10 mA/V and r_d is usually greater than 50 kΩ.

F.e.t. amplifier and oscillator circuits

When a small signal is applied about an operating point at say the middle of the straight part of the input characteristic, the f.e.t. will act as an amplifier. This is because the gate voltage causes the channel width to vary in a similar way. This, in turn, varies the drain current.

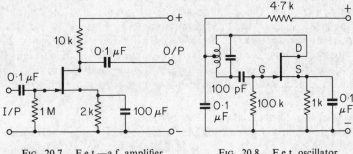

FIG. 20.7.   F.e.t.—a.f. amplifier   FIG. 20.8.   F.e.t. oscillator

An a.f. voltage amplifier with a f.e.t. is shown in Fig. 20.7, and a f.e.t. Hartley oscillator is shown in Fig. 20.8.   These circuits are very similar to the corresponding valve circuits, shown on p. 235 and p. 303.

As the junction capacitance is very small, a few pF, a f.e.t. has a high input impedance.   This makes it very suitable for an r.f. amplifier circuit, shown in Fig. 20.9.   The low noise of the f.e.t. is also a very useful property for a r.f. amplifier.

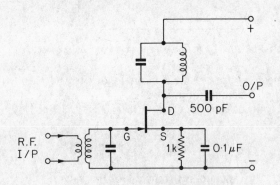

FIG. 20.9.   F.e.t.—r.f. amplifier

Other forms of f.e.t.

An important development of the junction f.e.t. is the *insulated gate f.e.t.* (i.g.f.e.t.), also known as the *metal oxide silicon transistor* (m.o.s.t.). In this f.e.t., shown in principle in Fig. 20.10(i), the gate G is insulated from the n-channel by a very thin layer of silicon oxide.   This may produce input a.c. resistances of the order of hundreds of megohms.

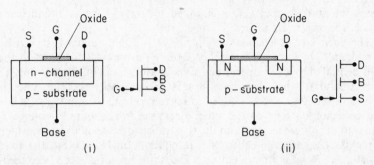

FIG. 20.10. Insulated gate f.e.t. or metal oxide silicon transistor (m.o.s.t.)

The oxide acts as a dielectric, so that the gate is coupled to the n-channel by capacitance only. When the gate voltage is made negative relative to the source, electrons are driven away from it and the conduction channel is thus reduced. As the channel is depleted of electrons near the gate, this i.g.f.e.t. is called a 'depletion' type. The base is connected to the source.

Another form of the i.g.f.e.t. is shown in Fig. 20.10(ii). Here the n-channel is separated in two parts by the p-type base. In operation, the gate has a positive bias, which attracts electrons to the gate region. This provides negative charges between the source and the drain.

The Differential Amplifier

Circuit of amplifier

The *differential amplifier* is widely used as a d.c. amplifier and as an operational amplifier in analogue computers. It is the basic unit in

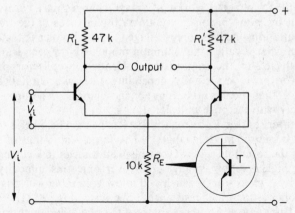

FIG. 20.11. Differential amplifier basic circuit

linear integrated circuits, that is, those integrated circuits intended for use as r.f. or a.f. amplifiers.

The basic circuit is shown in Fig. 20.11. The amplifier is driven by two signals, V_i and V_i', having *opposite* polarities. This is called the 'differential' mode of operation. The action is a 'push-pull' one, in the sense that when one transistor is driven positively, the other is driven negatively. So the collector current of one rises in value, while the collector current of the other decreases. The output voltage is equal to the *difference* between the two transistor output voltages, which explains the name given to the amplifier. In Fig. 20.11, the load resistances R_L and R_L' are equal. The 'tail' resistor R_E provides feedback for d.c. stability, as explained shortly. For differential inputs, however, there is no a.c. feedback. As the current in one transistor increases, the current in the other decreases, so the p.d. across R_E remains constant.

Stability of differential amplifier

If the characteristics and circuit components for each transistor were exactly the same, the potentials of the collectors would be the same when the circuit is in the quiescent stage, that is, no signal is applied. This is not the case in practice. No two transistors match exactly, their temperatures may be different and there are tolerances in the values of the circuit components. In the integrated circuit differential amplifier, the two transistors are laid beside each other so that their temperature is the same. Any departure from exact matching causes a resultant output voltage, since the collectors will have different potentials. A small voltage thus needs to be fed to the bases to offset this difference. It is called the 'offset voltage' and has a specified value for a given amplifier circuit.

When the amplifier is working, voltage changes may be induced in the circuit by 'hum' pickup, by temperature changes in the transistors and by variations in the supply voltage. The amplifier is then said to operate in what is called the 'common mode'. Now each transistor is largely affected to the same extent. Hence the collector potentials move up or down very closely, depending on how accurately they are matched. Thus there is no output voltage change. An output voltage occurs only with the push-pull signals.

The emitter resistor R_E also gives d.c. feedback, which helps to reduce or reject common mode changes. The larger the value of R_E, the greater is the rejection. However, this would mean low current working or a higher supply voltage. To overcome this difficulty, R_E is replaced by a transistor T which will allow a suitable working current and yet offer a high a.c. resistance. See inset, Fig. 20.11. The collector of T is connected to the emitters of the two differential transistors.

Changes in the collector voltage of T have little effect on the current through it and so, in effect, T acts as a high resistance.

Owing to its high degree of d.c. stability, the differential amplifier transistors can be d.c. coupled.   This is particularly important in integrated circuits because the relatively large coupling capacitor need not be used.   Integrated circuit amplifiers consist of cascaded differential amplifiers, which are compensated against d.c. and temperature changes.   Very high gains are obtainable which may exceed 50,000. F.e.t.s. are now used in such circuits.

Finally, mention may be made of the *Darlington pair*, shown in

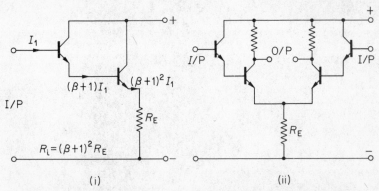

FIG. 20.12.   (i) Darlington pair (ii) Darlington pair with differential amplifier.

Fig. 20.12(i).   In this arrangement, the emitter current of one transistor is used for the base current of a second transistor.   Thus the input current is increased considerably.   They also provide a very high input resistance.   Fig. 20.12(ii) shows the use of a Darlington pair with the differential amplifier.

REFERENCES

Introduction to Semiconductor Devices—Bailey (Allen & Unwin).
Radio Circuits—Miller & Spreadbury (Iliffe).
Transistor Circuits—Amos (Iliffe).
MULLARD Transistor Audio & Radio Circuits.
Electronic Applications & Fundamentals—Ryder (Pitman).
Transistor Circuit Analysis—Fitchen (Van Nostrand).
Radio Communication—Reyner (Pitman).

Answers

EXERCISE 2 (p. 31)

1. (a) 1,200, (b) 72,000 C. **2.** 200 μA. **3.** 64 V. **4.** 2,500 Ω, 0·02 mA. **5.** (a) 3,333, (b) 15,000 Ω. **6.** (a) 20 Ω, (b) 3, 2, 5 A; 30 V. **7.** 0·0243 Ω. **8.** (a) 0–120 mV, (b) 499,500 Ω. **9.** 110 Ω. **10.** 16, 8 mA. **13.** 40, 80 V; 30, 60 V. **14.** 2 A. **15.** 0·34 Ω. **16.** 8·1 × 10^{-8} Ω m. **17.** 8·25 m. **18.** 5 × 10^{-7} m^2; 136 Ω. **19.** 1·8 V. **20.** 0·4 Ω. **21.** 50. **24.** 0·29 Ω. **25.** 0·14 A. **26.** 1·4 V. **27.** 11 V, 12·5 V. **29.** 203 Ω. **30.** 0·75. **31.** 188 Ω.

EXERCISE 3 (p. 42)

1. energy; power. **2.** time. **3.** decibel. **4.** e.m.f. **5.** 180 W. **6.** no. **7.** yes. **8.** 40 dB. **9.** (i) 40, (ii) 200 mW. **10.** 0·66 kW, 0·88 h.p. **11.** (a) $\frac{1}{2}$ A, (b) 200 Ω, (c) 180,000 J. **12.** 1·8 Ω. **13.** 576 Ω. **14.** 88%. **15.** (a) 60 J, (b) 4:2:1. **16.** 1·5 h.p. (approx.). **17.** (i) 9%, (ii) 0·8 Ω. **18.** (b) 100 Ω. **19.** 1·7, $\mu\Omega$, 44 × 10^{-4} cm^2. **20.** 13·7, 31 dB, 17·3 dB. **21.** (i) 5, (ii) 12·25, (iii) 15·8, (iv) 70·7 mA. **22.** 5$\frac{1}{3}$, 2$\frac{2}{3}$, 16 W. **23.** 4 min. **24.** 1·9 kWh.

EXERCISE 4 (p. 70)

1. 200 μC. **2.** (i) air, (ii) electrolytic. **4.** 0·002 μF. **6.** (i) B, (ii) C, (iii) A; C (most), A (least). **7.** 0·02 J. **8.** $\varepsilon A/d$; 89 pF. **9.** 177 pF; 0·71 mA. **10.** 160 μC; 40,160 V. **11.** 120 V, 400 μC. **13.** (a) 106 pF, (b) 0·106 μC, (c) 2,000 V, (d) 400 V. **15.** (a) 0·2 (b) 10^{-4} s; (a) slower. **16.** 5·3 × 10^{-4}, 15·9 × 10^{-4} μF; 10·6 μJ. **17.** 221 pF; 33 μJ, 1,500 V. **18.** 50 V. **19.** 1,800 V (approx.). **21.** increased 1$\frac{1}{3}$ times. **22.** (a) 50 μC, (b) 25 μA, (c) 16 μA.

EXERCISE 5 (p. 91)

7. 0·04 N. **8.** (i) 0·1 N, (ii) 0·002 N m. **9.** 1·2 × 10^{-3} N. **10.** (i) 4 × 10^{-3} N m, (ii) 0. **12.** 16%. **13.** 0·01 N; 0·5 N m; zero. **15.** 8 × 10^{-7} N m; 8 × 10^{-4} deg. **16.** 7·9 × 10^{-3} N per mA. **20.** 2 × 10^{-7} N m.

EXERCISE 6 (p. 113)

4. 8 V. **5.** 0·05 H. **9.** $\frac{1}{2}$ LI^2, (iv) 8 J. **10.** (a) 2 A, (b) 10 A per sec. **12.** (ii) 0·1 A. **13.** 1,000 (approx.). **15.** (a) 800, (b) 16 J. **16.** (i) 280, (ii) 120 mH. **17.** 2; 50 Ω; transformer. **19.** (a) 0, (b) 0·25 A.

EXERCISE 7 (p. 151)

2. 113 V. **9.** (a) 80, (b) 0·08, (c) 318 kΩ, (d) 79·6 kΩ, (e) 530 Ω. **11.** (i) 125·6 kΩ, (ii) 628 kΩ. **13.** 20, 6·4 V. **14.** 3·2 mA. **15.** X = 0·8 μF, Y = 0·13 H. **16.** 0·005 sec, 200 Hz, 2·828, 2. v = 225 sin (400πt − π/2), r.m.s. = 159. **17.** (a) i_m = 10, v_m = 20, (b) 100 Hz, (c) v leads by 90°, 2 Ω inductive. **20.** 4·5 V. **21.** 330 Ω, 0·03 A. **22.** 40 V. **23.** 252 V. **24.** 55 μH. **25.** (a) 53, (b) 85 V, 1·59.

EXERCISE 8 (p. 182)

1. 100 V. **2.** 55 μH. **3.** (a) 7,725, (b) 7,725, (c) 150 V. **4.** (i) 0·1 A, (ii) 180 V, (iii) 90. **5.** (i) 6·4, (ii) 20 A, **6.** 4 V. **7.** 120 V, 271 V, 34°. **8.** 503 Hz. **9.** 800 kHz. **10.** 910 kHz. **11.** 0·92 A. **12.** (a) 700 V, (b) 4 A, (c) 3 A. **13.** 0·33 A, I lags by 73°. **14.** (a) 796 kHz, (b) 62·5 kΩ, (c) 500 V. **15.** (i) 4,000 Ω, (ii) 20, (iii) 50 mA. **16.** 784 kHz, 102; bandwidth = 7·7 kHz. **17.** 2:1; d.c. = 0, a.c. reduced. **18.** 8 mW. **19.** 13·5 V, 5 W, 0·37. **20.** 40,000 (approx.). **21.** 0·1 A; (a) 10^{-4} rad, (b) 10^{-2} Ω, (c) 10^6 Ω. **22.** (a) 6 Ω, (b) 5 A, 5 A (r.m.s.), (c) 60°, (d) 33 mH.

EXERCISE 9 (p. 196)

1. temperature. **2.** positive. **3.** rate of emission. **4.** electrons, space-charge, cathode. **5.** electrons. **6.** half-wave. **7.** peak. **8.** varying, steady. **9.** d.c.; a.c.

EXERCISE 10 (p. 208)

1. silicon, germanium. **2.** decreases. **3.** silicon, germanium. **4.** electrons, holes. **5.** electrons. **6.** n-type. **7.** donors. **8.** p-type. **9.** electrons, holes. **10.** holes, electrons. **11.** opposes. **12.** conducts, low. **13.** much less. **14.** minority. **15.** reverse. **16.** Zener, high. **17.** Zener, stabilize. **25.** 1 MΩ, 1·2k Ω (approx.). **27.** 850 Ω.

EXERCISE 11 (p. 224)

1. grid, anode. **2.** negative. **3.** load. **4.** V_g. **5.** V_a. **6.** undistorted. **7.** cut-off. **8.** class B. **9.** grid voltage. **10.** I_a, V_g. **11.** 2 V. **12.** 1 V. **13.** 100 V. **14.** 1 kΩ. **15.** (i) 12 mA, (ii) 120 V. **16.** 15,700 Ω, 0·4 mA/V (approx.). **17.** 1·5 mA/V. **19.** $r_a = 6$ kΩ, g_m, $\mu = 6$. **20.** 5·3, 4·3, 3·1 mA. **21.** (i) 3·8 mA, (ii) 5·75, 2·5 mA.

EXERCISE 12 (p. 235)

1. 0·2 V (r.m.s.). **2.** a.c. resistance, r_a. **3.** 4. **4.** grid. **5.** input. **6.** h.t. voltage. **7.** self-capacitance, less. **8.** stray-capacitance of R. **9.** 12. **10.** 15. **12.** 6. **13.** (a) 1·2 V, (b) 1·9 V. **14.** (i) 18, (ii) 23 Hz.

EXERCISE 13 (p. 262)

1. (a) p-n-p, (b) 1 = collector, 2 = base, 3 = emitter. **2.** 1 = emitter, 2 = base, 3 = collector. **3.** (i) X = collector, Y = base, Z = emitter, (ii) common base, (iii) common terminal of L, M, Y. **5.** (a) n-p-n, (b) p-n-p. **6.** (i) 1·5 V, (ii) 0·5 V, (iii) 4·05 mA, (iv) 1·0 V. **7.** (i) 4·1 mA, (ii) 50, (iii) $V_{BE} = 0·5$ V, $V_{CE} = 1·5$ V. **9.** (ii) 49. **11.** (i) X, Y, (ii) A, Y, (iii) P, Q, (iv) 2·7 k, (v) counteracts temperature rise, (vi) electrolytic decoupling, (vii) base bias, (viii) isolates base from input d.c. **16.** 5 kΩ, 60. **17.** (i) 46, (ii) 12·75 kΩ; 30 μA. **20.** 1·96 mA, 0·98. **21.** 49. **22.** 1·2 kΩ. **23.** (i) 55, (ii) 10 kΩ. **24.** $I_C = 2·2$ mA, $V_{CE} = 3·4$ V; 3·8 V (approx.). **25.** $R_1 = 28·6$ kΩ, $R_2 = 10·7$, $R_E = 1$ kΩ, $R = 2$ kΩ. **26.** 0·66 V (approx.).

EXERCISE 14 (p. 281)

1. 25 kΩ. **2.** 675 Ω. **3.** (a) 12·5 W, (b) 4 W, (c) 32%. **4.** 1:35. **5.** 870 mW.
6. 6 mW. **7.** 120 mW. **8.** (i) 250 Ω, (ii) 60.5 mW, (iii) 1:7 (approx.). **10.**
1:10, P_{ac} = 680 mW, 74%. **11.** 48, 0·24%. **13.** 250 kΩ, 125 kΩ.

EXERCISE 15 (p. 295)

10. 6 kHz. **11.** 74. **12.** 19·2 kHz (approx.). **13.** (i) 12·5, (ii) 21·8.
17. 450 pF.

EXERCISE 16 (p. 306)

1. L–C (tank); $f = 1/2\pi\sqrt{LC}$. **2.** in phase, positive. **3.** C, efficiency.
4. h.t. supply. **5.** zero. **6.** becomes negative. **7.** (i) 10,070 Hz, (ii) provides
feedback, (iii) base bias, (iv) decouples to r.f., (v) stabilizer, (vi) P, Q.

EXERCISE 17 (p. 320)

1. h.f. **2.** audio. **3.** shift-frequency. **4.** side-bands. **5.** C–R. **6.** modulating,
carrier. **7.** 50%; 202, 205, 208 kHz. **8.** 696, 700, 704 kHz. **9.** 796 Ω, 796 kΩ.
11. 1·2 V, 25%; 305, 310, 315 kHz. **14.** 16 kHz, 100. **15.** 10,025 and 9,975
kHz, 60 kHz, 5 kHz per sec.

EXERCISE 18 (p. 336)

1. (i) low (ii) high (iii) low. **2.** $V_{CE} = V_{CC} - I_C R$. (i) high (ii) low. **3.** Input
1, output 0; input 0, output 1. Gate = inverter. **4.** (i) inverter (ii) NOR (iii)
AND. **8.** (iii) capacitors, in parallel with feedback resistors.

EXERCISE 19 (p. 342)

13. $S_1 = \overline{A + B}$, $S_2 = \overline{A + B}$. $C = \overline{\bar{A} . \bar{B} . C}$.
14. $S_1 = \overline{A + B}$, $S_2 = A . B$, $S_3 = \overline{A + B + A . B}$.

Index